ASSESSING LANGUAGE PRODUCTION USING SALT SOFTWARE

A Clinician's Guide to Language Sample *[...]*

2nd Edition

ASSESSING LANGUAGE PRODUCTION USING SALT SOFTWARE

A Clinician's Guide to Language Sample Analysis

JON F. MILLER   KAREN ANDRIACCHI   ANN NOCKERTS

ASSESSING LANGUAGE PRODUCTION USING SALT SOFTWARE
A Clinician's Guide to Language Sample Analysis

edited by Jon F. Miller, Karen Andriacchi, and Ann Nockerts

with chapters contributed by
   Chapters 1–6: Jon F. Miller, Karen Andriacchi, and Ann Nockerts
   Chapter 7: Raúl Rojas and Aquiles Iglesias
   Chapter 8: Julie Washington
   Chapter 9: Joyelle DiVall-Rayan, Nikola Nelson, Karen Andriacchi, and
          Ann Nockerts
   Chapter 10: Joyelle DiVall-Rayan and Jon F. Miller

Printed in the United States of America.

Published by SALT Software LLC, Middleton, WI.

Printing History:
November, 2011: First Edition.
December, 2015: Second Edition.
January, 2016: Revised Edition

SALT Software, LLC
7006 Hubbard Avenue
Middleton, WI 53562
1-888-440-7258
www.saltsoftware.com

CONTENTS

FOREWORD

Updates on our views on the language sample analysis (LSA) process and the release of a new version of SALT software (Miller & Iglesias, 2015) motivated creating a second edition of this book. This second edition addresses the challenges of assessing language production through the life span. The unfolding of language through childhood requires us to be mindful of the change in language knowledge, the demands on language use for school, home, and community, and the role spoken language plays in mastering literacy skills. This book provides an overview of how LSA provides the tools to carefully evaluate language performance in a variety of speaking contexts. It details how SALT reduces the burden of the LSA process, creating functional measurement options for everyday use. It is written to overcome the bias against LSA as too difficult to learn and too variable as a measurement tool. It is written to convince you of the value of LSA and to show you how SALT reduces the effort up front and provides consistent results.

Revisions were made to reflect changes in the software. New language measures and analysis reports have been added to SALT and a number of the reports have been reformatted to provide a more transparent view of the results. The Expository reference database has been expanded and a new Persuasion database was added to include typical students in grades 9 – 12. These two major additions to the databases provide access to language expectations for adolescents as they transition into adulthood. We were fortunate to also include a contributed database of monolingual Spanish story retell samples, elicited from typical 1st – 3rd grade students in Guadalajara, Mexico. These changes to the software are documented in this second addition.

A new chapter was added on additional uses of SALT, focusing on coding written samples and fluency behaviors. Written language has been of increasing interest, particularly for middle and high school students. A written language transcription format has been developed with input from Nicki Nelson. The reciprocal nature of spoken and written language has been the focus of increased research and clinical interest. The written language transcription format allows for the comparison of spoken and written language performance to advance the focus of intervention services. A flexible coding scheme was developed to capture behaviors unique to stuttering, such as prolongations, blocks, and concomitant behaviors. Once coded, these behaviors are summarized in a new fluency report.

This second edition follows the format of the first edition with an introductory chapter followed by chapters on each of the key components of the LSA process; sample elicitation, transcription, analysis, and interpretation. Each of these chapters walks you through challenges and solutions for that component to provide you with a broad understanding of the process. Each step in the process provides the foundation for the next. A representative sample, transcribed accurately, will provide valid and reliable analysis results available for your clinical interpretation. The next two chapters are included to bring attention to special populations, Spanish-English bilingual children and speakers of African American English. These chapters describe the challenges facing clinicians when evaluating oral language in these populations. The last chapter is filled with case studies, to test your knowledge of using SALT to document performance. You should be able to anticipate the analyses outcomes as they unfold for each case. These cases are intended to emphasize the power of LSA to document specific language deficits and strengths of each individual. At the same time we bring attention to the importance of integrating your clinical experience and judgment into the process.

When all is said and done, SALT continues to provide you with abundant data about spoken language performance. But you must use your clinical skills to figure out what the analyses mean for each individual. LSA is a powerful assessment measure that can enhance clinical services for individuals with spoken language deficits. It will aid in identification of language disorder by documenting language use in everyday communication tasks. SALT provides many tools for making LSA faster and more manageable. It provides reference databases to use for comparison with typical speakers. Elicitation protocols are simple and well defined. Online help is comprehensive and readily accessible. LSA is particularly well-suited for monitoring change associated with intervention, supporting frequent language sampling, as any length of sample from any communication context can be analyzed.

This book could not have been written without the help of so many people. Students and colleagues over the past 30+ years have weighed in on previous versions of the software. Special thanks to John Heilmann, Raúl Rojas, Thomas Malone, Marleen Westerveld, Mary-Beth Rolland, and Sue Carpenter for their help with reading early drafts and discussions of content and organization. We particularly want to thank our contributors. Aquiles Iglesias and Raúl Rojas wrote an eloquent chapter on how language sample analysis can be used to evaluate language knowledge in Spanish and English. They demonstrate the importance of making sure comparisons across languages use the same units of analysis; words, morphemes, and utterances. Julie Washington details the complexities of distinguishing African American English (AAE) from language disorder. She provides a roadmap for recognizing the features of AAE thereby not confusing them with errors and omissions in Standard American English. Nicki Nelson provided special commentary and advice on the written language transcription system. Joyelle DiVall-Rayan provided clinical expertise on several chapters. The case studies chapter is mostly her work; finding the children, securing the language samples, talking with parents about the process, gaining permission to publish their children's language samples, and then writing up the results. I would also like to thank the SALT group of the Madison Metropolitan School District who, over the past 30+ years, critiqued existing SALT measures and suggested new ones. They also spearheaded the collection of the first SALT reference databases, providing leadership for the statewide effort to collect representative language samples. The MMSD SALT group has had a tremendous influence on how the software performs.

Finally, I would like to thank my co-editors, Ann Nockerts and Karen Andriacchi. Ann is my longtime partner in this work. She has written almost every line of computer code across many operating systems including this new version. Without her, SALT software would not exist. She has provided the vision and enthusiasm to transform a complicated research tool into a practical clinical instrument. Karen has worked on several large research projects involving SALT, bringing special expertise on transcribing and analyzing language samples. She contributed extensively to the content of this book and provided detailed organizational help, within and across chapters, to make sure the information flowed in a cohesive manner.

We hope you enjoy reading this Second Edition of the SALT book. We expect to continue to provide you with the most powerful language analysis tools to advance your assessment of language production.

Jon
December 2015

Jon F. Miller, Ph.D., CCC-SLP

Jon is a Professor Emeritus in the Department of Communicative Disorders at the University of Wisconsin–Madison. He is also Co-founder and CEO of SALT Software, LLC. Jon is a Fellow of the American Speech-Language-Hearing Association and has conducted research for the past 40 years on language development and disorders in children with a variety of disabilities.

Karen Andriacchi, M.S., CCC-SLP

Karen graduated from the University of Wisconsin-Madison with a Bachelor's degree in secondary education and a Master's degree in Communicative Disorders. She worked for many years as a clinician in the public schools with students in grades K-12 with speech-language and/or cognitive impairments. She also managed multiple child-language research projects at UW-Madison. In her role as Director of Services for SALT Software, LLC, Karen manages transcription and consultation Services. Her expertise is in the many aspects of using language sample analysis to assess oral language.

Ann Nockerts, M.S.

Ann is Co-founder and lead programmer for SALT Software, LLC. She is responsible for the design and development of the SALT software as well as numerous other tools for analyzing language samples. She has consulted with researchers, clinicians, and students to design coding schemes, adapt SALT for other languages, and to provide general guidance for using the software.

ABOUT THE CONTRIBUTORS

Joyelle DiVall-Rayan, M.S., CCC-SLP
Director of Education for SALT Software, LLC

Ms. DiVall-Rayan received her Master's degree in Communicative Disorders at the University of Wisconsin-Madison. She worked several years in an outpatient medical setting working with adult and pediatric patients as well as in the public school setting. In her current position with SALT Software, she is responsible for continuing education and course development.

Chapter 9: Additional Applications of SALT
Chapter 10: Pulling it All Together: Examples from our case study files

Aquiles Iglesias, Ph.D., CCC-SLP
Professor and Founding Director in the Department of Communication Sciences and Disorders at University of Delaware

Dr. Iglesias is a Fellow of the American Speech-Language-Hearing Association. His major area of research is language acquisition in bilingual children and his research, funded by IES, focuses on developing assessment protocols for bilingual (Spanish/English) children.

Chapter 7: Assessing the Bilingual (Spanish/English) Population

Nickola Nelson, Ph.D., CCC-SLP
Professor in the Department of Speech Pathology and Audiology at Western Michigan University, and Program Director of the Ph.D. program in interdisciplinary health sciences.

Dr. Nelson's research involves curriculum-relevant language assessment and intervention and working with doctoral students to extend interdisciplinary evidence-based interventions across populations and contexts. She is the author of many books, chapters, and articles on children with language disorders and has been the editor of Topics in Language Disorders (Lippincott, Williams, and Wilkins/Wolters-Kluwer) since 2006. Dr. Nelson is a Fellow of the American Speech-Language-Hearing Association and the International Academy for Research in Learning Disabilities.

Chapter 9: Additional Applications of SALT

Raúl Rojas, Ph.D., CCC-SLP

Assistant Professor at the University of Texas at Dallas, Callier Center for Communication Disorders

Dr. Rojas's research focuses on child language from a longitudinal and processing perspective, specifically bilingual language development in typically developing children and in children with language impairments. He is particularly interested in bilingual language growth and in validating paradigms to index processing load and early language learning in bilingual children. Dr. Rojas has provided bilingual (Spanish-English) speech-language pathology services in multiple settings, including schools and early intervention.

Chapter 7: Assessing the Bilingual (Spanish/English) Population

Julie Washington, Ph.D., CCC-SLP

Professor in the Department of Educational Psychology and Special Education: Communication Disorders Program at Georgia State University

Dr. Washington is a Fellow of the American Speech-Language-Hearing Association. Her research, which addresses language and literacy development in diverse populations, has focused on understanding cultural dialect use in young African American children with a specific emphasis on language assessment, language impairment, and academic performance. In addition, her work with preschoolers has focused on understanding and improving the emergent literacy skills necessary to support later reading proficiency in high risk groups.

Chapter 8: The Dialect Features of African American English and Their Importance in LSA

Introduction to LSA Using SALT

Jon F. Miller
Karen Andriacchi
Ann Nockerts

Language sample analysis (LSA) is the only assessment measure that captures a speaker's typical and functional language use. Although traditional standardized tests play an important role in oral language assessment, LSA shows how language is put to use in the home, with friends, at school, and within the community.

The goal of this book is to show how LSA using *Systematic Analysis of Language Transcripts* (SALT) software can be used to measure the real-life oral language of essentially any speaker. SALT standardizes the entire LSA process from selecting the sampling context to interpreting the results, thus giving consistent and reliable measures of oral language.

Background: The History of LSA

Language sample analysis has a long history as a tool used to investigate language development. Studying what children said over time was seen as a reasonable index of what they knew. Since the stream of speech is transitive, writing down exactly what was said created a permanent record. This record made evident the words and sentence structures used and how they changed through childhood. Because this process required writing down by hand what was said as it was spoken, it was limited by the rate of speech and by the attention of the investigator. Also, there was no way to verify the accuracy of the record. As electronic recording equipment emerged, investigators recorded speech samples for later transcription. They were no longer limited by the speaking rate or the length of the sample. Larger samples increased the likelihood of capturing every vocabulary word and grammatical feature the child was capable of using at that time. Systematic investigations of several children at a time were undertaken in the 1960s, electronically recording samples every few weeks. These studies made a number of ground breaking discoveries that radically changed our views of language development from a passive imitation-based process to an active rule-based process. This work revived research interest in language development and promoted interest in children who experienced difficulty developing language.

The most prominent example of this work was Roger Brown and his students at Harvard (Brown, 1973). Brown and his students recorded samples of more than 700 utterances from three children every few weeks, capturing their advancement from single-word utterances to utterances that were four to five morphemes in length. These samples were transcribed and grammars were written for each child following linguistic discovery methods. This approach revealed two major discoveries; first, children were constructing grammatical rules for producing utterances longer than one word that were consistent across children. Second, these grammars advanced systematically as utterance length increased. Mean utterance length defined stages of syntactic development up to utterances five morphemes in length. These concepts seem commonplace to us now but at the time they were revolutionary and prompted a great deal of research on all aspects of language development. Those of us interested in language disorder followed this work with great interest and used the LSA methodology to develop measures of syntax using the findings of the research on language development in typical children. These measures focused on identifying the types of sentences used at the different stages of development.

The use of very large language samples was impractical for clinical work but LSA was still viewed as an essential part of clinical problem solving. Several clinical measures of syntax which emerged from research have withstood the test of time and are in use today; Developmental Sentence Scoring (DSS, Lee & Canter, 1971); Language Assessment, Remediation, and Screening Procedure (LARSP, Crystal, Garman, and Fletcher, 1976); Assigning Structural Stage (Miller, 1981).

These measures were calculated by hand from conversational samples between mothers and children. As time consuming as these measures were, the results provided a detailed account of a child's syntactic development.

This early work provided the pathway for identifying language delay in children using tested methods that had at least some data from research studies. These efforts elevated LSA from a descriptive method to a criterion referenced method when using summary data from the developmental literature to interpret the results (Miller, 1981). The key components from this early research, powerful for both researchers and clinical practitioners, have driven the revitalization of the LSA process with the use of computer technology. It is agreed within the field that LSA is an essential component to the assessment of spoken language. Best practice guidelines (per ASHA) across a number of populations, including developmental delays, specific language impairment, and autism spectrum disorders, suggest LSA as an approach to 1) problem solve language differences or deficits, 2) generate clear goals for intervention, and 3) assist in monitoring progress.

LSA Has Stood the Test of Time and Should Be Part of Your Clinical Tool Set

Re-thinking the LSA process
The LSA process provides a way to preserve the auditory speech signal for analysis. Representative samples of spontaneous language provide direct access to language use in everyday communication. Historically, listening to and transcribing the sample by hand, using paper and pencil, was the method for this procedure. This wasn't as simple as one might think. In order to accurately and authentically capture the language, rules to define utterances, words, and morphemes had to be created, and they had to remain consistent. To analyze the transcript required manually counting words and morphemes per utterance as well as the number of different words produced across the sample. To interpret those results required knowledge of language development through direct experience with children and knowledge of the research literature on language development. Without this knowledge one was unable to document what constituted typical, or atypical, oral expression of three, four, or five year olds. Rigorous as LSA was, it did not fall to the wayside even when it was all

done by hand. This difficult and time-consuming process was far too valuable to abandon, and our efforts have focused on making the process more accessible for clinical use. Since the mid-1980s SALT has employed computer technology to standardize the LSA process. We now have a defined transcription system, high-speed analyses at all levels of language, and databases of typical speakers to facilitate the interpretation process.

How LSA provides insight into language use
Even difficult-to-test individuals have some means of communicating. Usually direct observation of communication with familiar partners, such as family members, provides insight into the frequency and complexity of their language use. Recording and transcribing this language allows for a detailed analysis at all language levels. Additional samples can be recorded at home or school to complete the communication profile. Analysis and interpretation of these samples is enhanced with the use of SALT by providing instant analysis at all language levels. Reference databases provide sets of typical age-matched or grade-matched peers for comparison to aid interpretation of the results. LSA provides a key resource for the resolution of complex clinical problems and allows for monitoring change over time in everyday communication contexts.

A review of key features
There are a number of key features of the LSA process that have prompted its continued use and motivated its revitalization and improvement.

1. *LSA is flexible*. It allows for multiple analysis of the same sample, offering many different views of the speaker's performance at each of the language levels; syntax, semantics, and discourse. LSA can be used with anyone who can produce language regardless of cognitive, perceptual, or motor ability. Speakers who have challenges such as learning a second language, speaking a dialect, developmental disabilities, or who are on the autism spectrum are excellent candidates for LSA. Additionally, LSA is culturally unbiased; if the examiner is sensitive to cultural characteristics, bias will be eliminated.

2. *LSA is repeatable*. Language samples can be recorded daily, weekly, or monthly to document change in performance or to note differences between oral language tasks such as conversation and narration. "Everyday"

language, authentic to the speaker, is elicited in natural and functional communication contexts (i.e., in an uncontrived setting) as often as deemed necessary. Because a language sample is basically a snapshot of the speaker's typical oral language, realistic therapy goals, which highly impact communication and language learning, can be developed directly from the analyses. From the assessment we learn how the speaker puts to use his or her knowledge of the language. As soon as we know this, we then have an avenue for remediation. Once intervention is underway, generalization of skills can be readily assessed and documented by eliciting another language sample. Test-retest reliability issues, which can be a problem with standardized measures, are not a factor in LSA.

3. *LSA is valid*. It documents change in everyday communication skills or in oral language requirements in school. Performance on grade-level state and school district standards can be documented through the use of LSA. Examples might include the ability to debate or produce an exposition such as "how the heart pumps blood" or "how a bill becomes a law". Research by Miller, et.al. 2006, found significant correlations between several measures of oral narrative performance and reading achievement in both Spanish and English. The higher children's oral narrative language skills were in either language, the higher their reading scores. The measures of oral narrative skill taken from Miller's story retell protocol predicted reading scores better than the Passage Comprehension subtest from the Woodcock Language Proficiency Battery Revised: English and Spanish (1991).

4. *LSA is accountable*. It can measure language growth at all levels and at frequent intervals to meet evidence-based practice standards. LSA augments standardized measures and can substantiate the results of those measures as well as the reason for referral. It is important to know how a child performs compared to his or her peers using the norms from standardized tests. Standardized tests are required by school districts to qualify students for speech-language services but their sensitivity in diagnosing language disorders is inconsistent. They tend to look at language use narrowly, requiring only morpheme, word, or phrase responses. Whereas, LSA assesses oral language from a functional use perspective. A student with language impairment could score within the average range on

some standardized measures yet fail to retell a coherent narrative or provide an organized exposition.

5. *LSA aligns with Common Core State Standards.* Implementation of the Common Core State Standards inherently requires methods to measure outcomes, or progress, related to those standards. Speech-Language Pathologists are held responsible for measuring the progress of students on their caseload. Appendix T contains a table which illustrates how to link LSA using SALT software to the Common Core State Standards for Speaking and Listening in grades K-12. The table suggests the appropriate language sample contexts for eliciting samples that will reflect achievement of, or progress on, the Speaking and Listening core standards. Additionally listed are suggested measures in SALT that can quantify progress on a standard.

Streamlining the Process to Make LSA Accessible

LSA has always been time consuming, particularly in clinical settings. Transcription and analysis, sometimes still completed by hand, can take hours. Streamlining the process was a necessity in order for the benefits of the process to outweigh the arduousness of the procedure. Consistency of the process was historically a problem in terms of the types of samples, the length of sample, the different transcription procedures and rules used, and the specific analyses generated. Until computers came into general use, interpreting the results of language samples relied solely on the users' knowledge of language development. There were no databases of typical children's language performance in specific speaking contexts.

Over the past 40 years there have been three groups of researchers using computer technology to work out solutions to the LSA implementation problems. One group developed tools for child language researchers to enhance research productivity (McWhinney, 2000). A second group computerized analyses from classic research on language development (Long, Fey, & Channell, 2008). The third group, the focus of this book, automated the LSA process, making it as standardized as possible by providing reference databases for comparison (Systematic Analysis of Language Transcripts (SALT), Miller & Iglesias, 2015).

SALT Solutions to Improving LSA Accessibility: Overcoming the barriers to efficient clinical use of LSA

Since its inception, SALT has continually focused on developing solutions to make the LSA process quicker, easier, and more accessible for both clinicians and researchers. The improvements in computer technology, including more advanced programming languages, more sophisticated operating systems, and higher performing hardware, have improved the process of LSA. Fast-forward to the present day and consider how the current version of SALT improves the LSA process by addressing the most common misconceptions.

Time: *It takes too much time to transcribe and analyze a language sample.*
The practice of eliciting 100 utterances (or 15 minutes) of oral language was the standard for many years. LSA research shows that shorter, focused samples provide robust measures of language performance (Miller, et al., 2006). SALT's transcription format uses minimal coding to gain maximal analysis outcomes. A story retell narrative, for example, with 3 – 6 minutes of talking, will take, on average, 15-30 minutes to transcribe, less time than it takes to give most standardized language tests. Our research has shown it takes roughly five minutes for a trained transcriber to transcribe each minute of oral language. This assumes that the speaker is fluent and intelligible, the context is familiar, and the recording is of high quality. SALT analyses are generated in seconds.

Consistency: *Consistency of the process is a problem in terms of the types of samples, sample length, transcription procedures and rules used, and the specific analysis performed.*
The SALT language sample elicitation protocols, transcription format, and computer analyses guarantee consistency across language samples. This consistency allows for comparison across speakers or within the same speaker over time. Sample length can be controlled within SALT. Comparisons can be made using same amount of elapsed time, same number of utterances, or same number of words.

<u>Interpreting the results</u>: *Interpretation of the results relies solely on the user's knowledge of language development. There are no databases of typical speaker's language performance in specific speaking contexts.*
SALT has moved beyond charts of typical development, though they are still useful. Our databases of several thousand typical speakers allow the user to compare an individual speaker to age-matched or grade-matched peers in the same speaking conditions. An individual's performance can be monitored relative to typical language growth over time.

SALT has improved the entire process of LSA at the sampling, transcription, analysis, and interpretation levels with:

- detailed elicitation protocols used to collect the samples from typical speakers
- transcription tools to facilitate the process, e.g., specialized editor and error checking routine
- online contextual help systems to provide information wherever you are in the program; available using F1 key when in the SALT editor
- instant analysis reports from standard measures of syntax, semantics, discourse, rate, fluency, errors, and omissions
- databases of more than 7,000 typical speakers in a variety of speaking contexts to aid interpretation
- automated comparison of the target sample to a set of age or grade-matched peers selected from the relevant database in standard deviation units
- routines to search transcripts for specific features, e.g., responses to questions or a list of the different words used and their inflections
- analysis tables and selected utterances which can be incorporated into clinical reports
- online courses to take the learner through each step of the LSA process

The strength of language sample analysis is its flexibility to capture language use in everyday communication contexts, accurately measuring lexical, morphemic, syntactic, discourse, rate, and fluency features of the same sample. This procedure has been a research staple for more than sixty years and has provided the means to document language development in typical and atypical populations. The validity of this procedure is beyond question, and the reliability has been documented (Heilmann, et al., 2008). We established standardized protocols and transcription procedures for several genres and across ages (Miller, Andriacchi, and Nockerts, in press). This led us to confirm the stability of the LSA measures calculated by SALT.

Over the years, our research on LSA measures has produced a range of results that inform us about how these measures can characterize oral language performance. Here is a summary of what we have learned about typical children and how LSA measures inform us about language production.

- Mean length of utterance (MLU), number of different words (NDW), number of total words (NTW), and words per minute (WPM) significantly correlate with age in $3 - 13$ year olds, $r = .65 - .72$.
- MLU is longer and WPM is higher when producing a narrative than a conversation.
- Children produce more mazes in narration than conversation suggesting narration is the more difficult context.
- Number of mazes increase as utterance length increases.
- Measures of MLU and SI increase as the difficulty of the context increases: conversation -> narration (story retell) -> exposition-> persuasion.
- Short conversational samples produce relatively the same data as longer samples, i.e., 50 vs. 100 utterances.
- Narrative story retell samples of $35 - 65$ utterances provide stable and robust samples.
- Measures calculated from story retell samples predict reading achievement in Spanish and English better than the Passage Comprehension subtest from the Woodcock Language Proficiency Battery Revised: English and Spanish (Miller, et al., 2006).
- Expository samples result in significantly longer samples with more complex syntax than conversation or narrative retell samples.
- Persuasion samples are shorter than expository samples, but facilitate the production of more complex language.
- Standardizing the LSA process results in reliable measures across ages and speaking conditions.
- LSA produces valid measures of functional language use.

The remainder of the book provides detailed considerations of each step in the process; elicitation, transcription, analysis, and interpretation. Our goal is to walk you through the process of learning to use SALT to facilitate the clinical use of LSA.

Eliciting Language Samples

Jon F. Miller
Karen Andriacchi
Ann Nockerts

We have learned a great deal about language sample analysis as an assessment tool through our research and that of others over the past 40 years. Eliciting "the best" sample for an individual can be considered from several perspectives at this point in time.

- Developmental. Sampling contexts expand with advancing age and ability level. Up through age four, children are acquiring conversational skills. After age four narrative skills emerge and branch into several narrative types such as personal narratives, story retell, and exposition.

- Functional. Functional considerations focus on how language difficulties manifest themselves. In the preschool years, this will be language use in conversation. In elementary school years, language problems usually concern aspects of the curriculum which require oral narrative ability. This can involve written language as well. In the late elementary and early adolescent years, the curriculum requires expository abilities in oral and written form, that is, explaining how to do something (*find a library book*) or how to play a game. Adults may experience difficulties in any one or all of these language genres.

- Precision of interpretation. SALT offers an additional consideration to selecting the type of sample to elicit, databases of typical speakers to improve the precision of interpretation. We have assembled databases of more than 7, 000 language samples from children 3 – 188 years of age in conversation, narrative, expository, and persuasive sampling contexts. Because we do not have complete sets of language samples for all ages across all possible speaking conditions, we are left with the challenge of finding the best sampling context to optimize language use and exhibit the language difficulty, with optimum opportunity to interpret the results. Ideally we want to select an elicitation context that fits the speaker's oral language abilities and reveals the language difficulty, with a SALT database to quantify the results.

Selecting the Optimum Language Sample

The optimum language sample for an individual will meet as many of the following objectives as possible.

1. Provide maximum information about the speaker's language
   - Vocabulary, syntax, semantics, and discourse
   - Structure and organization
   - Fluency, efficiency, and accuracy
2. Motivate the speaker to do their best talking
   - Age appropriate
   - Attentive listener or conversational partner
3. Identify speakers' oral language strengths and weaknesses within:
   - Community
   - School
   - Workplace
   - Family
4. For school-aged children, clearly demonstrate the student's difficulties with functional language regarding:
   - Classroom curriculum
   - State-wide oral language standards
   - Social language use

5. Optimize opportunity to interpret results
   - Follow the relevant elicitation protocol
   - Adhere to SALT transcription conventions
   - Where possible, compare performance to typical speakers (SALT databases)

These objectives will help guide you in choosing the sampling condition that best captures the oral language issue(s) in question.

Sampling Contexts or Genres

A clear understanding of the different types of sampling contexts is inherent to a valid and effective language sample, and is central to implementing the objectives listed in the previous section. Research has demonstrated that each of the speaking contexts places different demands on the speaker and produces somewhat different results. For example, conversational samples help document discourse skills, while narrative, expository, and persuasion samples work well to illustrate organizational skills. The reference databases in SALT consist of samples from the following sampling contexts:

- Conversation in play

  Conversation, where adults speak to children about ongoing events, is the basic platform for learning language. Children begin to respond with gestures or verbalizations, such as ba-ba, da-da, ma-ma, that are received with delight and interpreted to mean whatever is relevant. As understandable words appear and word combinations signal the emergence of grammar, language learning accelerates with rapid gains in every aspect of verbal communication. Samples of conversation can be recorded as soon as children can be understood and throughout the life span.

  Young children are most comfortable conversing while playing and are likely to talk more with familiar partners than strangers, e.g., parents versus newly encountered adults. Although most young children tend to talk more in play situations, this should be confirmed for each child. The play context can be adjusted to meet individual preferences, individual interests, gender, culture, and experience. Consider that some children may prefer novel versus familiar toys. Discussion with parents may be helpful in selecting the optimum talking contexts and partners. Parents are usually the most familiar conversational partners, and often can elicit the most talk. Professional examiners can direct the language sample by pointing out situations to talk about and asking questions of increasing complexity; yes/no, what, where, why, or when, for example. Play samples are most productive up to about age four or five, after which the child will usually talk to an adult about a topic without physical interaction with objects. This is a somewhat variable ability in typical children. Remember, the goal is to record the best language use possible. When the play session is completed, confirm with the parents as to the validity of the sample.

Play-based language samples are particularly useful when evaluating the communication skills of late talkers, individuals with developmental disabilities, those on the autism spectrum, and those with neurological disorders. Consider that recording language samples in play offers the opportunity to evaluate communication in the individual's most productive medium, demonstrating his or her optimum language use.

Play is the natural context for language learning and the most comfortable method of interaction with toddlers when evaluating language. A good sample of play is child initiated. Samples of interactive play not only give an authentic picture of current levels of language production, they can also reveal non-verbal behaviors that go along with communicative development. Where non-verbal behaviors are important to analyze, samples of play should be videotaped in order to assess both verbal and non-verbal communication skills.

Samples of children producing utterances of two words or less can probably be transcribed by an observer as the child is talking. With utterances longer than two words, a recording of the speech is necessary to insure an accurate record of language use. Keep in mind that children talk more as they get older. The length of the sample will need to be sufficient to allow opportunity to display their best oral language skills.

- <u>Conversation with adult partner</u>

Conversational samples uniquely document the use of oral language to exchange information at a spontaneous level. Conversations are governed by the rules of discourse and, as such, they offer insight into the social aspect of language use. From a conversation we can assess the speaker's ability to orchestrate turn taking, topic initiation and maintenance, and ability to repair breakdowns in communication. In a conversation speakers must follow certain conventions. For example, they must listen attentively, limit interruptions, say only what needs to be said, and say what is true. These conventions are learned by talking. Speakers get better at conversing as they get older and have more experiences initiating topics, staying on topic, responding to questions, providing more utterances per turn, and using more diverse vocabulary and longer utterances.

Conversation, with both familiar and unfamiliar partners, allows for careful description of the social use of language. Eliciting conversational samples places more responsibility on the examiner than any other context. Examiners need to monitor their language to engage the speaker in conversation while having the least influence on the speaker. To do this, examiners should ask open-ended questions rather than yes/no questions, and should allow the target speaker to introduce new topics. Eliciting a conversational sample is like talking with your grandmother to find out what life was like when she was growing up; you get to listen a lot and say encouraging things to express your interest. Hopefully she will do most of the talking – which is the point of the conversation.

Conversational samples are particularly useful in documenting language abilities of children and adults diagnosed with autism spectrum disorder and the related diagnosis of social communication disorder. These samples provide access to the social aspects of communication, such as listening, initiating and responding on topic, adding new information, responding to requests for clarification, answering questions, and allowing the partner to speak.

- Narration - story tell or retell

  We engage in narrative language when we tell someone about an event attended, a book, a T.V. episode, or a movie. Narrative samples, in general, require less interaction from the examiner as the focus is on the target speaker to tell or retell a story. The examiner introduces the task, helping the speaker identify a story to tell or reviewing a specific story to retell. After that, it is up to speaker to proceed with as little coaching as possible. Narratives require remembering sequences of actions or events that must be told in order to form a coherent text. Narratives emerge between three and four years of age. However, our research reveals that narrative ability is not consistent until after age four. Our work also documents that children produce longer and more complex utterances in narration than in conversation.

  Where conversations are utterance based, narratives are text based, formed by many utterances produced in a logical order to convey the information. Narratives fall into two groups for language sample analysis purposes, 1) narratives where the speaker knows the content but the examiner may not, and, 2) narratives where both the speaker and the examiner know the content. Event narratives entail relating an event experienced directly. Telling a story from memory, relating a movie or an episode of a TV show, making up a story, or retelling a story just heard are also types of oral narratives. There are excellent reasons to consider each type of narrative, determining the optimum language sample to collect. If you let the speaker choose the story, you may foster individual motivation to tell the best story. If you choose the story, you can interpret the content and vocabulary in detail.

- Narration - expository

  When we impart information, such as how to do something or how to play a game, we are engaging in exposition, also called procedural narration. Expository skills are acquired later in childhood through adolescence. Research documents exposition produces more complex syntax than story retelling or conversation (Nippold, 2010). Exposition in spoken and written language is part of every state's instructional standards from middle elementary through high school. This suggests that expository language samples are an excellent choice for late elementary, middle, and high school students, as well as adults. The most common expository task used in oral language research is the telling of how to play a favorite game. This can be an individual sport, a team sport, or a board game. Our research on exposition corroborates other studies documenting that speakers produce more complex language in exposition than in conversation or story narratives (Malone, et al., 2008; Malone, et al., 2010). Our research also documents that game types are equivalent in eliciting valid expository language samples.

- Narration - persuasion

Persuasion can be defined as "the use of argumentation to convince another person to perform an act or accept the point of view desired by the persuader" (Nippold, 2007). It figures prominently in academic standards, such as the Common Core State Standards, that cut across modes of communication: speaking, listening, reading, and writing (National Governors Association, 2010). The ability to persuade is required across the secondary curriculum. Acquiring persuasive skills is critical to success in college and career, and to full participation in social and civic life. Persuasion challenges students to take into account their audience's perspective and to use complex language to express complex ideas. Our preliminary research indicates that this sampling context produces shorter samples than the expository task, but facilitates the production of more complex language.

In general, consider eliciting conversational samples for children less than 4 – 5 years of age because narrative skills are just emerging at about four years. We have found that narrative samples, particularly story retell, exposition, and persuasion expand the information we can glean from the language sample as they are more challenging than conversation and are central to language arts curricula in schools. The SALT narrative databases allow measures of vocabulary, syntax, rate, fluency, and textual content and structure relative to age or grade-matched peers reported in standard deviation units. Narrative samples require less examiner vigilance, increasing examiner confidence in the reliability of the sample.

Sample Length

How long does a language sample need to be to ensure a valid reflection of oral language performance? This question has been asked repeatedly over the years. The answer is, as you might expect, it depends. We have spent a great deal of effort addressing this issue as it reflects on all other aspects of the LSA process. Shorter samples are faster to elicit and transcribe. *But will they include the important features of language under scrutiny?* Our original target sample size of 100 utterances, which turned out to produce consistent results across children of the same ages, could be recorded in 10-12 minutes and transcribed in 60 – 90 minutes. Subsequent research determined that smaller samples produced similar results in a much shorter time frame. Conversational samples of 5 minutes in duration resulted in approximately 50 utterances, cutting transcription time in half. We also learned that children talk more as they get older so it takes longer to elicit a sample of 50 utterances from a three year old than a 5 year old. In fact, there is a linear relationship between age and amount of talking per unit time. Children having difficulty with oral language usually take longer to produce a reliable language sample. For more information on the impact of sample size on outcome measures, read the article *Language Sampling: Does the Length of the Transcript Matter?* by Heilmann, Nockerts, and Miller, J. (2010).

SALT Reference Databases

Participants included in the SALT databases vary in age, gender, socioeconomic status, and geographic location. Different elicitation protocols were used to collect the samples, and each sample included in a database was elicited following the corresponding protocol. The participants in each database were all typically developing and reflected the range of SES and school ability in their communities, with no history of special education. Each database was the product of one or more research studies confirming stability of performance within ages and grades, and documenting changes associated with advancing age across a range of measurements. Selecting a sample type using these sampling protocols allows you to create an age or grade-matched set of peers to document strengths and weaknesses. You can also elicit more than one sample type to make sure language production is representative of a variety of speaking conditions found in daily use.

SALT Reference Database	Samples	Ages	Grades	Location	Appendix
Play	69	2;8–5;8	P,K	Wisconsin	A
Conversation	584	2;9–13;3	P,K,1,2,3,5,7	Wisconsin & California	B
Narrative SSS (Student Selects Story)	330	5;2–13;3	K,1,2,3,5,7	Wisconsin	C

Narrative Story Retell
  Frog, Where Are You? (FWAY)
  Pookins Gets Her Way (PGHW)
  A Porcupine Named Fluffy (APNF)
  Doctor De Soto (DDS)
	
	145
	101
	53
	201
		
		4;4–7;5
		7;0–8;11
		7;11–9;11
		9;3–12;8
			
			P,K,1
			2
			3
			4,5,6
				Wisconsin & California	D

Expository	354	10;7–18;9	5–7, 9–12	Wisconsin	E
Persuasion	179	12;10–18;9	9–12	Wisconsin & Australia	F

Bilingual Spanish/English Story Retell
  Frog, Where Are You? (FWAY)
  Frog Goes To Dinner (FGTD)
  Frog On His Own (FOHO)
	
	2,070
	1,667
	930
		
		5;0–9;9
		5;5–8;11
		6;0–7;9
			
			K,1,2,3
			K,2
			1
				Texas & California	G

Bilingual Spanish/English Unique Story *One Frog Too Many* (OFTM)	 475	 4;1–9;7	 K,1,2,3	Texas & California	H

Monolingual Spanish Story Retell
  Frog Goes To Dinner (FGTD)
  Frog On His Own (FOHO)
  Frog, Where Are You? (FWAY)
  One Frog Too Many (OFTM)
	
	360
	188
	366
	154
		
		6;4-10;6
		6;1–10;1
		5;10–9;11
		6;9–10;7
			
			1,2,3
				Guadalajara, Mexico	I

ENNI (*story generation from pictures*)	377	3;11–10;0		Canada	J
Gillam Narrative Tasks	500	5;0–11;11		4 US Regions	K

New Zealand/Australia Databases
  Conversation
  Story Retell (*Anna Gets Lost*)
  Personal Narrative
  Expository
	
	350
	476
	355
	107
		
		4;5–8;4
		4;0–8;9
		4;5–8;4
		6;1–8;4
				New Zealand & Australia	L-1
					L-2
					L-3
					L-4

Figure 2-1

Figure 2-1 lists the reference databases included with SALT software. Language samples you collect, following SALT's protocols, may be compared to age or grade-matched peers selected from these databases. For each database, the number of samples, the age range, grade range (*if available*), and the geographic locations are listed.

- Play database

  Language samples from young children, ages 2;8 to 5;8, were collected in a play format allowing the child to talk about ongoing events and refer to past and future events as they were able. Like other conversational samples, the examiner was required to follow the child's lead, expand utterances, comment on ongoing actions and events, and ask open-ended questions to encourage talking when necessary. See Appendix A.

- Conversation database

  The SALT Conversation database was one of our earliest databases, driven by the wealth of developmental data from research studies on language development. This SALT database uses a protocol prescribing face-to-face talk with an examiner on general topics of home, school, or holidays for children 3 - 13 years of age. Conversation requires examiners to introduce topics, then encourage speakers to expand on their own experiences, responding to open-ended questions and requests for clarification. See Appendix B.

- Narrative SSS (Student Selects Story) database

  The SSS narrative protocol was developed to provide speakers with the most motivation to tell their best story. The protocol allows the speaker to select a story, movie, or TV program to retell with minimal prompts from the examiner. The advantage of this genre is the speaker's familiarity with the story, which optimizes motivation to tell as complete a story as possible. The disadvantage is that the content of the story and specific vocabulary may not be known by the examiner, which may limit interpretation of vocabulary use and story structure.

This protocol was the earliest narrative protocol examined in our research. It was developed as part of a project focused on comparing conversational and narrative language from school-aged children. Children younger than 4 - 5 years had difficulty with this task, which allowed us to identify the baseline for documenting narrative language. For children older than 4 - 5 years, this protocol worked very well. The Narrative SSS protocol is a more linguistically challenging task than conversation. See Appendix C.

● Narrative Story Retell database

The next narrative protocol examined in our research was story retelling where children narrated a story just told to them. This protocol allowed us to develop methods to analyze narrative structure and specific content because the story was known or familiar to both the examiner and the speaker being assessed. This protocol required us to select specific stories that would be age appropriate and motivating for speakers of both genders, and be as culture-free as possible. We began by using the story *Frog, Where are You?* (Mayer, 1969) which had been used in language development research for decades with children 4 - 10 years of age. Different stories had to be identified for children beyond first grade, as research, and our experience, indicated that children did not use more complex language after about age eight. We used different stories for the 2nd, 3rd, and 4th - 6th grades (*see Figure 2-1 for the story titles*). These stories increased in complexity while providing age-appropriate interest. Our research on children's story retells indicates that children retell increasingly complex stories with advancing grades. Their stories are longer with more complex syntax, larger vocabularies, and more complete story structures.

The databases can be used to compare age or grade-level expectations. Using the same stories allows you to compare what the child included in their retell as well as what they left out. Specific vocabulary for each story can also be compared. Our research has shown story retells produced short consistent samples that were easily transcribed. The examiner introduces the task, reviews the story while sharing the pictures, then asks the speaker to tell the story. This context places minimal demand on the examiner, and results in stories that are short, focused, and consistent over age and grade. See Appendix D.

- Expository database

The expository protocol involves describing how to play a favorite game or sport. This can be an individual or team sport, a board or yard game. Our initial research project involved 7th and 9th graders and we found that, no matter which type of game was described, the language produced was similar in amount and complexity (Malone, et al., 2008). This finding is very helpful when helping a student select a familiar game to talk about and compare to the database samples.

The Expository database was recently expanded and now contains language samples from 5th - 7th, and 9th - 12th grade students. Research on language development in adolescents and the experience of clinicians providing services for middle and high school students motivated the creation and subsequent expansion of this database. Research on exposition documents that students produce more complex language in exposition than in conversation or narration, making it a more challenging sampling context (Malone, et al. 2008; Nippold, 2010). Expository sampling using SALT requires the examiner to introduce the task and help select the game or sport to talk about. The examiner then monitors the speaker, who makes notes using a matrix of topics that should be covered when providing a complete rendition of the game or sport. The speaker's notes are used to guide the speaker through the task. This task is linguistically challenging and research is still exploring the limits of its use for children and adults (Miller, Andriacchi, & Nockerts, in press). See Appendix E.

- Persuasion Database

The persuasion protocol requires the student to present a persuasive argument for a change in their school, workplace, or community. The argument is to be directed at the student's principal, supervisor, or government official. The student can choose an issue of personal interest or select from a list of suggested issues. The student is given a few minutes to complete a planning sheet which contains six topics (Issue Id and Desired Change, Supporting Reasons, Counter Arguments, Response to Counter Arguments, Compromises, and Conclusion). Next to each point is a brief description of what is covered within that topic and space for making notes. The student is then asked to present his or her persuasive argument. The persuasion task reflects a skill essential for success across the secondary curriculum and for success as a friend, family member, employee, and citizen. Oral persuasion is under-represented in standardized speech-language assessment tools and is a linguistically challenging task that we believe is sensitive to language impairment.

The Persuasion reference database consists of 179 samples from typically developing adolescents fluent in English. Students were drawn from public schools in two geographic areas of Wisconsin: Milwaukee area school districts, and Madison Metropolitan School District and from public schools across the state of Queensland, Australia. There are students from a variety of economic backgrounds and ability levels. See Appendix F.

At the time of this writing, we are collaborating with clinicians from the San Diego Unified School District to elicit additional persuasive samples.

- Bilingual (Spanish/English) Story Retell & Bilingual (Spanish/English) Unique Story databases

The Bilingual (Spanish/English) databases were the result of a collaborative research project supported by the NIH - NICHD and the Institute for Educational Research, U.S. Office of Education. The goal of this research was to investigate factors associated with successful reading and school achievement among bilingual children whose first language was Spanish. Several thousand children living in Texas and California attending K - 3rd grade served as participants. Language samples were collected from each child retelling the same story in both Spanish and English. A subset of these children also told a similar, but unfamiliar, second story in each language. The databases were created to provide clinical access to typical, Spanish/English bilingual children allowing comparison of their English and Spanish language skills. These databases are unique, as they are the largest set of oral language samples from bilingual children nationally or internationally. See Appendices G and H.

- Monolingual Spanish Story Retell Database

  The Monolingual Spanish Retell stories were contributed by Dr. Claude Goldenberg as part of the NICHD grant R01 HD44923, "Language and Literacy Development in Mexican Children" on which he was a P.I.

  The Narrative story retells in Spanish were elicited using a standard protocol which included a story script to aid the examiner when modeling the story, from a wordless picture book, in their own words. Examiners were trained to use minimal open-ended prompts when eliciting the samples. The child was seated next to an examiner who told the story in Spanish. The examiner and child looked at the story together as it was told. The examiner then left the book with the child, moved slightly away from the child, and instructed the child to tell the story back using his/her own words. See Appendix I.

- ENNI Database

  The Edmonton Narrative Norms Instrument (ENNI) was developed by Phyllis Schneider who was interested in providing normative data for typical children in Edmonton, Canada (Schneider, Dubé, & Hayward, 2005). The Province provided grant funds for the project.

  Stories were written and children aged 4 - 10 retold them using a specific protocol. The major outcome of this work was the consistency of their oral narrative performance within age groups and the consistent progress across the entire age range. This work confirms our findings that oral language samples do provide a consistent and powerful index of language skills over time and across genres. The ENNI project, along with the stories and elicitation protocols, can be found at ww.rehabmed.ualberta.ca/spa/enni/. See Appendix J.

- Gillam Narrative Tasks Database

  The Gillam Narrative Tasks database came from Ron Gillam's normative testing of the Test of Narrative Language (Gillam & Pearson, 2004). He was interested in adding his transcribed oral narratives to SALT to allow users to examine the oral narratives elicited from the test in more detail. The 500 samples are the completed normative data set from the test. This database can provide users with the opportunity to examine word, utterance, and narrative structure using objective measures. See Appendix K.

- New Zealand – Australia Databases

  The New Zealand databases were the result of collaboration with Gail Gillon and Marleen Westerveld. They were interested in creating a national database of oral language samples which would document language development for New Zealand children and allow these data to be used to document disordered language performance. A practice-based research project was undertaken with volunteer speech-language pathologists from around the country. Each recorded 5 - 7 samples from typical children of specific ages. The result was a database of several hundred children 4 - 8 years of age producing conversations, story retells, personal narratives, and expositions. Several published research papers have resulted from this work (Westerveld, Gillon, & Miller, 2004; Westerveld, Gillon, & Moran, 2008; Westerveld and Gillon, 2010a, 2010b), the most recent comparing the New Zealand and American data sets (Westerveld & Heilmann, 2010). The results revealed remarkable similarities across the two countries. The most significant difference occurred with the five year olds who, in New Zealand, seem to be slightly more advanced than their American counterparts. It is suggested that this difference may be due to when they enter school. Children in New Zealand enter school on their fifth birthday rather than waiting for the start of the next school year as is done in the U.S. This research collaboration led to the creation of the first national database of New Zealand language development.

Marleen Westerveld expanded the databases by collecting samples from students in Queensland, Australia following the same protocol as was used when collecting the New Zealand samples. See Appendix L.

Eliciting Samples for Comparison with the SALT Reference Databases

The SALT databases provide the opportunity to compare an individual language sample to age or grade-matched peers. In order for the comparison to be valid, however, language samples must be elicited following the same protocol as was used to collect the database samples. Conversations must be all conversation without narratives intruding. Similarly, narratives must be all narratives without conversation intruding. Comparison of narratives requires following the specific protocol used in eliciting the narratives in the comparison database. Narratives where the student selects the story (SSS narratives) can validly be compared to any story the speaker selects following the SSS protocol. Story retell narratives, where the speaker retells the same story they've just heard or followed, should only be compared to other story retells of the same story. And expository and persuasive narratives must be compared to their respective database samples in order to get valid results. In each case the protocol will result in samples that are comparable, with reliable outcomes, as long as they were collected under the same conditions and transcribed using SALT's transcription conventions.

From a developmental perspective, our research documents that the language produced by these different sampling contexts provides speakers with increasing challenges. From conversation to narration to exposition to persuasion, speakers produce more complex language, longer sentences, and more different words, as well as more errors, repetitions, and revisions. As students progress through the curriculum, conversational skills become less important, with the exception of some students on the autism spectrum. Narrative and expository skills underlie much of the literacy curriculum, particularly written language.

What if There Isn't a Comparable Database?

Even without a reference database to use for comparison, a good language sample can provide a wealth of information about a person's expressive language. The SALT *Standard Measures Report* groups together some of the most informative language measures to give an overall summary of the speakers' language performance. This report provides data on transcript length, syntax/morphology, semantics, discourse, intelligibility, mazes and abandoned utterances, verbal facility and rate, and omissions and errors.

Two samples from the same speaker may be linked for a Time1/Time2, Pre/Post, Language1/Language2, or Protocol1/Protocol2 comparison. This information can be extraordinarily useful for diagnostic purposes as well as for tracking response to intervention.

Suggestions for Eliciting the Best Language Sample

Speakers are more likely to converse if they believe listeners are really interested in what they have to say. If they doubt a listener's sincerity, younger speakers may simply refuse to cooperate. Older speakers may cooperate but may provide only minimal responses that do not reflect their language ability. The speaker who has difficulties is often reticent and requires an environment of trust to achieve optimal communication. *How can the examiner create this environment and gather the most representative sample of the speaker's expressive language skills?*

The first few minutes of the language sample interaction are critical. If the examiner fails to establish a comfortable rapport with the speaker, the resulting language sample may be strained and lack the necessary spontaneity to function as a valid index of the speaker's expressive language performance. Taking a few minutes to visit before moving on to the sampling protocol is helpful. The goal is to elicit a sample which is representative of the communicative behaviors in question. The following are suggestions to help achieve this goal:

- Be friendly and enthusiastic. Give the speaker your undivided attention, showing interest with smiles, vocal inflection, and eye contact.
- Be patient. Allow the speaker space and time to perform and don't be afraid of pauses. Use a relaxed rate of speech as a fast rate can cause communicative pressure.

- Get the most language by using open-ended prompts and following the speaker's lead. If the protocol allows, ask for clarification. This indicates interest and is informative to the assessment.
- If the protocol allows for questions, avoid yes/no and specific "wh" questions, such as what-are questions, as they tend to elicit one word responses. Ask age-appropriate questions and avoid asking questions when the speaker knows you already have the answer. Don't ask more than one question at a time.

These suggestions are relevant for all speakers regardless of their cultural, economic, or language background, or their cognitive, physical, or speech and language differences. The goal is to provide the speaker the maximum opportunity to communicate to the best of his or her ability. There is no substitute for experience in talking with speakers of various ages and ability levels. But even the most experienced examiner must guard against behavior that might inhibit the speaker's performance.

What constitutes a valid language sample?

1. The examiner follows the elicitation protocol.
2. The elicitation protocol challenges the speaker's production abilities.
3. The speaker produces a sample that is representative of his or her language.
4. At least 80% of the sample is intelligible (*find a quiet area and use a quality recording device*).

What materials are needed to elicit the samples?

1. An audio recorder. Digital is preferred. An external microphone is usually not necessary with a digital recorder.
2. A quiet area, preferably with a table and two chairs.
3. Any books, pictures, audios, or other materials required for the specific elicitation protocol.

Summary

Keep in mind that the people you are trying to evaluate may not have a successful history talking spontaneously. The SALT elicitation protocols have been very effective in eliciting language under a variety of conditions. Eliciting samples still requires your clinical skill to encourage optimum productive language from individuals who may be poor communicators. The language sample process allows you to take several different samples without affecting the outcome of each. So if the first sample does not work out, try again. The databases will allow you to bring precision to your interpretation of the results. Be clear about your clinical objectives as they are central to collecting a sample relevant to meeting your goals. Keep in mind that the better the sample you record, the better the analysis results will reflect the speaker's language skills. The next step in the process is to render the sample into a form that SALT can analyze. That requires converting the acoustic recording to text, in other words, transcription.

Transcribing Language Samples

Jon F. Miller
Karen Andriacchi
Ann Nockerts

Why Transcribe?

Transcribing oral language into orthographic text has a long history. It has been used to preserve meeting outcomes with "Minutes", to record legal proceedings for trial transcripts and depositions, to provide access to oral language for the Deaf community with closed captioning on television, and, for many years, stenographers had to "take a letter". These few examples serve to point out that transcribing oral language captures what was said at various events and provides access to that language at a later time. Today, there are software applications which convert speech to text. With little or no training, these applications can produce fairly accurate text. *So can we use them for our language samples?* The answer, unfortunately, is "not at this time". Certainly speech recognition keeps improving, but it still requires intelligible speech which follows standard grammar rules. Our speakers are not so considerate. We could have the speech recognition software create a first draft of the text that we could then edit. Or we could speak the sample into the computer while listening to the recording. We have tried these approaches and find that they actually take more time to edit and review for reliability than simply transcribing the original oral sample. SALT requires a transcript which follows specific transcription rules. These rules specify words, morphemes, and utterances. Exact transcription ensures accurate counts for the measures SALT calculates.

For now, transcription using software such as SALT, with live listeners and typists, is the best and most accurate option for populations seen in the field of speech-language pathology.

Transcription is often thought of as an activity that is difficult and time consuming. In truth, once the coding conventions are learned, transcription is not difficult and the process provides a wide scope of insight into oral language skills, showing both strengths and weaknesses. You might consider it to be detailed listening. We have created a transcription format that ensures accuracy (Heilmann, et al., 2008) and provides for many levels of detail. At the basic level, you can code words, morphemes, and utterances and the software will provide measures like mean length of utterance, number of different words, and total words. Marking pauses and transcript duration produce measures of speaking rate and can pinpoint frequency, duration, and location of pauses. Add marking for repetitions, revisions, and filled pauses, and get an analysis of their frequency as well as a breakdown of repetitions and revisions as partial words, whole words, and phrases. These measures allow you to say something about whether verbal fluency problems are at the word level, as in word retrieval, or at the phrase level having more to do with syntactic formulation. The next deeper level of linguistic analysis allows for coding of words or utterances for specific features. An example we have incorporated into our analysis set, the Subordination Index, is a fast measure of clause density associated with complex sentence use. This measure requires coding for each utterance in the sample using the SALT coding routines (see Appendix O). The SALT transcription process is designed to provide the most information for the least transcription effort. Utterances need to be identified with appropriate ending punctuation, and words are defined by spaces on each side. Everything else is optional. The more you mark or code, however, the deeper and more thorough the subsequent analysis will be.

Overview of SALT Transcription

The record of oral language created with a SALT transcript allows for a variety of immediate analyses and offers the opportunity for additional analysis in the future. Transcription may seem like a daunting task when just beginning, but working through the transcription process has incalculable rewards as the first step for problem solving an individual's oral language skills. Practice leads to proficiency.

The basic transcription protocol in SALT (see Appendix M) specifies conventions to identify utterances, words, morphemes, pauses, unintelligibility, omissions, and errors used to calculate specific language measures. Our first goal was *time efficiency*, keeping coding to a minimum for basic level analysis. Subsequent coding, if desired, would be guided by the results of the initial analyses across all language levels.

It was also important to create a readable transcript that could be easily followed and understood by family and other professionals. Transcripts can be shared with colleagues to increase accuracy in diagnosis and intervention. This process is particularly important for complex problems. Clinicians have reported sharing transcripts with diagnostic team members, parents, teachers, and administrators to clarify oral language concerns and to support other diagnostic results. Transcripts, along with the audio/video files, can be stored as part of clinical records to facilitate sharing of information.

SALT provides you with helpful tools. A specialized editor facilitates every step of the transcription process, from setting up descriptive information about the speaker and context to a transcript error routine that identifies format errors and guides correction. SALT has built-in help at every level. When transcribing, specific transcription coding features can be easily accessed, producing a list of all transcription features, their definitions, and examples for use. This is particularly useful for infrequently used conventions. Once a transcript is completed, a variety of analyses can easily be calculated. This transcription format ensures that all analyses are calculated accurately. The uniformity of the process overcomes the major weakness cited for completing LSA by hand, *consistency*. With SALT, all transcription is completed using the same method, regardless of the type of sample or age of the speaker.

Transcription Requirements

The SALT software and some method for audio/video playback are required for transcription. Digital recordings greatly improve the overall sound quality of a language sample which, in turn, improves the ability to accurately and more efficiently transcribe what was spoken. Digital recordings also allow for easy and fast manipulation of the audio or video file, e.g., moving forward and back, or repeating segments of language. File transfer and copying is fast and simple with digital recordings. There are a number of options for controlling the playback of digital files for transcription. For those who plan on transcribing frequently, we have found foot pedal controls (*hands free*) reduce transcription time and improve the overall accuracy of the transcript. There are also a number of software programs available for controlling the playback of digital files which are often free downloads or come installed on your computer. The SALT web site has recommendations for digital recorders and play back hardware and software.

You do not need to be a speech pathologist to transcribe a language sample. Transcribing oral language into the SALT editor requires the ability to type, fluency in the language recorded, knowledge of the elicitation protocol, and familiarity with SALT transcription conventions. With experience, you develop the ability to rapidly and accurately code samples using the SALT transcription conventions. A number of school districts have set up transcription stations staffed by speech pathology aides or individuals with clerical experience. These transcribers produce transcripts that can be used to create the basic reports leaving more technical coding, when necessary, to individual SLPs.

How long does it take to transcribe a language sample? The transcription tools available with SALT greatly speed up the transcription process. In our review on frog story retells, transcription time took an average of 40 minutes. This included specialized coding for clause density and story structure. These audio files were 3 – 6 minutes in length and averaged about 60 utterances. Longer samples take more time of course. Conversational samples generally take longer because topics can vary so much. Story retells have the advantage of providing the same expectations, characters, vocabulary, and story line for the transcriber. Experience also makes a difference. Just as in typing or keyboarding, practice makes perfect.

The Underpinnings of Transcription

The first transcription decisions to be made are *what is a word?* and *what is an utterance?* This sounds simple enough, but consistency is required.

<u>What is a word?</u>
The SALT transcript format defines a word as a set of characters bound by spaces. In SALT, *fsqwú* is a word, though not recognizable in English. We transcribe what is said using standard orthography. This means that we transcribe the words used but not the pronunciation used by the speaker. Articulation errors are not typed in a SALT transcript. Word transcription is driven by using the same spelling for words heard regardless of articulation. For example, a speaker who reduces /r/ clusters might say "tuck" for "truck". Contextually, the transcriber would know the speaker intended to say "truck" and thus would type the word "truck" to get accurate vocabulary measures. Similarly, pronunciation differences due to regional dialects are not typed in a SALT transcript. As an example, the speaker drops the "g" and says "waitin" for "waiting". This would be transcribed as "waiting" (see Chapter 8 for a discussion of dialectal variations in African American English). Note that clinicians interested in tracking articulation errors and dialectal variations could mark the instances using word codes (see the "Customized Coding" section later in this chapter).

The reason for using the intended word rather than the pronounced word is consistency. Standard spelling conventions are needed to avoid increasing the number of different words used within and across transcripts. Six different spellings of the same word would be counted as six different words in the program. Uniform spelling is essential to obtaining accurate counts of the number of different words used in a sample. "Ahhhh I see", and "Ah I see", although spoken with different intonation, should be spelled consistently, e.g., "Ah".

<u>What is an utterance?</u>
A number of rules to define utterances have been used in the research literature. Utterances can be segmented using Phonological Units (P-units) which are based on speakers' pauses and intonation in the speech sample

(Loban, 1963). Communication Units (C-units) are the most commonly used method of segmenting (Loban, 1976). They are defined as a main clause with all its dependent clauses. Minimal Terminable Units (T-units) are a variation of C-unit rules, originally defined to segment written language (Hunt, 1965). Over the years we have moved from using P-units to using C-units because the more syntax-based rules of the C-unit provided greater consistency. This was particularly true as we increased the age of the children we studied. Despite using consistent rules that have been time-tested through research, children and adults still say things that are puzzling to segment. These surprises have led to the creation of the "utterance of the week" in our lab which has led to many spirited discussions on how to segment or code properly. Typically, 95% of the transcription process is straight forward with 5% of the decisions requiring more thought or creativity.

SALT is focused on word, morpheme, utterance, and discourse features of the language, and transcription decisions define the measures calculated for each language feature. Language production, rather than speech production, is the focus. As you learn the transcription coding rules, you will begin to appreciate that each decision for a specific feature has an impact on how other features are defined for analysis. Learning to transcribe will help you understand the interrelationship among the features of our language.

Anatomy of a Transcript

Figure 3-1 shows an excerpt from a SALT transcript. The lines at the beginning of the transcript make up the transcript header. Header information is entered into a dialogue box presented when you create a new transcript in SALT. The information you enter in the header dialogue box is inserted at the beginning of the new transcript. The speaker label line, which begins with a dollar sign, identifies the speakers in the transcript. The identification lines begin with a plus sign and contain identification information such as the target speaker's gender and current age. The initial timing line begins with a hyphen. The example given here is one possibility of what the header information may look like at the beginning of a transcript. Your header will vary depending on what information you choose to fill in.

Figure 3-1

Once the header information is specified, you are ready to type what was spoken during the language sample. Each utterance must begin with a speaker identification letter. These letters should correspond to the first letter of the speaker label as specified in the $ speaker label line. For example, if your speaker label line is $ Child, Examiner, each child utterance will begin with C and each examiner utterance will begin with E, as shown in the example above. Each utterance is segmented according to the rules chosen for the sample. For the most thorough and accurate analysis results each utterance should be marked and coded following the basic SALT transcription conventions (see Appendix M).

Customized Coding

SALT allows you to devise your own codes to analyze any feature of the language sample that you are interested in. These codes can be inserted anywhere within a word or at the end of specific words or utterances, depending upon the features of interest. One example of custom coding includes marking responses to questions as appropriate [AR], inappropriate [IR], or no response [NR]. The transcript might look like the following:

> E Do you have any plan/s for the weekend?
> C No **[AR]**.
> E Did you know there/'s a track meet here on Saturday **[NR]**?
> : 0:05
> E Do you know anyone on the track team?
> C I don't like track **[IR]**.

Codes could be created to mark suprasegmental features if important to the diagnostic, e.g., [PR] for pitch rise and [FI] for falling intonation. These codes can then be pulled up in the analyses for further investigation of frequency or patterns of use. Coding schemes for articulation errors and dialectal variations can be created, or existing schemes can be implemented. With bilingual or multilingual speakers we often see code switching. Code switches can be marked at the word and/or utterance level with a code, e.g., [CS], to be further reviewed or counted. When transcribing from video samples, non-verbal communication behaviors such as points, nods, or shrugs can be marked. Unique coding is also useful for tracking progress made in therapy with specifically coded repeat samples. An example might include work on increasing specific referencing with pronoun use. Pronouns with unclear referents in the sample can be marked with a code during transcription and later pulled up in the analysis. There are endless possibilities for unique coding schemes since the coding is so flexible.

When creating new codes or when using less frequently used codes in SALT, it is helpful to insert plus lines at the beginning of the transcript to define the codes for the reader. See Figure 3-2.

```
$ Child, Examiner
+ Gender: F
+ CA: 6;8
+ Context: Con
+ [EW] = word-level error
+ [EU] = utterance-level error
+ [CS] = code switching
```

Figure 3-2

Transcription Reliability

At the end of the day, can you learn the basic transcription codes and use them reliably to create an orthographic record of oral language? We addressed this question in a research project to document transcription accuracy and reliability (Heilmann, et.al. 2008). This project looked at English and Spanish narrative samples elicited from bilingual children retelling the story *Frog, Where Are You?* by Mercer Meyer (1969). All samples were digitally recorded and later transcribed by a trained master's-level student majoring in speech-language pathology. On average, it took the transcribers 30 minutes to transcribe each sample.

Transcript protocol accuracy was analyzed by having a proficient transcriber review transcripts for adherence to the SALT coding conventions; checking for accuracy in utterance segmentation, words within the main body of the utterance, words in mazes, and maze placement. Percent agreement was high across the board (90% - 100%) suggesting the transcribers consistently adhered to the transcription procedure. *Transcription consensus* was analyzed to identify differences in transcripts completed by a single transcriber against the "gold standard" transcript; checking for accuracy in words and morphemes, utterance segmentation, maze placement, pauses, and utterance type. Transcribers were very reliable in transcribing samples with percent agreement of 90% - 99%, with the exception of marking pauses (60% - 70%). *Test-retest reliability* was also calculated for samples collected within a two week period. Results revealed significant correlation values from r=.69 to r=.79 noting a very high level of agreement that is statistically the same. These data, however, indicate some variability across transcripts. To determine the impact of this variability, SALT analyses were calculated for each transcript. Statistical analysis found that both transcripts (test-retest) provided the same values across measures of syntax (mean length of utterance in words), semantics (number of different word roots), and total productivity (number of total words and words per minute). While some variability is inevitable when making decisions during transcription, these analyses document that the impact on the measures of language performance is negligible.

This work demonstrates that language samples can provide consistent data for documenting language performance across individuals and within the same client over time. You can have confidence that using SALT transcription codes will result in reliable transcripts of oral language use. This work also dispels the myth that language samples are too variable to provide robust clinical data. On the contrary, your transcription of individual samples will provide you with the tools to document your practice.

Transcribing in Other Languages: Challenges and Rewards

Our bilingual Spanish/English research project (Miller, et al., 2006) presented us with a major challenge; how to make consistent transcription decisions for Spanish that would allow comparison with English transcripts. In order to compare an individual's Spanish language skills with their English language skills we needed to be sure we were counting the same elements; words, morphemes, and utterances. Aquiles Iglesias and Raúl Rojas, who at the time were at Temple University, collaborated with us to design the Spanish transcription format for SALT (see Chapter 7 for details). It took the better part of a year to work out how to code specific features of Spanish which are inherently different than English, such as verb inflections and bound versus unbound clitics. Once the transcription rules were defined, the final product, which included reference databases for comparison in both English and Spanish, proved to be such a valuable tool that we built it into the SALT software. This has been well received and frequently used by both researchers and clinicians.

Through collaboration with Elin Thordardottir at McGill University (Thordardottir, 2005) and Elizabeth Kay-Rainingbird at Dalhousie University, SALT now supports French transcription and reporting. Funda Acarlar, a colleague at Ankara University in Turkey, used SALT to transcribe samples in Turkish to produce its own database for comparison in the language, in essence creating local norms which resulted in a customized version of SALT (Acarlar & Johnston, 2006).

There has been interest in using SALT with other languages as well. The challenge is always to make consistent transcription decisions within the language. Words and utterances must be clearly defined. The end product, however, will offer the benefit being able to analyze functional language produced in real-life settings.

Summary

Suffice it to say that transcription is the core of LSA. If done with care and consistency you will have a valuable snapshot of spoken language to evaluate. Understand that there will be a few puzzling features of almost every transcript. To accurately capture the speaker's language, think about what was said and how it was intended. Work toward typing and coding precisely what was communicated while appreciating the diversity of human communication within and across age (see Appendix M).

Analyzing Language Samples

Jon F. Miller
Karen Andriacchi
Ann Nockerts

Analyzing the sample is where we begin to see the tremendous power that computers bring to the task. SALT can be used to create a series of reports of word, morpheme, discourse, rate, fluency, and error measures. To make this happen it is important to understand the overall structure of the program and learn the specifics of the menu choices available. This chapter focuses on the organization of the SALT measures, explaining why they are included in the software, what you can learn from each score, and where to go to further evaluate a specific problem. The software calculates a wide variety of measures which are accessed from the menus. In this discussion, the focus is on two of these menus: Analyze and Database.

When analyzing language samples, it is important to create an approach that examines each transcript systematically, making sure that all levels of language performance are evaluated. The transcript includes utterances from one or more speakers, representing features of the sample such as unintelligible segments, repetitions, revisions, pauses, overlapping speech, abandoned utterances, and words or bound morphemes omitted in obligatory context. This transcribed sample is the basis for all measures.

Review the Transcript

It's easy to get excited at this point and plunge into the detailed analyses of the transcript. It is important to remember, however, that the results of the analyses need to be placed in context to create an overall description of oral language performance. Prior to analyzing the transcript, it is strongly suggested you follow these steps:

1. Re-read the transcript while listening to the recording. This will help you to consider the reliability of the recording as a valid index of the targeted speaker's oral language.

2. Make changes to the transcript where necessary. If transcription was done by someone other than yourself, there may be unintelligible segments that you, as a familiar listener, can understand. Or, it is possible that the transcriber upheld the speaker to a higher or lower standard of proper syntax than you desire for the speaker's age or the sample context. You should be aware of coding decisions made by the transcriber and make changes to ensure the transcript is authentic to the speaker's intent.

3. Look back on the issues raised in the referral by teachers, parents/family, by you, or by a fellow team member. *Does the transcript provide a sample of oral language which reflects the reasons for referral?*

Analysis Menu Options

Analysis of the language in the transcript is completed using two main menu options in SALT: Analyze and Database. They are introduced here but are discussed, in greater detail, later in this chapter.

The Analyze menu produces reports which summarize information from the current SALT transcript *independent of the reference databases*. These reports provide information for two speakers in the sample, as defined by the $ speaker line at the beginning of the transcript.

The *Database* menu produces reports which compare language measures from an individual's transcript to age or grade-matched samples selected from one of the SALT reference databases.

SALT Reference Databases

Language sample analysis has long been held as a valid indicator of expressive language performance in children. Several factors, however, have limited its general use including a lack of standardized procedures for eliciting language samples, validated measurement categories, normative data, and relevant interpretation strategies. Over the past several years, each of these issues has been addressed through research projects. Analyses of data obtained from these projects have led to the development of standardized language sampling procedures, language sample norms, and interpretation strategies that can be used in the evaluation process for determining the existence of a handicapping condition in expressive language. These data also have direct implications for determining special education program intervention strategies and in monitoring student progress. The language sample norms obtained from these research projects have been stored in the SALT reference databases (see Chapter 2).

Underlying Constructs

Let us take a look at three important underlying constructs that are the backbone of the SALT analysis process. There are default settings for each of these constructs which can be changed to suit your needs using the *Setup* menu.

- **Analysis Set (C&I Verbal Utts)**

  The *analysis set* in SALT is a subset of the total utterances which is used for many of the calculations. Although you may change the analysis set, the default analysis set includes those utterances which are complete (not abandoned or interrupted), intelligible (do not contain any unintelligible segments), and verbal (excludes utterances that do not contain at least one verbalized word, e.g., gestures). To illustrate the importance of the analysis set, consider the calculation of mean length of utterance (MLU). To avoid negatively influencing the outcome, the only utterances included in the calculation of MLU are those in the analysis set, i.e., those utterances which are complete, intelligible, and verbal (C&I Verbal Utts). Contrast this with the measure of percent intelligibility which is calculated on all of the utterances in the sample.

Many of the reports selected from the Analyze menu provide the same language measures calculated from both the analysis set utterances and from total utterances. Other reports selected from the Analyze menu give you the option of specifying the set of utterances to use for the calculations. Reports selected from the Database menu, on the other hand, decide for you the measures which are based on analysis set utterances and those which are based on total utterances.

As stated earlier, the analysis set can be changed to meet your needs. As an example, consider that, when eliciting conversational samples, examiners are often forced to ask questions to encourage talking. Responding to yes/no questions, however, often results in one-word responses. Because of this, early research on language development calculated MLU from "spontaneous" C&I verbal utterances, eliminating responses to questions. Using the *Setup menu: Analysis Set* option, you can change the current analysis set so that it excludes responses to questions. Subsequent analyses would then be based on the new analysis set. If the speaker's MLU is significantly longer when responses to questions are excluded, we can assume that responses to questions limited verbal output.

- **Word Base**

The *word base* defines which words you want included in the analyses. By default, the word base includes all words except those coded as ((parenthetical remarks)). You have the option of including parenthetical remarks as well as excluding, or only including, words that have specific [codes] attached to them. Words excluded from the current word base are not included in any analyses except the count of all words which is used to calculate speaking rate. In all other respects, they are treated as though they were commented out.

An example of the utility of the word base option might include a transcript which contains signed words. The signed words would have been coded in the transcript to flag them for analysis, e.g., typing the code [SIGNED] at the end of each signed word. Using the *Setup menu: Word Base* option you may choose to exclude, or to only include, the signed words.

- **Transcript Cut**

  The *transcript cut* setting determines which section of the transcript to include in the analyses. All analyses are based on those utterances within the current transcript cut. The default transcript cut is the entire transcript (*nothing cut*), but it may be changed to restrict the analysis to a specific section of the transcript. The transcript cut is determined by the location of the utterances within the transcript (*contrast this with the current analysis set, which is determined by the contents of the utterances*). The *Setup menu: Transcript cut* option is used to change the current transcript cut. You specify the transcript cut in terms of a starting point (*beginning of transcript, specified utterance, timing line or code*) and either an ending point (*end of transcript, specified utterance, timing line or code*) or until the transcript contains a specified number of utterances, words, or elapsed time.

  The transcript cut could be used, for example, to limit the analysis to the first 50 utterances or to the first 200 words. Suppose your transcript contains a series of conversational topics. You could set the transcript cut to analyze only those utterances pertaining to a specific topic.

As stated previously, each of these constructs has a default setting that will more often than not be used for running measures in SALT. It is, however, important to understand that you have the option to change them and how those changes might affect the outcome of your analyses.

Running the Measures

The Analyze Menu

The Analyze menu provides the opportunity to generate measures for each speaker in the transcript. A few of the options are discussed here. Others are covered later with specific clinical case examples (see Chapter 10).

The *Standard Measures Report* (SMR) is the first analysis option in the Analyze menu. The SMR calculates summary measures across syntax, semantics, discourse, rate, fluency, omissions, and errors. This report is designed to provide a profile of strengths and weaknesses in individual speakers.

Follow-up analyses are available in the Analyze menu to examine particular issues. If MLU or number of different words (NDW) is low, for example, you may want to generate a summary of the words and bound morphemes found in the transcript (*Word and Morpheme Summary*), an alphabetical list of all the different words in the transcript and their frequency (*Word Root Tables*), a list of common words and their frequency (*Standard Words Lists*), a list of bound morphemes with their word roots (*Bound Morpheme Tables*), and lists of words categorized by parts of speech (*Grammatical Categories*[1]). Generate a *Maze Summary* when filled pauses, repetitions, and/or revisions are high. The *Standard Utterance Lists* option pulls up utterances containing specific features, e.g., responses to questions, abandoned utterances, and utterances containing omissions. The organization mirrors clinical decision making by presenting a look at strengths and weaknesses and then offering further analysis options to explore each area in more detail (see Appendix S).

The Analyze menu lists outcomes for each speaker in the transcript. The reports have particular utility when eliciting samples for which there is no database for comparison such as adult speakers or the hearing impaired. Perhaps you used an elicitation protocol different than those used for the SALT databases, or perhaps you simply want to look at change over time comparing transcripts

---

[1] The grammatical category algorithm, dictionary, and software code have been generously provided by Ron Channell, Ph.D., Brigham Young University.

from the same speaker at different intervals. Even without a reference database to use for comparison, a good language sample can provide a wealth of information about a person's expressive language.

The Database Menu

The Database menu is used to compare a speaker's performance to age or grade-matched peers to generate comparison data. The databases allow you to answer the question, *is this speaker's performance across measures typical?* There are multiple analysis options available in the Database menu.

Selecting the Database Samples for Comparison

In order to utilize the analysis options in the Database menu, you must first select a database comparison set. There are three steps to the process (Figure 4-1).

Figure 4-1

1. Select the appropriate SALT database for comparison. The plus lines at the beginning of the SALT transcript (Figure 4-2) direct the software to pre-select the appropriate database. In the example we are using, the *Narrative Story Retell* database was chosen with subgroup/story FWAY (*Frog, Where Are You?*, Mayer, 1969). This database selection step typically requires only that you agree with the selection made by the software. The selection can, of course, be changed.

   $ Child, Examiner
   + Name: Timmy
   + Gender: M
   + CA: 5;8
   + Grade: K
   + Context: Nar
   + Subgroup: FWAY

   Figure 4-2

2. Choose criteria for matching samples. The options are to match your sample to samples in the database by age, grade, and/or gender. An age match is the most common criteria used for comparison and is usually the default selection.

3. Select a method to equate your sample and the database samples by length in terms of words, utterances, elapsed time, or entire transcript. Most language measures vary depending on the length of a sample. Consider, for example, the number of total words (NTW) and the number of different words (NDW). The longer the sample, the greater the opportunity to produce words. If the target speaker's sample was far longer than the samples in the database, his or her opportunity to use more and different words was greater. Reversely, a target speaker who produced a very short sample had less time, thus opportunity, to produce more and different words. Equating samples by length offers a more fair comparison of the target speaker's performance to the performance of the speakers in the database samples; apples to apples.

Once the comparison set criteria have been selected, all of the analysis options in the Database menu become available.

The Database Menu Reports

The *Standard Measures Report* (SMR) is designed to provide an overall summary of how the target speaker compares to a selected peer group in standard deviation units. The report produces measures for sample length, syntax, semantics, discourse, verbal facility, and errors. The results produce a profile of strengths and weaknesses for individual speakers. The measures included in this report come from the research literature on language production, e.g., MLU, NDW, TTR, mazes (false starts, repetitions, revisions, and filled pauses), and from the requests of SLPs who were interested in measures of speaking rate, pauses, intelligibility, and certain features of discourse. The *SMR* is the backbone of SALT analysis, providing general measures of language performance essential for identifying strengths and deficits at all levels of language use. The individual sections in this report are discussed in detail below.

The heading at the beginning of the *Standard Measures Report* (Figure 4-3) gives information about the target speaker and the database comparison sets that were selected. In this example, Timmy, age 5;8, produced a story retell sample using FWAY (*Frog, Where Are You?*, Mayer, 1969). The comparison sets chosen included, first, a match from the *Narrative Story Retell* database of Timmy's entire sample to the entire samples of his age-matched peers (69 samples), and next, a comparison to 66 of the 69 samples in the database that were cut to 139 Number of Total Words (the same NTW as found in Timmy's sample). Note that 3 of the 69 samples were excluded because they contained less than 139 NTW.

TRANSCRIPT INFORMATION	DATABASE INFORMATION
Speaker: Timmy (Child)	Database: Narrative Story Retell
Sample Date:	69 Samples Matched by Age
Current Age: 5;8, Grade: K	66 Samples Cut at 139 Number Total Words
Context: Narration (FWAY)	Context: Narration (FWAY)

Figure 4-3

The *Standard Measures Report* is broken into two main sections based on the comparison sets selected. The top section of the report shows the comparison of the target speaker to database samples selected by age, grade, and/or gender using the entire transcript. The bottom section of the report shows the target speaker's performance compared to database samples equated by length, e.g., same number of words or utterances, same amount of elapsed time, or the entire transcript.

SMR Top Section: Analysis comparing samples matched by age (+/- 6 months)

The top section of the report (Figure 4-4) shows the comparison of the target speaker to database samples selected by an age, grade, and/or gender match. The speaker's age is listed, followed by measures calculated on the entire transcript.

STANDARD MEASURES REPORT							
LANGUAGE MEASURE	Child		DATABASE				
	Score	+/-SD	Mean	Min	Max	SD	%SD
Current Age (5:8)	5.67	-0.10	5.69	5.17	6.17	0.29	5%
Compared to 69 Samples Matched by Age (ENTIRE TRANSCRIPT)							
TRANSCRIPT LENGTH							
Total Utterances	26 *	-1.35	38.59	22	60	9.30	24%
# C&I Verbal Utts	24 *	-1.34	34.84	20	56	8.08	23%
All Words Including Mazes	154 *	-1.72	285.57	150	458	76.58	27%
Elapsed Time (1:54)	1.90 *	-1.71	3.52	1.72	7.03	0.95	27%
INTELLIGIBILITY							
% Intelligible Utterances	96.2%	0.21	94.75	70.59	100.00	6.77	7%
% Intelligible Words	99.4%	0.12	99.23	94.92	100.00	1.04	1%
NARRATIVE STRUCTURE							
NSS Composite Score	13 *	-1.83	18.83	11	26	3.18	17%

Calculations based on C&I Verbal Utts
* At least 1 SD (** 2 SD) from the database mean
Database selection criteria: age +/- 6 months (5;2 - 6;2)

Figure 4-4

Let's look at the numbers.

As you scan the report (Figure 4-4), note that one of the measures is preceded with a # sign (far left side). Measures preceded by a # sign are calculated using the subset of utterances, the analysis set (C&I Verbal Utts). Measures which are not preceded by a # sign are calculated using all of the utterances.

Following the measures column are the scores for the target speaker reported as raw scores and in standard deviation units relative to the database mean. Note that values which are highlighted and followed by one asterisk are used to denote scores that are at least 1 standard deviation (SD) from the database mean. Values followed by two asterisks are 2 or more SDs from the database mean. The SD interval, which affects how measures are asterisked, can be changed from the default setting of 1 SD to any value, e.g., 1.5, 1.75, to accommodate diagnostic criteria. Careful consideration of the plus and minus standard deviation values relative to each score is necessary to make the correct interpretation of performance. For example, scores of negative 2 SDs for mazes is considered to be a strength while negative 2 SDs for MLU indicates a significant problem. Think about the direction the speaker's performance must deviate to be considered a problem.

The final five columns in the report include database values of mean, range of scores (min and max), SD, and %SD. The percent standard deviation is an index of the variability of each score for the dataset. The higher the %SD value, the greater the variability of the scores in the comparison set.

Transcript Length: Measures of transcript length provide data on the length of the transcript in terms of utterances, words, and elapsed time. Sample length should always be kept in mind when interpreting language measures. Some language measures, e.g., NTW, NDW, number of errors and omissions, vary depending on the length of a sample.

Intelligibility: The speech intelligibility measures provide an index of how many unintelligible segments there are in the transcript. This is important when evaluating the language performance in speakers who have articulation issues. Speakers with intelligibility scores less than 80% may generate language measures that are influenced by their ability to produce understandable utterances. Utterances may be shorter and word selection may be reduced to fewer syllables. Also, keep in mind that this measure is not speech intelligibility per se. This score also reflects the quality of the recording (hopefully improved with digital equipment), the skill of the transcriber, the number of unique proper names, and limiting listening to three passes of a segment during transcription. The intelligibility scores reflect understanding of the recording which may be different than face-to-face speech recognition.

Narrative/Expository/Persuasion Structure: Scoring procedures were developed to assess the structure and content of narrative, expository, and persuasion samples (see Appendices P, Q, and R). When a transcript is scored following these procedures, the composite score is included in this section of the report.

SMR Bottom Section: The analysis comparing samples equated by length

The bottom section of the report (Figure 4-5) shows the target speaker's performance compared to database samples equated by length, e.g., same Number of Total Words (NTW).

	STANDARD MEASURES REPORT							
LANGUAGE MEASURE	Child			DATABASE				
	Score	+/-SD		Mean	Min	Max	SD	%SD
Compared to 66 Samples Equated by Same Number of Total Words (CUT AT 139 NTW)								
SYNTAX/MORPHOLOGY								
# MLU in Words	5.79 *	-1.25		7.16	4.93	9.33	1.09	15%
# MLU in Morphemes	6.54 *	-1.19		7.95	5.21	10.47	1.18	15%
# SI Composite Score	1.05	-0.74		1.13	0.94	1.47	0.11	10%
SEMANTICS								
# Number Total Words (NTW)	139	0.00		139.00	139	139	0.00	0%
# Number Different Words (NDW)	62	0.53		59.02	47	70	5.60	9%
# Type Token Ratio (TTR)	0.45	0.53		0.42	0.34	0.50	0.04	9%
# Moving-Average TTR (100)	0.49	0.53		0.47	0.39	0.54	0.04	8%
VERBAL FACILITY								
Words/Minute	81.05	-0.17		84.38	44.58	129.17	20.12	24%
# Maze Words as % of Total Words	4.1%	-0.93		9.87	0.00	24.46	6.14	62%
Pauses Within Utterances	1	-0.16		1.27	0	10	1.76	138%
Pauses Between Utterances	9	0.86		5.26	0	18	4.33	82%
Abandoned Utterances	1	0.65		0.50	0	3	0.77	154%
ERRORS								
# % Utterances with Errors	20.8%	0.59		15.83	0.00	38.89	8.45	53%
Number of Omissions	2	0.71		1.12	0	5	1.23	110%
Number of Error Codes	3	0.31		2.50	0	6	1.64	66%

 # Calculations based on C&I Verbal Utts
* At least 1 SD (** 2 SD) from the database mean
Database selection criteria: age +/- 6 months (5;2 - 6;2)

Figure 4-5

Syntax/Morphology: Measures of syntax and morphology include MLU in words and morphemes which are highly correlated with age from 3 – 13 years (Leadholm & Miller, 1992). MLU is one of the measures central to the identification of language disorder (Paul, 2007; Rice, et al., 2010). The SI composite score is included with samples coded for subordination index (see Appendix O).

Semantics: Number of Total Words (NTW) is the total count of all words. Number of Different Words (NDW) is a direct index of vocabulary diversity. It is derived from the production of unique free morphemes (the part of the word that precedes the /). For example, *play*, *play/ed*, and *play/ing* would be treated as one word root (*play*) occurring three times. Only words located in the main body (excludes mazes) of the utterance are counted to calculate these measures. Type Token Ratio (TTR) provides an index of the ratio between NTW and NDW. Typically, as the sample length increases, the TTR decreases because fewer different words are used on the same topics. TTR was created by Mildred Templin (1957) who noted that TTR was a constant ratio for 50-utterance conversational samples at .43 -.47 for ages 3 - 8 years. The Moving-Average TTR estimates TTR using a moving window. Initially, a window length is selected, e.g., 100 words, and the TTR for words 1–100 is calculated. Then the TTR is calculated for words 2–101, then 3–102, and so on to the end of the sample. For the final score, the individual TTRs are averaged. Unlike the traditional calculation of TTR, the Moving Average TTR is independent of sample length (Covington & McFall, 2010). If desired, the MATTR window length can be changed using the Setup menu in SALT.

Discourse: Discourse measures are available for conversational samples where percent responses to questions, mean turn length in words, utterances with overlapping speech, and number of interruptions inform you about responsiveness to a conversational partner. These measures are an excellent first step in identifying speakers who fail to attend to partner speech.

Verbal Facility: Verbal facility is described by providing a measure of speaking rate (in words per minute), a percentage of the number of total words that were in mazes (Maze Words as % of Total Words), the number of silent pauses marked in the sample, and the number of abandoned utterances. The words per minute score significantly correlates with age and is considered by bilingual researchers to be an index of language facility (Miller, et al., 2006). The more fluent you are in a language, the higher your words per minute score. "Maze" is the term used for false starts, repetitions, revisions, and filled pauses. Increased maze use has been linked to word retrieval and utterance formulation problems. The maze words to total words ratio captures the overall impact of mazes on the whole sample. Silent pauses, both within and between utterances, affect overall verbal facility and rate. A high number of pauses within the speaker's utterances might be indicative of language processing, word retrieval, or fluency problems. Pauses between utterances may indicate processing or formulation difficulties. Abandoned utterances can be thought of as severe mazes where the speaker does not complete the utterance. These utterances can impact overall fluency of oral productions.

Errors: The errors and omissions scores are captured during transcription. "% Utterances with Errors" calculates the percent of analysis set utterances (C&I Verbal Utts) which contain at least one instance of either an omission or an error code. Omission codes are used to mark missing words or bound morphemes that have obligatory contexts signaling required use. Error codes at the word or utterance level are used to note inappropriate word choice or syntactic form. These codes are meant to signal errors that may need further review.

Using the Databases

There are more than 7,000 transcripts in the SALT databases across speaking genres. As mentioned, the software helps you to identify the correct database from which you will select the transcripts for comparison. The first time you select a report from the Database menu, you are prompted to choose the specific database matching your sample type, the age or grade-match criteria, and the basis for comparison by length. This is best illustrated with examples.

Example 1: Blake 8;4 PGHW[2]

Blake is 8 years and 4 months old. In this example, he is retelling the story *Pookins Gets Her Way* (Lester, 1987). To select a report from the Database menu, you are prompted to select the database comparison set. Based on the +Context and +Subgroup information lines at the beginning of Blake's transcript (Figure 4-6), the Narrative Story Retell database (see Appendix D) is pre-selected. This database contains samples from participants retelling several different stories. Only those participants retelling the same story, *Pookins Gets Her Way* (PGHW), are considered.

$ Child, Examiner
+ Name: Blake
+ Gender: M
+ CA: 8;4
+ Ethnicity: Caucasian
+ Grade: 2
+ Context: Nar
+ Subgroup: PGHW

Figure 4-6

Age, grade, and gender criteria are then specified to further refine the comparison set. For Blake's sample, the age criterion is pre-set to +/- 6 months, i.e., all database participants in the age range 7;10 – 8;10. The grade and gender criteria are not specified using the default settings. They can be selected if desired. In this example, 74 participants matched the age range specified (Figure 4-7).

> *The rule of thumb we have developed over the years is to aim for at least 20 participants for comparison to reduce the variability as much as possible. The more participants you have in the comparison set, the better it represents language performance of typical speakers of the same age or grade, speaking under the same conditions.*

The next step in selecting database samples for comparison is to find a set of samples that are equated by length. When comparing an individual's sample with selected database samples, it is important to understand what portion of the database transcripts are included in the comparison. The default setting is to compare the target sample to samples in the database with the same number of total words (NTW). Other options include a comparison using the same number of analysis set utterances, the same amount of elapsed time, or the

---

[2] *Blake 8;4 PGHW* is one of the sample transcripts included with the software.

entire transcript regardless of the length. In this example, we use NTW to equate the length of the samples. After making this selection, you are presented with the best comparison set options varying in number of participants and number of words (Figure 4-8).

Figure 4-7

Figure 4-8

In this example, 58 of the 74 participants contained at least 247 NTW (same NTW as found in Blake's sample). You want to maximize the number of participants with the most language. Often the choice is obvious. In this example, six options are provided, ranging from 58 samples with transcripts containing at least 247 words, to 74 samples with transcripts containing at least 139 words. The 58 samples provide the longest transcripts (247 words versus 139 words), hence the most language to be included in the comparison set. The 74 samples maximize the database participants but minimize the sample length. Since 58 samples are sufficient, this option was selected. SALT then calculated the database values with the selected database participants and generated the reports.

Example 2: Timothy 6;1 Con[3]

Timothy is 6 years and 1 month old. In this example, a conversational sample was elicited between Timothy and a speech pathologist. Based on the +Context information line at the beginning of the transcript (Figure 4-9), the Conversation database (see Appendix B) is pre-selected.

$ Child, Examiner
+ Name: Timothy
+ Gender: M
+ CA: 6;1
+ Grade: K
+ Context: Con

Figure 4-9

The age criterion is pre-set to +/- 6 months. The database has 147 samples for comparison in that age range. The same number of total words was chosen to equate this sample to the database samples by length. With an open-ended elicitation context, such as a conversation, you wouldn't base the comparison

---

[3] *Timothy 6;1 Con* is one of the sample transcripts included with the software.

on the entire transcript since the transcript lengths are so variable. Rather, you would equate the transcripts by basing the comparison on the same number of words, utterances, or time. Using the same number of words in the both Timothy's sample and the database samples ensures that measures, such as number of different words, number of pauses, and errors are not influenced by sample length. If your target speaker's MLU is low and you compare samples based on the same number of utterances (rather than words), the typical speakers in the comparison set will likely have longer utterances and hence more different words because they produced more words per utterance. Basing the comparison on the same length in words eliminates this confound. 146 of the 147 samples had at least as many words as Timothy's sample (53 NTW).

At this point you could consider narrowing the age range of the analysis set, reducing it from 12 months (+/- 6 months) to perhaps 8 months (+/- 4 months) which provides 104 participants with transcripts containing at least 53 words. Narrowing the age range even further to 6 months still results in a group of 77 participants with 53 words. By reducing the age range of the comparison set, we improve the match between the individual speaker and the comparison group of typical speakers. This reduces the variability inherent in larger age ranges. You might also consider matching the database participants by grade and/or gender. Some databases are large enough to allow you to adjust the selection criteria and still have sufficient participants to create a valid comparison set. Some do not allow for this adjustment because the number of participants was limited at inception.

What we have done in selecting a comparison set is to create a customized set of transcripts that best match the target language sample. In this example, there are two comparison sets. The first includes all samples which match the age criteria selected and calculations are based on the entire transcript. In the second, and length-matched, comparison set, the comparison is based on 53 words (Timothy's NTW). The matching database samples are all cut at 53 words, i.e., transcript processing stops when the 53rd word is reached in each of those samples. The SALT program produces the unique set of measures for each comparison set providing the best possible measures of typical performance. Each of these comparison sets constitutes a table of normative values like that found in any standardized test. Instead of one look-up table, SALT creates unlimited look-up tables tailored for each target transcript.

Following up on the Standard Measures Report

A variety of analyses have been created to provide more insight into the strengths and deficits identified on the *Database menu: Standard Measures Report*. The remaining examples in this chapter are used for illustration.

Example 3: Steven 15;3 Expo transcript[4]

Steven is 15 years and 3 months old. In this example, an expository sample was elicited. The Verbal Facility variables in the *Standard Measures Report*, generated from comparing Steven's sample to age-matched peers selected from the Expository database (see Appendix E), show reduced words/minute and an increase, by 1.86 standard deviations, in the number of maze words as a percent of total words (Figure 4-10). They also show an increased use of unfilled pauses and abandoned utterances.

STANDARD MEASURES REPORT							
LANGUAGE MEASURE	Child		DATABASE				
	Score	+/-SD	Mean	Min	Max	SD	%SD
Compared to 72 Samples Equated by Same Number of Total Words (CUT AT 294 NTW)							
VERBAL FACILITY							
Words/Minute	82.04 **	-3.07	151.78	89.42	208.60	22.70	15%
# Maze Words as % of Total Words	18.3% *	1.86	8.85	1.34	25.19	5.10	58%
Pauses Within Utterances	4 **	7.55	0.25	0	2	0.50	199%
Pauses Between Utterances	7 **	10.38	0.18	0	4	0.66	364%
Abandoned Utterances	3 **	5.07	0.28	0	2	0.54	193%

Figure 4-10

The *Analyze menu: Rate and Pause Summary* provides a breakdown of within- and between-utterance pauses produced by Steven and the examiner as well as the total pause time in the sample (Figure 4-11). It is important to determine if silent pauses contribute to a slow rate of speech.

---

[4] *Stephen 15;3 Expo* is one of the sample transcripts included with the software.

PAUSE SUMMARY			
	No. of Pauses	Total Pause Time	Average Pause Time
Within Child Utterances			
Main body	0	0:00	
Mazes	4	0:09	
Total	4	0:09	0:02
Between Child Utterances			
Within Turn	6	0:17	
Preceding Turn	0	0:00	
Total	6	0:17	0:03
Within Examiner Utterances			
Main body	0	0:00	
Mazes	0	0:00	
Total	0	0:00	0:00
Between Examiner Utterances			
Within Turn	0	0:00	
Preceding Turn	1	0:06	
Total	1	0:06	0:06

Figure 4-11

The SMR also revealed 18.3% of Steven's total words were in mazes. This is 1.86 standard deviations higher than the database mean. Based on these values, this area appears to be a relative weakness for Steven and indicates a more in-depth look at the contents of the mazes. The *Database menu: Maze Summary* report provides the break-down of the maze contents. Using this report, we learn that there were a significant number of phrase-level revisions and repetitions when comparing to samples in the database. This can be indicative of utterance formulation problems. (Figure 4-12).

Over eighteen percent of Steven's words were in mazes. This has a considerable impact on his oral communication. In addition, he produced repetitions and revisions at the phrase level. Reviewing the utterances with mazes may provide additional insight. To do this, use the *Analyze menu: Standard Utterance Lists* option (Figure 4-13). Looking at the mazes in context will help identify where they appear in each utterance. *Do they seem to indicate utterance formulation problems, word retrieval issues, or some of each?* SALT provides you with the data to make these decisions which will guide you in developing an intervention plan.

MAZE SUMMARY
Calculations Based on C&I Verbal Utts, Transcripts Cut at 294 Number Total Words (72 samples)

LANGUAGE MEASURE	Child		DATABASE				
	Score	+/-SD	Mean	Min	Max	SD	%SD
% Maze Words/Total Words	18.3% *	1.86	8.85	1.34	25.19	5.10	58%
Revisions							
Part Word	3 **	2.39	0.61	0	4	1.00	164%
Word	4	0.89	2.25	0	10	1.96	87%
Phrase	7 *	1.08	3.68	0	18	3.06	83%
Repetitions							
Part Word	1	0.11	0.72	0	20	2.43	336%
Word	1	0.13	0.81	0	9	1.51	187%
Phrase	3 *	1.94	0.54	0	8	1.27	234%
Filled Pauses							
Single Word	17	0.66	11.08	0	36	8.97	81%
Multiple Words	0	-0.43	0.25	0	3	0.58	230%

* At least 1 SD (** 2 SD) from the database mean

Figure 4-12

STANDARD UTTERANCE LISTS
Total Utterances
1st Speaker

Utterances with Mazes - Repetitions & Revisions

11 C (Um) the object in tennis is (to score) to score eleven point/s to win the game.

14 C And whoever win/3s (:02 mo* um) four out of the seven game/s win/3s.

15 C (The prep*) the preparation/s for tennis is[EW:are] you need the following equipment, tennis ball/s, and racket/s.

17 C And what player/s do to get ready is warm up (volley*) volleying the ball back and forth between the court/s.

20 C (How the contest) how the contest begin/3s is (um :02) one of the two opponent/s decide/*3s who get/3s to serve during the game.

23 C To serve (you s*) you go behind the baseline and serve.

26 C (The um) the rule/s for singles tennis is[EW:are] (um) >

28 C The major rule/s are (um) penalty/s for foul/s (if it/'s) if you serve (if) to your opponent (is) if it is not *in the diagonal front box.

30 C Then, if you don't do it a second time it (is a score to your other opponent) is a point to your other opponent.

31 C (A way one way to score in tennis is um is the ten*) the scoring go/3s love, fifteen, thirty, forty, and then game.

32 C (Um how the contest) how long the contest last/3s is depending *on how (um) good you are.

35 C And you just keep go/ing until (to) one person win/3s by two point/s.

37 C (Um) some strategic move/s in tennis are to (um :02 really smash the ball when it come/3s like) smash the ball into the (on*) other opponent/z court.

44 C (Um when) how you win in tennis is (um af*) if you/'re at forty point/s and you score another point then you would win the game.

Figure 4-13

Using the *Analyze menu: Standard Utterance Lists* option, you can pull out a whole range of utterances from each speaker, e.g., utterances with omissions, errors, or pauses. Utterances can be displayed individually or with preceding and/or following utterances.

Example 4: Jeremy 3;3 Play transcript[5]

Jeremy is 3 years and 3 months old. A play-based sample was elicited and compared to age-matched peers selected from the Play database (see Appendix A). The Syntax/Morphology variables in the *Standard Measures Report*, generated by comparing Jeremy's performance to database samples equated by same Number Total Words (NTW), show that Jeremy's MLU in morphemes was 2.64 standard deviations below the database mean (Figure 4-14).

STANDARD MEASURES REPORT							
LANGUAGE MEASURE	Child		DATABASE				
	Score	+/-SD	Mean	Min	Max	SD	%SD
Compared to 30 Samples Equated by Same Number of Total Words (CUT AT 102 NTW)							
SYNTAX/MORPHOLOGY							
# MLU in Words	1.62 **	-2.57	3.15	2.37	5.00	0.60	19%
# MLU in Morphemes	1.71 **	-2.64	3.44	2.51	5.50	0.65	19%

Figure 4-14

The Semantics variables in the same section of the *Standard Measures Report* show that his number of different words (NDW) and type token ratio (TTR) were more than three standard deviations below the database mean (Figure 4-15). Low NDW and TTR are indicators of limited vocabulary.

STANDARD MEASURES REPORT							
LANGUAGE MEASURE	Child		DATABASE				
	Score	+/-SD	Mean	Min	Max	SD	%SD
Compared to 30 Samples Equated by Same Number of Total Words (CUT AT 102 NTW)							
SEMANTICS							
# Number Total Words (NTW)	102	0.00	102.00	102	102	0.00	0%
# Number Different Words (NDW)	38 **	-3.16	55.13	40	63	5.42	10%
# Type Token Ratio (TTR)	0.37 **	-3.16	0.54	0.39	0.62	0.05	10%
# Moving-Average TTR (100)	0.38 **	-3.09	0.55	0.40	0.62	0.05	10%

Figure 4-15

---

[5] *Jeremy 3;3 Play* is one of the sample transcripts that comes with the software.

The *Database menu: Word Lists, Bound Morphemes, & Utterance Distribution* report can be generated to further evaluate these measures. In the first section of this report (Figure 4-16), we see that Jeremy produced more question words than his peers but used only two types. No negatives (where three are expected), one conjunction, no auxiliary verbs, and limited personal pronouns.

WORD LISTS, BOUND MORPHEMES, & UTTERANCE DISTRIBUTION Calculations Based on C&I Verbal Utts, Transcripts Cut at 102 Number Total Words (30 samples)							
LANGUAGE MEASURE	Child		DATABASE				
	Score	+/-SD	Mean	Min	Max	SD	%SD
WORD LISTS							
Question Words							
Total	7 **	2.29	2.60	0	6	1.92	74%
Type	2	0.55	1.47	0	3	0.97	66%
Negatives							
Total	0 *	-1.24	3.83	0	15	3.10	81%
Type	0 *	-1.46	2.17	0	7	1.49	69%
Conjunctions							
Total	1	-0.77	3.07	0	10	2.69	88%
Type	1	-0.48	1.60	0	5	1.25	78%
Modal Auxiliary Verbs							
Total	0	-0.95	1.53	0	6	1.61	105%
Type	0	-1.19	0.90	0	3	0.76	84%
Personal Pronouns							
Total	4 **	-2.33	15.40	8	27	4.90	32%
Type	3 *	-1.21	4.67	1	7	1.37	29%

Figure 4-16

The next section of this report focuses on bound morphemes (Figure 4-17). Jeremy produced one 3rd person singular morpheme, no regular past tense /ed or /ing, four plurals, and no possessives.

WORD LISTS, BOUND MORPHEMES, & UTTERANCE DISTRIBUTION Calculations Based on C&I Verbal Utts, Transcripts Cut at 102 Number Total Words (30 samples)							
LANGUAGE MEASURE	Child		DATABASE				
	Score	+/-SD	Mean	Min	Max	SD	%SD
BOUND MORPHEMES							
/3S	1	0.74	0.40	0	3	0.81	203%
/ED	0	-0.68	0.50	0	2	0.73	146%
/ING	0	-0.85	1.07	0	4	1.26	118%
/S	4 *	1.35	2.07	0	6	1.44	70%
/Z	0	-0.31	0.13	0	2	0.43	326%

Figure 4-17

The final section of the report (Figure 4-18), which shows the utterance distribution tables, allows you to evaluate the low MLU score. The number of utterances at each utterance length in both words and morphemes can be found in these distribution tables. Jeremy does not have any utterances longer than 5 morphemes where 7 - 9 morpheme lengths are expected. If a speech motor problem were evident we might see utterances severely restricted in length with utterances only at 2 - 3 morphemes. It is important to review these tables when there are low MLU scores. The longer utterances produced may give insight into the next level of syntax to be mastered.

NUMBER OF UTTERANCES BY UTTERANCE LENGTH																
Utterance Length in Words																
	0	1	2	3	4	5	6	7	8	9	10	11	12	13	14	15+	Total
Child	0	38	16	6	1	2	0	0	0	0	0	0	0	0	0	0	63
DB Mean	0	12	4	5	5	4	2	1	1	0	0	0	0	0	0	0	34
Utterance Length in Morphemes																
	0	1	2	3	4	5	6	7	8	9	10	11	12	13	14	15+	Total
Child	0	35	18	5	3	2	0	0	0	0	0	0	0	0	0	0	63
DB Mean	0	12	3	4	5	4	3	2	1	1	0	0	0	0	0	0	35

Figure 4-18

The *Database menu: Grammatical Categories* examines specific vocabulary use in more detail by sorting the words Jeremy used into 23 grammatical categories (Figure 4-19). Each word in the analysis set (C&I Verbal Utts) is identified as belonging to one of these categories. This is done using a large dictionary of English words and a set of grammatical rules (Channell & Johnson, 1999).

To list the vocabulary words spoken within the language sample from a specific grammatical category, use the *Analyze menu: Grammatical Category Lists* option and select categories of interest. It may be beneficial to look at words produced from categories highlighted as areas of relative weakness when compared to the database samples. In Jeremy's case there were a number of grammatical forms more than one standard deviation from the database mean Jeremy's use of interjections may be of interest when reviewing the context of the transcript. It may be informative to ponder why these forms were so prevalent in his language sample as there were 20 productions compared to the average of just under 8 in the database comparison set (Figure 4-20).

GRAMMATICAL CATEGORIES
Calculations Based on C&I Verbal Utts, Transcripts Cut at 102 Number Total Words (30 samples)

LANGUAGE MEASURE	Child		DATABASE				
	Score	+/-SD	Mean	Min	Max	SD	%SD
Initiators	0	-0.33	0.10	0	1	0.31	305%
Determiners	9	-0.58	11.23	4	18	3.85	34%
Adjectives	0 *	-1.22	3.67	0	13	3.01	82%
Nouns	20	0.38	18.17	5	27	4.86	27%
Personal Pronouns	4 *	-1.96	14.27	6	26	5.24	37%
Other Pronouns	11 *	1.29	7.33	3	13	2.83	39%
Auxiliary Modals	0 *	-1.14	1.87	0	6	1.63	88%
Auxiliary Operators	0 *	-1.53	3.50	0	9	2.29	65%
Verbs	11 *	-1.27	17.20	11	30	4.89	28%
Copula Forms	4	-0.05	4.13	0	10	2.79	67%
Verb Particles	2	0.05	1.90	0	8	1.84	97%
Adverbs	12 **	2.53	4.80	1	12	2.85	59%
Intensifiers	5 **	5.18	0.77	0	2	0.82	107%
Prepositions	2 *	-1.53	5.70	1	12	2.42	43%
Existential	1 *	1.13	0.23	0	3	0.68	291%
Question Words	7 **	2.47	2.43	0	6	1.85	76%
Coordinators	0 *	-1.16	2.10	0	5	1.81	86%
Subordinators	0	-0.85	1.00	0	4	1.17	117%
Infinitives	0	-0.95	1.00	0	4	1.05	105%
Possessives	0	-0.36	0.17	0	2	0.46	277%
Negation Words	0 *	-1.35	2.00	0	6	1.49	74%
Lets Words	0	-0.39	0.13	0	1	0.35	259%
Interjections	20 **	3.75	7.90	3	14	3.23	41%

Figure 4-19

GRAMMATICAL CATEGORY LISTS
C&I Verbal Utts

Interjections	Child	Exami
HEY	0	1
HUH	0	3
MHM	1	0
OH	5	7
YEAH	7	1
YEP	7	0
Total Frequency	20	12

Figure 4-20

Example 5: Timothy 6;1 Con

This final illustration uses the same transcript as Example 2 where a conversational sample was elicited between Timothy (age 6;1) and a speech-language clinician. Timothy's sample was compared to age-matched peers selected from the Conversation database. The discourse section of the *Database menu: Standard Measures Report* revealed less than expected responses to questions at 42.9%. The *Database menu: Discourse Summary* report can be selected to follow up this score (Figure 4-21). This table reveals that the examiner asked 7 questions of which 3 were answered = 42.9%. An answer is defined by a child response to an examiner question. You will need to read the questions to determine if they were correct responses in terms of syntax and semantics. The length of Timothy's speaking turns was within the typical range when compared to his age-matched peers.

DISCOURSE SUMMARY
Calculations Based on Total utterances, Transcripts Cut at 53 Number Total Words (146 samples)

LANGUAGE MEASURE	CHILD		DATABASE				
	Score	+/-SD	Mean	Min	Max	SD	%SD
Responses to Questions							
Other Speaker Questions	7	-0.12	7.92	0	59	7.55	95%
Responses to Questions	3	-0.56	5.51	0	29	4.46	81%
Y/N Responses to Questions	0	-0.88	1.40	0	7	1.58	113%
% Responses to Questions	42.9% *	-1.23	73.57	0.00	100.00	24.87	34%
TURN LENGTH SUMMARY							
Mean Turn Length (utts)	1.14	-0.69	1.66	1.00	7.00	0.75	45%
Median Turn Length (utts)	1.00	-0.39	1.32	1.00	7.00	0.82	62%
Mean Turn Length (words)	3.24	-0.88	8.98	1.94	59.00	6.53	73%
Mean Turn Length (words)	2.00	-0.76	7.20	1.00	59.00	6.84	95%
OTHER							
% Words Mentioned First	51.5%	-0.50	55.65	36.51	78.95	8.43	15%
Utts. with Overlapping Speech	0	-0.81	1.16	0	8	1.44	124%
Interrupted Other Speaker	0	-0.35	0.13	0	2	0.38	289%

*At least 1 SD (** 2 SD) from the database mean*

Figure 4-21

The *Analyze menu: Standard Utterance Lists* option can be used to display the examiner's questions in the context of the entries which follow each question (Figure 4-22). In this example, the examiner's questions are displayed with the following two entries. The examiner's second and last three questions were not answered. It is informative to look at the questions to see what types of questions were asked and to see whether or not the examiner provided sufficient time for the child to respond.

STANDARD UTTERANCE LISTS Total Utterances 2nd Speaker

Questions	
28	E WHAT ELSE?
29	C A X.
30	C SOMEONE BROUGHT THE CAKE.
70	E A CHOO_CHOO_TRAIN?
71	E OH THAT SOUND/3S FUN.
72	; :10
101	E A REAL LIVE TRAIN?
102	C FIVE.
103	E FIVE WHAT HON?
103	E FIVE WHAT HON?
104	C FIFTEEN.
105	E FIFTEEN.
108	E GO BACKWARDS?
109	; :06
110	E SOUND/3S FUN.
123	E AND GRANDMA AND GRANDPA TOO?
124	E I BET THEY LIVE UP.
125	C MHM.
130	E HAVE YOU EVER BEEN BACKWARD IN A TRAIN?
131	E AND I DID/N'T UNDERSTAND THE FIFTEEN.
132	C FIFTEEN TRAIN/*S.

Figure 4-22

Chronological Age versus Cognitive Age

You can use the databases to create an age-matched comparison set based on the cognitive age of the target speaker. This is useful, for example, when you are working with children with developmental disabilities. Comparing to typical peers based on this method provides you with reference scores based on cognitive abilities. Creating a second comparison set based on chronological age provides you with contrasting scores to help describe the speaker's communication ability comparing cognitive ability with current age expectations.

Arguments about which scores qualify for services are still debated in the literature and vary across states and school districts. With this contrast so easily accessible, you will be able to document performance to address criteria using chronological age versus cognitive age as the reference point.

Analyzing Samples without using the Reference Databases

There may be times when you do not require the databases, or the appropriate database is not available for the target speaker's age or for the sampling condition you prefer to use. You may be working with older adults, or a speaker who has a native language other than English, or a speaker who uses alternative/ augmentative communication. You may prefer to assess language use in the home, in a supervised work setting, or while participating in a classroom activity. Perhaps you have designed your own elicitation protocol to capture specific language use.

The reports in the Analyze menu provide scores for all language levels and elicitation contexts. Without a database for comparison, you can use clinical judgment or find other sources of information to interpret language ability. Books on language development will refresh your information about expectations through the developmental period. Paul (2007) provides an invaluable resource on developmental expectations extracted from the literature through adolescence.

Examining the relationship between communication partners in conversation does not require a database, only comparison scores for each language measure. The *Analyze menu: Discourse Summary* provides you with the amount of talking for each participant. You can quickly see who is asking questions, who is answering, how much each speaker holds the floor, the number of utterances containing overlapping speech, and the number of interruptions. Communication partners may diverge from following the same topic. Examining each speaking turn relative to the preceding turn of the partner allows you to interpret if the speaker stayed on topic. This may be an important index for children and adults on the autism spectrum or who have sustained brain injury.

There may be other aspects of the language sample you want to evaluate such as specific vocabulary or pronoun use. The *Analyze menu: Word Root Tables* provides an alphabetical list of the words used in the sample. The *Analyze menu: Grammatical Categories* option breaks down the speaker's vocabulary into twenty-three categories based on parts of speech. The *Analyze menu: Standard Word Lists* provides eight different pronoun lists, including personal pronouns and possessive pronouns. Suppose you want to flag those pronouns where the reference was not clearly established. The *Edit menu: Insert Code* option can be used to help code any aspect of the transcript you are concerned about. You can create a code list and save it for future use across time or individuals. Once your transcript is coded, the *Analyze menu: Code Summary*, *Analyze menu: Word Code Tables*, and *Analyze menu: Utterance Code Tables* provide summary reports of your codes.

SALT provides an important tool to facilitate the side-by-side comparison of two transcripts. Link your transcripts using *Link menu: Link Transcripts* and then select reports from the Analyze and Database menus to compare the target speaker from each transcript. The *Link* option can be used to compare transcripts recorded at different times to chart progress. Samples taken at time-one and time-two can be compared directly to document changes across language levels. This is particularly important when working with individuals with brain injury where documenting change is crucial for continuing therapy. Also, because of the wide range of measures available, unexpected changes can be documented. You can also use the *Link* option to make comparisons across languages, e.g., English and French. Language samples for each language can be compared, allowing a precise index of the speaker's fluency in each language. The Link menu is also helpful in comparing performance across linguistic contexts such as conversation vs. narration. A speaker on the autism spectrum, for example, may perform differently in a conversational context than a more text-based context such as a narrative story retell.

Summary

In this chapter we reviewed the major concepts for using SALT to analyze language transcripts. Chief among them are the analysis set, which determines the utterances to be included for each measure, and the comparison set for selecting database participants. Awareness of the analysis set and the comparison set will facilitate accurate interpretation of the results provided for each measure. The reference databases are unique to SALT and provide comparison data on typical peers. SALT is an assessment tool with vast capabilities. The more time you spend with it the more it will reveal about oral language performance.

Interpreting Language Samples

Jon F. Miller
Karen Andriacchi
Ann Nockerts

This chapter focuses on using SALT to build a thorough description of language use. SALT provides a range of measures which describes oral language performance and creates a profile of strengths and weaknesses. Understanding the measures is key to interpreting the outcome of the SALT analysis. It is important to be clear what is being measured and how that measurement relates to oral language performance. This is the most difficult, but most interesting, part of the language sample analysis (LSA) process.

The major outcome of the LSA process is a description of language use in functional speaking contexts. LSA, along with other potential measures and clinical judgment, can be used to identify language disorder or delay.

Describing Language Use via SALT Measurement Outcomes

The *Standard Measures Report* (SMR) provides an overview of performance across measures of all language levels. When examining a *Database menu: Standard Measures Report*, consider plus or minus one standard deviation (SD) as significant in terms of identifying areas that need further examination. This criterion allows you to quickly form an impression of strengths and weaknesses, or the "profile" of language production exhibited in the sample. The measures in the SALT *Standard Measures Report* are organized into language performance areas that have been identified by research and/or by clinicians as central to a thorough examination of language production, and frequently relate to academic performance. The measures cover transcript length, semantics, syntax/morphology, verbal facility, intelligibility, and errors. The report provides the target speaker's raw score and standard deviation for each measure as well as the database mean, range, and percent SD. Each of the measures is considered to be a general score, sensitive to disordered performance identified by parents, teachers, and SLPs. This range of measures is necessary as there are a number of different types of oral language deficits. In other words, not all language disordered children show the same profile of scores across the SMR. The array of measures allows us to identify strengths as well as weaknesses in oral language, an essential ingredient in developing intervention plans.

Profiles of Performance

We don't expect all children with language difficulty to communicate alike, nor do we expect them to exhibit the same linguistic profiles within and across age. We know that disorders of language production take several different forms and, further, that these forms seem to be stable over time. Our own research documented this by identifying a number of different problem areas in children receiving speech-language services in the schools (Leadholm & Miller, 1992).

The rest of this section discusses how deficit areas converge to create profiles of performance.

Delayed language

The most common problem area is the classic language delay. Indications of language delay on the SMR are noted by a low mean length of utterance (MLU). Additionally, low number of different words (NDW), and/or low number of total words (NTW) are frequently noted with this type of language difficulty. Often speaking rate is low, i.e., low words per minute (WPM). Multiple errors at the word and utterance level can be evident. And, for younger children, we see frequent omissions of bound morphemes and auxiliary verbs. Further examination of the low MLU reveals a reliance on simple syntax. These children may just be reticent talkers, producing shorter samples with sparse vocabularies and elemental syntax. In these cases, SLPs need to refocus on overall language proficiency. Not talking very much may be a function of family style (Hart & Risley, 1999), cultural background (Crago, Annahatak, & Ningiuruvik, 1993), or lack of language proficiency. Careful review of family status and performance across speaking situations can help sort this out. Ultimately, the primary intervention target may be to increase talking by providing varied opportunities to use language.

Word retrieval and utterance formulation

Speakers having trouble finding the right word or completing utterances with intended semantic content and appropriate syntax frequently repeat and revise. We refer to these repetitions and revisions as mazes, after Walter Loban whose seminal work coined the term (Loban, 1976). The SMR contains the measure *percent maze words to total words*; which indexes the impact of mazes on the entire sample. When this measure is high, it is important to look further at the number and types of mazes in both the *Database menu: Maze Summary* and *Analyze menu: Maze Summary.* Here you will find important essential information breaking down the contents of mazes, the distribution of mazes, (percent of the 1-morpheme, 2-morpheme ... 15+ morpheme utterances which contain mazes), the number of mazes (some utterances may have more than one maze), the total number of maze words, and the average number of words per maze. All of these measures provide information which, together, form a picture of the extent and nature of the speaker's difficulty. Where samples are short, percent maze words to total words is the best measure, as the other measures are confounded by frequency. To distinguish between a word-level and an utterance-level problem we need to examine the sample in more detail. Repetition and revision of words and part-words point to word retrieval issues. Repetitions and revisions of phrases are indicative of utterance formulation problems. The number of abandoned utterances may also be indicative of either of these problems and is significant in that the speaker did not resolve the word or utterance conflict. Consider abandoned utterances to be failed utterances which should be reviewed in detail to determine if a pattern exists. *Are these partial utterances similar relative to form and/or content?*

We have documented cases where speakers produced three and four mazes per utterance. When examining these utterances in detail, it was evident that they were attempting to string three or more propositions together in a single utterance, but didn't have the necessary command of complex syntax to accomplish the task. This is an example of how LSA can provide detailed evidence of the language deficit with a clear direction for organizing an intervention plan.

Pauses can also be indicative of word retrieval or utterance formulation problems. Our clinical experience suggests that either mazes or pauses are used when having difficulty finding the right word or formulating an acceptable utterance. Seldom are both pauses and mazes used by the same speaker. The *Analyze menu: Rate and Pause Summary* provides several telling pause measures such as pauses within utterances and pauses between utterances. The total time for all pauses in each category is provided as well. The total time measure allows a fast check on the impact of pausing on the overall sample. Pauses within utterances may be associated with word-level problems. An analysis of where pauses occur in the utterance will help confirm this interpretation. Pauses which occur before main verbs, subject or object nouns, or adjectives are indications of word selection issues. You can also confirm this by asking individuals older than seven or eight who have the capacity to reflect on their own language use. Pauses between utterances may be related to utterance-level problems. Some individuals pause both within and between utterances. More assessment should be done to confirm the nature of difficulty. Pauses can be a significant deficit. As an example, a middle school student was disciplined for not responding to a school administrator, judged to be insolent, and sent home. The school SLP intervened with a language sample showing a pattern of significant pausing; more than five minutes total pause time in a 15 minute sample. This is perhaps an extreme case, but it illustrates how oral language deficits can be misinterpreted within the school and community.

Narrative organization

Documenting this type of problem requires collecting a narrative sample where the examiner knows the content expected. Examples include a story retell or an exposition of a game or sport familiar to the SLP. Narrative organization problems are usually evident when listening to the sample. The scope and sequence of the narrative may be confused, characters may be left out, conflicts or resolutions might be missing. The SMR provides only a few helpful measures. Frequently, high numbers of pauses both within and between utterances are evident and there may also be high maze values. Non-specific referencing, which may also occur, can be flagged by inserting word codes within the transcript. These codes can then be counted and the words and utterances containing them pulled up for analysis. Differentiating word retrieval or utterance formulation problems from narrative organization deficits will require additional measures such as the Narrative Scoring Scheme (see Appendix P), the Expository Scoring Scheme (see Appendix Q), or the Persuasion Scoring Scheme (see Appendix R). These applications will be reviewed in the next chapter which entails following up the SMR with more detailed measures to confirm language production difficulties. Basically, listening to the sample will provide clinical evidence of whether the problem is at the word, utterance, or overall text level. Further analyses are necessary to document these clinical impressions.

Discourse deficits
Discourse or pragmatic deficits can take many forms. The SMR provides several measures to assist with discourse analysis. Discourse requires an interaction between two speakers, in other words a conversational sample. SALT calculates the percent of responses to questions and the average speaking turn measured in words. It also quantifies overlapping speech and interruptions. Research shows that length of speaking turn increases with age as does the number of responses to examiner questions. Responses to questions provide a direct index of attending to the speaking partner. A closer look at questions within the language sample is recommended. This should include reviewing the examiner questions and the responses to determine the types of questions that were posed and their relative level of difficulty, e.g., yes/no versus "WH" (what, where, when, why, or how). Additionally, this analysis should include a review of the type of utterance that followed the examiner question, e.g., another question, an appropriate response, an inappropriate response. SALT bases the calculation of responses to questions on who spoke following the question, the examiner or target speaker. If the target speaker spoke and is credited with a response, the content and form of the responses should be examined to determine if the syntax and semantic content are accurate. Failing to answer questions appropriately, or at all, may also be associated with delayed language development. A significant amount of overlapping speech and/or interruptions may be an indication of poor discourse skills. Examine the transcript to look for patterns.

<u>Fast speaking rate with low semantic content</u>
Individuals who speak very fast do not necessarily have a language problem. Our esteemed colleague Liz Bates spoke very fast but with extraordinarily clear and precise language form and content. In relatively infrequent cases, a fast rate appears to be an adaptation to not being able to organize thoughts into utterances or texts. This is most evident in conversational samples where the speaker is sharing information or responding to requests. Rate accelerates and content is circumlocuted. The speaker talks around the target adding relatively little new information, often without giving the conversational partner opportunity to speak. Also the speaker may lack specific referencing using pronouns in the place of specific referencing nouns. So WPM is very high, turn length is high, and MLU is high, though not always related to complex sentence use. The contrast between a conversational sample and a narrative sample may reveal the pattern only appears in conversation, or possibly across all genres. Clinical experience suggests that these cases, while rare, are very resistant to intervention. Perhaps we do not yet understand the basis for these problems. Perhaps written language samples would be informative about these semantic issues.

Identifying Language Disorder

Speech-Language Pathologists are the experts in determining if a language disorder is present. When oral language issues are in question, we know best practice includes language sample analysis. An essential component of the LSA process requires a definition and clear understanding of what is a language disorder. Once in place you can relate that knowledge to the oral language measures calculated by SALT. The American Speech-Language-Hearing Association (ASHA) has defined language disorder as "impairment in comprehension and/or use of a spoken, written, and/or other symbol system. The disorder may involve the 1) form of language (phonologic, morphologic, and syntactic systems), 2) the content of language (semantic system), and/or 3) the function of language in communication (pragmatic system), in any combination." (1993, p. 40 as cited in Paul, 2007). Paul (2007) explains language disorder in her own words as follows: "Children can be described as having language disorders if they have a significant deficit in learning to talk, understand, or use any aspect of language appropriately, relative to both environmental and norm referenced expectations for children of similar developmental level" (p. 4). Both definitions of language disorder agree there must be impairment in receptive or expressive language. However, Paul's definition includes the terms "significant", "environmental expectations", and "norm referenced" which provide the diagnostician more thoroughly defined criteria from which to align their assessment. Significant environmental deficit judgments are made relative to communication success at home, school, and community. Norm referenced deficits refer to performance on standardized or norm referenced tests. Paul advocates the position that deficits be identified by testing to define age-level expectations and by assessing the ability to use language for communication in the activities of daily living. This is particularly important for us to keep in mind as we consider the outcomes of LSA. LSA is the gold standard for documenting everyday communication, which is a critical part of defining language disorders (Paul, 2007). *But does SALT's LSA process qualify as a standardized test or a norm referenced procedure?*

Standardization

To document "impairment", as required by the definition of language disorder, best practice includes documenting performance relative to age-matched peers, usually using a standardized test. There are several concepts that make up the standardization process. The first part of "standardization" is doing the same thing with everyone, following a consistent testing protocol. From its onset, SALT has worked toward standardizing the process of language sampling. First, we've developed detailed protocols for eliciting conversational and several types of narrative samples. See Appendices A-L for detailed protocols for each sample type, including guides to examiner behavior, scripts for encouraging reticent individuals, books for story retelling, and expository and persuasion note-taking matrices. Second, language samples are transcribed using a very specific and consistent set of rules to identify words, morphemes, utterances, and errors. Detailed transcription rules ensure the accuracy of each analysis. Uniformity in collecting and transcribing samples has produced consistent analysis results, both within and across speakers (Heilmann, et al., 2010a). SALT does meet the first condition necessary for "standardization" with standardized administration and transcription protocols.

The next condition of standardization to review is the creation of an index of typical performance by administering the "test" to a large group of individuals. This process generates a normative sample or comparison group that can be used to document performance relative to age-matched peers. The composition of the normative sample usually includes stratification of, 1) typical development, including high, average, and low performers, 2) geographical distribution, to satisfy perceived "Lake Woebegone" bias ("where all the children are above average" - Garrison Keillor), and, 3) socioeconomic and ethnic diversity. The SALT databases were created following the premise of stratification. The databases provide access to the performance of typical speakers under the same standardized speaking conditions. The SALT databases have some limitations relative to geographical distribution and ethnic diversity. Where we have tested geographical differences we have found no significant differences between children in Wisconsin and San Diego. Some differences do exist between American and New Zealand children at five years but not six or seven. And it has been suggested that the difference at five years is because children in New Zealand begin kindergarten on their 5th birthday, typically earlier than their American counterparts (Westerveld & Heilmann, 2010). Research on ethnic diversity has not shown differences in language development for the core features of English. SLPs are responsible for recognizing dialect differences that are not consistent with Standard American English (SAE). Many features of African American English (AAE), for example, could be inappropriately considered as errors from an SAE perspective. The over inclusion of AAE speakers into special education has prompted a great deal of research which sites AAE as the major source of erroneous identification (see Chapter 8). SLPs are responsible for identifying dialectal features when transcribing, analyzing, and interpreting language samples.

Next we take up how these data can be used to interpret relative ranking of individual speakers. SALT uses standard deviation scores for each measure to document the relative ranking of individual speakers. This approach optimizes the descriptive value of the measures, sacrificing the "standard score" approach associated with standardized tests typically thought of as a scaled score, i.e., a standard deviation of 15 where 85 – 115 is considered typical performance. Creating scaled scores requires "smoothing" the data to create the same scaled scores for each measure or composite score. SALT, rather, relies on the standard deviation scores calculated for each comparison set that corresponds to the age and speaking conditions of the target speaker. Smoothing normative data allows test builders to interpolate missing data, e.g., data on 5 and 7-year-olds used to predict that of 6-year-old children. Creating standard scores makes interpreting the results more straight forward for users since all scores have the same statistical properties, such as mean and standard deviation. The measures included in SALT have come from the developmental literature or the clinical experience of SLPs working with language disorder. Measures like mean length of utterance, number of different words, and words per minute correlate highly with age and have very small standard deviations. Other clinically significant behaviors like mazes, pauses, and errors are not evenly distributed and have larger standard deviations. The SALT project has opted to keep these more descriptive measures that would certainly be discarded if creating a "standardized test" with smoothed standard scores for each measure. Creating standard scores assumes that each measure functions the same way across children over time. Some of the SALT measures that SLPs find useful in describing language production do not function the same way across speakers, but each captures an important aspect of oral language performance. As examples, consider pausing and mazing. Some speakers pause frequently to gain time to find the right word or to formulate the rest of an utterance while others do not. Similarly, some speakers produce frequent mazes, repeating and revising part words, words, and phrases. Both of these behaviors provide valuable clinical insight, but neither would appear in a standardized test because they do not correlate with age. The measures that are included in standardized tests are those that are significantly correlated with age and are sensitive to the identification of language disorder. Careful analysis of the standardized tests for language reveals that a great deal of work needs to be done to create measures that can identify language disorder beyond 70%. SALT identifies children with language disorder 76% of the time (sensitivity) and identifies children with typical language 82% of the time (specificity). These values were calculated from the measures in SALT's *Standard Measures Report* from 263 typical children and 231 children aged 3 – 13 receiving services in the Madison Metropolitan School District using -1 SD compared to the Conversation database (Miller & Klee, 1995). This means that SALT can identify disordered children at rates equal or better than most standardized language tests on the market today. But it can do more by describing specific language strengths and weaknesses. This profile of performance provides the information necessary to develop intervention plans to strengthen oral language skills essential for meeting everyday communication requirements.

The following is an email exchange on "standardization" between two SLPs who use SALT for LSA and a professor who conducts research on LSA. It addresses the issue of using LSA to qualify students for services.

Original question from Mary-Beth Rolland: SLP from Madison, Wisconsin:

Could I get some input from you all? The administration has been saying that we cannot use SALT to qualify students for speech and language because it is not a formal test measure. It is not standardized. You can use it to corroborate formal measures like the CELF (Semel, Wiig, & Secord, 2003). Can you speak to "formal", "standardized" and why LSA is a better measure of a child's actual performance than a test like the CELF? I have had this discussion so many times I need new info from the 'experts'.

From Tom Malone: SLP from Brown Deer, Wisconsin:

I have always viewed language sampling, including SALT, as one of the informal measures needed to meet state eligibility criteria for language impairment (Wisconsin Administrative Code, 2011). Although SALT does give you norm referenced measures, it does not give you the sort of composite scores that formal (i.e., standardized) tests, like the CELF, can provide. The requirement to use composite scores (either receptive, expressive, or total) in reporting standardized norm referenced test results is spelled out in a technical assistance guide published by the Wisconsin Department of Public Instruction (Freiberg, Wicklund, & Squier, 2003) to help implement the then-new SL criteria. With SALT you get a wide variety of measures on which a student can be compared to his/her peers, but no single measure (at least not yet) that tells you whether the student is language impaired. And that, I believe, puts SALT firmly in the informal measures camp.

I will defer to Jon (*referring to Jon Miller*) & John (*referring to John Heilmann*) on whether the SALT databases have the other necessary properties of a standardized test, such as normal distribution. The criteria do, however, give you an out for qualifying a student using SALT instead of formal tests. In those cases in which formal testing is "not appropriate or feasible," such as when such tests are not culturally appropriate for that student, informal measures can be substituted.

I might also mention that in selling SALT to administrators over the years I have gotten some traction in arguing that SALT can often make a compelling case for dismissing secondary students, who typically have been receiving SL services for a decade or more. That's because SALT, much better than formal testing, can address the issue of whether a student 'has a functional and effective communication system' which, according to the technical assistance guide (p. 29), is a major factor in considering dismissal.

From John Heilmann: Assistant Professor, University of Wisconsin – Milwaukee:

This is a great discussion. I'll add my two cents. Before doing so, I just want to say that this is my opinion and that these issues are not clear cut (obviously).

The word "standardized" can be used many different ways. Typically, when we say standardized test, we think of the CELF or TOLD (Hammill & Newcomer, 1988). However, I think it's more appropriate to apply the word "standardized" to the test administration procedures. In Ch. 3 of Haynes and Pindzola (2011), they state: "Standardization may imply only that the procedures for test administration are standard, not that norms are provided with the instrument." So, in that sense, LSA could be considered standardized, assuming the clinicians are adhering to the protocols used in the databases. There could be some debate here, as not every child is completing the same items. But, if the children are completing the same protocol and the protocol is pretty structured, e.g., narrative retell, expository discourse task, I feel comfortable saying that it is using standardized procedures. Some (including me) would call that a standardized assessment. Some evidence for this are the differences observed when using different protocols. There are many examples in the literature. For example, I presented a poster with Marleen Westerveld showing that there were significant and clinically meaningful differences in children's retells based on the presence or absence of pictures.

The next term to think about is "norm referenced." Basically, that means that you compare it to a normative sample. On the surface, it's pretty clear that you can compare SALT to a sample of age/grade-matched children. Most of the SALT databases are drawn from the Madison area, which some could argue is not representative of the broader population. In your particular case, I think it strengthens your argument, as you are essentially using local norms (recommended by many). But, we have put together some data showing that geography alone doesn't really affect the measures. You can see that in the 2010 paper you referred to. In the poster with Marleen (that I mentioned above), we provide even stronger evidence. We showed that the differences due to presence or absence of pictures were much greater than the difference due to geography (WI vs. New Zealand).

The final issue is "standard scores." This is where LSA using SALT differs from traditional "standardized/norm referenced" tests. Tests that generate standard scores, e.g., CELF, TOLD, normalize their norm referenced data to generate standard scores. That is, they smooth out the differences across ages to predict performance of individual children. This is done to increase the consistency of the data and smooth out the variations across the norming sample. SALT simply finds a group of matched children, generates normative data for that particular group (means, SD), and lets you know how your child performs in comparison. Another difference is that you can get a composite standard score, while, with SALT, you have to rely on each of the specific measures.

So, I don't know if that answers your question any further. I guess I would be interested in knowing why your administrators are concerned about the use of SALT. Are they concerned about, a) over identifying children, b) under identifying children, or c) reducing costs of transcription? If it's identification accuracy, you can cite the 2010 "using databases" paper (Heilmann, Miller, & Nockerts, 2010b). In that paper we also cite the other two main articles that have shown that LSA can identify children with LI (Aram, Morris, & Hall, 1993; Dunn, et al., 1996). There are other papers out there that have cautioned against the use of LSA. But, there are also plenty of papers that show the ineffectiveness of standardized tests, e.g., Dollaghan & Campbell (1998); Plante & Vance (1994). Also, you would be amazed at the questionable properties of standardized tests when looking at their very own test manuals. That is, many don't do a great job identifying children with LI (i.e., not great sensitivity and specificity) and they often "stack the deck" for their results, e.g., comparing performance on the CELF to the TOLD; they're basically the same test, so they should perform similarly on both.

This doesn't even mention the general admirable properties of the task [LSA] - functional communication, potentially less format bias for cultural and linguistic minorities, gets descriptive information, etc. Let me know what you think. Like I said, these are my opinions. I may have a bias given that this is my line of research. But, there are others out there who share similar views.

From Tom Malone:

It may be that Mary-Beth's administrators, like me, have focused on the legal aspect of eligibility. Like it or not, we are stuck with state criteria that require both formal and informal measures, but never really defines what those are or how they differ. Based on the emphasis on composite scores that I cited from the technical assistance guide (which doesn't really have the force of law, but it's all we've got), it seems probable that "formal" was meant to refer to traditional standardized tests. What John is saying, I think, that the research is showing that there really isn't such a bright-line distinction between these two types of testing.

Now, I think you know that I'm no big fan of standardized tests. A major point of our ASHA case study was to show that SALT was way superior to standardized testing in reflecting teacher concerns over our subject's language skills (Malone, et al., 2010). But over the years I've had administrators that really want to see those standardized scores when making eligibility decisions at an IEP meeting. And over the years I've become fairly resourceful at coming up with the test scores I need when I want to qualify a student, even if the student's SALT results are actually the bigger influence in my decision making. I admit it's not the cleanest approach, putting me in mind of these lines:

Between the idea
And the reality
Between the motion
And the act
Falls the shadow

-T.S. Eliot, *The Hollow Men*[6]

From John Heilmann:

I think that's a fair summary. Part of this is probably a cultural issue - standardized tests are ingrained in special education. Part of this is a psychometric issue. In many situations, you may find that norm referenced tests are more stable, particularly when looking at a composite score. There isn't a composite SALT score, per say. Laura Justice developed an index of narrative microstructure, which may be a good way to go (Justice, et al., 2006). However, recall that Aram's work showed that MLU is a good general measure (superior to standardized test results when identifying children with LI). So, I still think the jury is out. And we have to acknowledge the limitations of standardized tests for making high stakes decisions (when used alone).

This is the end of their email conversation which highlights some of the issues involved in using LSA to diagnose language disorder and qualify individuals for services in the schools. These issues remain with us, but the SALT project has advanced our confidence in using LSA to evaluate language use in the everyday speaking situations necessary to advance through the language arts and literacy school curriculum. Standardizing the process of collecting, transcribing, and

---

[6] This poem was first published as now known on November 23, 1925, in Eliot's *Poems: 1909-1925*.

analyzing samples provides confidence in using LSA as a valid and reliable assessment tool. SALT, with its databases of typical speakers to use for comparison, advances language sample analysis to norm referenced status and provides a window into how a range of language measures creates profiles of performance. These profiles confirm clinician, teacher, and parent judgments of communication difficulties and provide face validity for LSA.

A similar project that confirms the stability of LSA when the process is standardized is the Edmonton Narrative Norms Instrument (Schneider, Dubé, & Hayward, 2005). The ENNI is aimed at developing norms for narrative story retells for children ages 4 – 9 years. While the procedures and stories were different from those used when collecting the SALT story retell samples, the results were similar in terms of consistency of performance, reliability, validity, and advancing language skills with age. This project serves as a replication of our research over the years, advancing the use of LSA as a valid and reliable index of oral language performance.

What constitutes a "significant" deficit?

Possibly the most accepted proof of "significance" is to supply a score from an assessment. The first step in the LSA interpretation process is to review what constitutes a score outside the typical range. The definition of language disorder uses the phrase "significant deficit" but does not define the target value. Presumably the word "significant" is used in the definition to denote a level of performance below that of typical speakers of the same age. It is usually stated in standard scores or standard deviation (SD) units. The specific level noting "significance" is not an agreed upon number. A significant deficit or delay ranges from -0.5 SD to -1.5 SD in the research literature, to -1 SD to -2SD in state standards across the country. The value in Wisconsin, -1.75 SD, may likely be a political decision as there is no evidence relating this number with oral language difficulty having an impact on school performance. These values are important as they determine what percentage of children can qualify for services. A review of the normal curve offers some insight into specifying the percentage of the population falling at or below standard deviation units from -1 SD, -1.5 SD, -1.75 SD to -2 SD. 68% of the population will fall between plus and minus 1 SD, 82% between +/-1.5 SD, 89% between +/- 1.75 SD, and 95% between +/- 2 SD. If we look at the minus end of the curve, 9% of the population fall below -1.5 SD, 5.5%

below -1.75 SD, and 2.75% below -2 SD. These standard deviation criteria define the percentage of children who can qualify for services using standardized tests if the population of children with language disorder is distributed along the normal curve. These values define "significant" deficit relative to typical children.

We began the chapter with the definition of language disorder that had two parts, documenting language performance relative to age-matched peers, and difficulty with oral language at home, school, and community. We have seen that LSA can provide norm-referenced data across a range of measures that are relevant for describing disordered language performance in natural speaking situations; conversation, narrative, expository, and persuasive language. SALT's version of LSA is norm referenced, indexing performance relative to age or grade status. SALT does not aspire to become a standardized test but it does aspire to a standardized language sampling process; it can both define typical performance across age and speaking conditions and describe, in detail, the specific language features that characterize individual disordered performance.

Conclusion

SALT Analysis provides evidence for several different profiles of language disorder: language delay, word retrieval problems, utterance formulation deficits, discourse problems, and fast speaking rate with low semantic content. We examine each of these problem types further in the next chapter where we investigate the more detailed measures necessary to illuminate each specific profile. So far we have focused on the clusters of measures on the SMR that constitute a distinct profile of performance. Further analysis of each type will reveal that there can be overlap among these profiles requiring all of our clinical skills and experience to unravel.

Beyond the Standard Measures

Jon F. Miller
Karen Andriacchi
Ann Nockerts

Introduction

The central focus of this chapter is the analysis of language samples using a database comparison set. We will also branch into analyses that do not require a set of samples for comparison. These measures are valuable to the assessment process through the *Analyze menu: Standard Measures Report* which contains the same language measures as the *Database menu: Standard Measures Report* but is generated without a comparison dataset. The same general principles, discussed in this chapter, apply to both reports. For every language measure in the *Standard Measures Report* there are follow-up measures in SALT that can support your questions and aid in your clinical interpretation.

The *Standard Measures Report* provides general measures of performance across areas of language that have been identified as significant for functional communication as well as academic performance. The task at hand is to figure out how the strengths and weaknesses highlighted from language sample analysis (LSA) form a complete picture of oral language performance. The true power in the diagnostic process comes when the strength of the SALT application is combined with clinical knowledge. SALT allows for a highly detailed and thorough analysis of language production, but the diagnostician must know how to interpret the measures and where to look further.

Our approach to interpreting LSA measures, outlined here, has evolved over the past 20 years working with SLPs, and from our own research and clinical experiences.

Step 1
Once the sample has been transcribed, generate the *Database menu: Standard Measures Report* (SMR) with the appropriate database comparison group. Notice the areas which are flagged as being at least one standard deviation above or below the database mean. Interpreting the values correctly is very important. Negative values, or those below the database mean, can indicate a problem for values like MLU or NDW. But positive values, higher than the database mean, can also document problems. Pauses and mazes are examples where positive values can indicate oral language issues which may need further investigation. Don't make the mistake of considering all areas that are above or below the database mean to be a problem. Think about that aspect of language and what impact it has for the speaker. It would be irresponsible to enroll a student, for example, who has negative values for mazes, as that student is actually more fluent than the average speaker his or her same age.

Look for clusters of measures which point toward a specific profile of language production problem. The profiles are meant to be descriptive of the oral language performance. They are not independent and, in many cases, may be overlapping. Their utility is in providing direction for how we spend our follow-up time to create a complete description of oral language performance, and to create a plan for intervention. Don't be surprised if you find unique performance deficits. We are constantly finding utterances that are distinct, as well as overlapping profiles not seen before. Focus on the speaker and his or her distinctive communication problems, and allow the SALT measures to document these oral language deficits.

Step 2
After running the SMR, listen to the sample again while reading the transcript. This tunes you back in to the speaker's overall oral language style. It also gives

an opportunity to review how well the SALT measures captured the language difficulties you might have heard in the sample. The SMR does not capture every aspect of language difficulty. So be prepared to be creative in documenting issues beyond this report such as problems with narrative organization or non-specific referencing. It is possible to create customized code lists to mark any word or utterance of interest. SALT provides useful utilities to facilitate this hand-coding process, making it easy and efficient. We discuss these options in more detail later in the chapter.

Step 3
Evaluate problem areas in more detail. Measures in the SMR that are above or below one standard deviation from the database mean should be evaluated in more detail for several reasons. First, we need to confirm that each of these measures represents a real problem. Second, it is important to look at the utterances and words on which these measures are based, e.g., abandoned utterances, utterances with mazes, and words with omitted bound morphemes. Third, multiple measures should be reviewed together to determine if they constitute a profile of language disorder. SALT often provides more detailed and specific analyses that are available as summaries, e.g., *Database menu: Maze Summary*, or as lists, e.g., *Analyze menu: Omissions and Error Codes*. Exploring these additional analyses provides details about areas of difficulty and resolves questions about the impact of the SMR measures. The SMR results direct the next steps to help understand the language difficulties presented. To work efficiently, further analyses are only run when justified by measures in the SMR. If mazes are produced in high numbers, for example, then we want to determine if they consist of filled pauses, or part-words, words, or phrases in repetition or revision. SALT produces such a table but it is only of interest if maze totals are significantly high. In this way, the SMR identifies areas requiring further exploration.

Follow-up Analyses Organized by Profile Type

The discussion of follow-up analyses has been organized by the profile types mentioned in the previous chapter. This allows for discussion of each of the standard SALT measures, the more detailed measures, and recommendations for hand-coded procedures where warranted.

LANGUAGE DELAY

The primary indicator for delayed language development is low mean length of utterance (MLU). This is often in conjunction with low number of different words (NDW), low words per minute (WPM), high number of errors, and/or high number of omissions. We often see minimal, if any, complex syntax use. Each of these areas may need to be examined in further detail to determine if it is an accurate reflection of performance, and to support initial findings.

MLU: We want to make sure MLU shows a range of sentence lengths with the mean reflecting an average. Question a low MLU. *Could it be limited by speech production issues or a lack of respiratory support? Or is it truly language based?* Look at the *Database menu: Word Lists, Bound Morphemes, & Utterance Distribution* summary. The utterance distribution table in this summary (Figure 6-1) shows the number of utterances spoken for each utterance length. This example shows a speaker's language sample which contained only a few utterances that were longer than six words in length, notably less than the database mean values for that age speaker.

		0	1	2	3	4	5	6	7	8	9	10	11	12	13	14	15+	Total
NUMBER OF UTTERANCES BY UTTERANCE LENGTH																		
Utterance Length in Words																		
Child		0	3	1	7	2	3	5	0	0	0	1	0	2	0	0	0	24
DB Mean		0	0	1	2	4	6	5	5	4	2	2	1	1	1	0	1	35

Figure 6-1

This same distribution can also be investigated at the morpheme level. We hope to find a range of utterance lengths around the mean, some longer and some shorter than the mean value. It is instructive to examine the database values relative to the target sample to identify the number of longer utterances produced. These utterances may likely be the syntactic forms the speaker is just learning. Analyzing the syntax of these utterances provides useful insight into the speaker's language development progress. A reasonable distribution of utterance lengths clustering around the mean, e.g., lengths from 1 – 7 with an MLU of 3.2, validates the MLU value. It is also good practice to check on the examiner's language for conversational samples (see the *Analyze menu: Word and Morpheme Summary*). Examiner language (MLU and NDW) should be equal to, or less complex than, the target speaker.

NDW and Vocabulary: Begin examining vocabulary use with the *Database menu: Word Lists, Bound Morphemes, & Utterance Distribution* summary. The Word Lists section of this summary (Figure 6-2) provides frequency data for five word lists: question words (for conversational samples), negatives, conjunctions (the 1st complex sentence type), modal auxiliary verbs, and personal pronouns. The type and total frequency for each list is provided.

WORD LISTS, BOUND MORPHEMES, & UTTERANCE DISTRIBUTION Based on C&I Verbal Utts							
LANGUAGE MEASURE	CHILD		DATABASE				
	Score	+/-SD	Mean	Min	Max	SD	%SD
WORD LISTS							
Question Words							
Total	0	-0.48	0.33	0	4	0.69	210%
Type	0	-0.53	0.29	0	3	0.54	188%
Negatives							
Total	5	0.34	3.97	0	19	3.02	76%
Type	3	0.28	2.57	0	6	1.53	59%
Conjunctions							
Total	39 **	2.24	24.14	12	43	6.62	27%
Type	6	0.58	5.21	2	8	1.35	26%
Modal Auxiliary Verbs							
Total	5 **	2.11	1.53	0	8	1.64	107%
Type	3 **	2.44	0.98	0	3	0.83	85%
Personal Pronouns							
Total	29	-0.53	31.74	22	49	5.23	16%
Type	10 *	1.80	6.95	3	11	1.69	24%
*At least 1 SD (** 2 SD) from the database mean							

Figure 6-2

Conversational samples offer the opportunity to examine question word use. Negative utterances have a specific form, so the frequency of these words provides evidence of use. Conjunctions provide insight into initial complex sentence use. The types and tokens provide evidence for the variety of conjoining words used. Modals are another unique form used increasingly as development advances. Personal pronouns give some insight into referencing. Pronoun use follows a specific reference with appropriate subject and object, gender, and number choice. You can find the words used in the sample by accessing the *Analyze menu: Standard Word Lists*. This option lets you explore other vocabulary lists as well.

Another useful list is the *Analyze menu: Grammatical Categories* (Figure 6-3) which organizes all the words used in the sample into the categories listed in this table. This is done using a large dictionary and a set of grammatical rules (Channell & Johnson, 1999). The *Analyze menu: Grammatical Category Lists* option shows the words in each category.

GRAMMATICAL CATEGORIES		
	Child	Examiner
Initiators	0	1
Determiners	21	28
Adjectives	5	10
Nouns	40	53
Personal Pronouns	23	52
Other Pronouns	13	14
Auxiliary Modals	3	11
Auxiliary Operators	7	17
Verbs	33	59
Copula Forms	11	16
Verb Particles	0	5
Adverbs	10	15
Intensifiers	1	1
Prepositions	9	18
Existential	0	0
Question Words	5	10
Coordinators	2	7
Subordinators	0	4
Infinitives	1	4
Possessives	0	1
Negation Words	0	1
Lets Words	0	0
Interjections	8	9

Figure 6-3

The *Analyze menu: Word Root Tables* produces an alphabetized list of all the words used in the sample (Figure 6-4). This can be invaluable for exploring the vocabulary used in story retell narrative and expository samples where the context is familiar to the examiner and certain vocabulary use may be obligatory.

WORD ROOT TABLE C&I Verbal Utts					
	Child	Examiner		Child	Examiner
*BRANCHES	1	0	IN	2	0
*WERE	1	0	LEAP	1	0
A	5	0	LIKE	1	0
AGAIN	1	0	LOOK	4	0
AND	15	0	MY	1	0
AT	1	0	NIGHT	1	0
BACK	1	0	OF	2	0
BARK	1	0	ON	2	0
BE	1	0	ONE	3	0
BEE	2	0	OUT	1	0
BOY	2	1	OVER	2	0
BRANCH	1	0	QUIET	1	0

Figure 6-4

Omissions and errors: Frequently, in younger children, omissions and errors are centered around bound morphemes. The frequency and type of bound morphemes used in the sample are listed in the *Analyze menu: Bound Morpheme Tables*. The *Analyze menu: Omissions and Error Codes* summary (Figure 6-5) provides a list of all omitted words and bound morphemes as well as all the words and utterances coded as errors. The utterances containing the omissions and errors are also included in this summary. It is useful to examine these utterances to look for patterns.

OMISSIONS AND ERROR CODES Total Utterances 1st Speaker		
	CHILD	
	Total	Expanded
Omitted Words	3	
*THE		1
*TO		1
*WERE		1
62 C (Um we went) we *were just drive/ing *the car.		
109 C And they were try/ing *to chase the other dog away and run all around the whole world {E laughs}.		
Omitted Bound Morphemes	1	
CHASE/*ED		1
82 C My mommy chase/*ed them all around {C laughs}.		
Word-level Error Codes	5	
BES[EW:BEING]		1
CANNOT[EW:COULD_NOT]		1
FELLED|FALL[EO:FELL]		1
FIND[EW:FOUND]		1
SAWED|SEE[EO:SAW]		1
43 C But we cannot[EW:could_not] find them.		
65 C And :02 they are always bes[EW:being] mean to me.		
117 C And she (a*) felled|fall[EO:fell] in the thing.		
120 C And the lady sawed|see[EO:saw] her.		
122 C (And) and they find[EW:found] Savanna when they came home.		
Utterance-level Error Codes	2	
[EU]		2
73 C (And :02 and) and I have never want the dog/s (r*) runed away again [EU].		
103 C And another times when he was so crazy all the times [EU].		

Figure 6-5

<u>Subordination Index</u>: We tend to think about language delay only with children under 5 years of age. However, our clinical experience and research have shown that these delayed patterns persist through childhood. An important analysis often supporting the diagnosis of delayed development is the Subordination Index (SI), a hand-coded analysis of clausal density (see Appendix O). SALT has utilities for simple insertion of an SI code at the end of each utterance (see *Edit menu: Insert SI Codes*). The *Database menu: Subordination Index* (or the *Analyze*

menu: Subordination Index if you are not comparing to database samples) summarize the results (Figure 6-6). A low SI score indicates the use of simple syntax, or lack of complex sentence formulation, which is often characteristic of speakers with language delay.

LANGUAGE MEASURE	SUBORDINATION INDEX							
	Child		DATABASE				
	Score	+/-SD	Mean	Min	Max	SD	%SD
[SI-0]	0	-0.53	0.25	0	2	0.47	189%
[SI-1]	21 *	-1.21	29.46	12	47	7.00	24%
[SI-2]	1 *	-1.00	3.22	0	9	2.22	69%
[SI-3]	0	-0.43	0.16	0	1	0.37	231%
SI Score	1.05	-0.76	1.10	0.96	1.27	0.07	6%
* At least 1 SD (** 2 SD) from the database mean							

Figure 6-6

WORD RETRIEVAL AND UTTERANCE FORMULATION

Word retrieval and utterance formulation problems must be differentiated from one another by examining the speaker's mazes and pauses if scores for these behaviors prove to be higher than normal.

Mazes: High numbers of mazes revealed on the SMR is the primary indicator that we are dealing with a word retrieval or utterance formulation issue. The *Database menu: Maze Summary* (or the *Analyze menu: Maze Summary* if you are not comparing to database samples) provides a breakdown of the total number of mazes that are revisions, repetitions, and filled pauses (Figure 6-7). The maze revisions and repetitions are further broken down into their components (part-word, word, and phrase) and filled pauses are broken down into single word, e.g., "um", and multiple words, e.g., "um um um". Speakers with word-level problems have a preponderance of part-word and word repetitions and revisions. Speakers with utterance-level issues have more phrase-level repetitions and revisions. The results can be mixed, requiring further exploration.

MAZE SUMMARY Based on C&I Verbal Utts							
LANGUAGE MEASURE	**CHILD**			**DATABASE**			
	Score	+/-SD	Mean	Min	Max	SD	%SD
Utterances with Mazes	17 *	1.25	11.60	0	23	4.32	37%
Number of Mazes	34 **	2.84	14.94	0	38	6.70	45%
Number of Maze Words	73 **	3.13	27.49	0	73	14.55	53%
% Maze Words/Total Words	24% **	2.80	10.44	0	24	4.91	47%
Revisions							
Part Word	0	-0.67	0.90	0	7	1.34	149%
Word	2	-0.04	2.05	0	6	1.45	70%
Phrase	10 **	2.52	3.84	0	11	2.44	64%
Repetitions							
Part Word	0	-0.71	0.61	0	4	0.86	141%
Word	5 **	2.01	1.65	0	8	1.67	101%
Phrase	1	0.20	0.79	0	4	1.07	135%
Filled Pauses							
Single Word	29 **	3.15	8.41	0	28	6.53	78%
Multiple Words	0	-0.48	0.22	0	2	0.47	209%
* At least 1 SD (** 2 SD) from the database mean							

Figure 6-7

The *Maze Summary* also includes maze distribution tables (Figure 6-8). The first table, % of Utterances with Mazes by Utterance Length in Morphemes, provides you with the percentage of utterances with mazes at each length (1, 2, 3, 4, etc.) in morphemes. This is informative as you expect more mazes to appear with longer utterances. Note which utterance lengths have fewer mazes than expected and which have more. Additional tables provide you with the distribution of mazes by maze length and by utterance length. Finally, you can examine the distribution of utterances by the number of mazes they contain which gives a clear index of how many utterances had one maze, two mazes, and so on. These tables provide you with insight into maze length relative to utterances attempted and how much material is in mazes relative to the total sample. Mazes are disruptive to listeners, making it difficult to follow the utterance and the message. Speakers with word retrieval problems tend to repeat or revise before subject or object nouns, and adjectives. They also repeat or revise before verbs, which is tricky, as the problem may be syntax based rather than a problem with word retrieval.

MAZE DISTRIBUTION TABLES

% of Utterances with Mazes by Utterance Length in Morphemes

	1	2	3	4	5	6	7	8	9	10	11	12	13	14	15+	Total
CHILD	0%	0%	100%	100%	20%	50%	33%	100%	50%	100%	100%	100%	0%	100%	100%	53%
DB Mean	6%	12%	19%	29%	22%	33%	33%	40%	30%	31%	33%	32%	27%	35%	59%	36%

Number of Mazes by Maze Length in Morphemes

	0	1	2	3	4	5	6	7	8	9	10	11	12	13	14	15+	Total
CHILD	0	22	4	3	0	1	1	0	2	1	0	0	0	0	0	0	34
DB Mean	0	9	3	1	1	0	0	0	0	0	0	0	0	0	0	0	14

Number of Mazes by Utterance Length in Morphemes

	1	2	3	4	5	6	7	8	9	10	11	12	13	14	15+	Total
CHILD	0	0	1	1	1	4	1	1	5	4	3	2	0	3	8	34
DB Mean	0	0	1	1	1	1	1	1	1	1	1	1	1	1	3	15

Number of Verbal Utterances by Number of Mazes

	0	1	2	3	4	5	6+	Total
CHILD	15	9	2	3	3	0	0	32
DB Mean	27	9	2	0	0	0	0	38

Figure 6-8

Utterance formulation problems can be linked to specific syntactic forms like complex sentences. When you see a high percentage of mazes in longer utterances as well as more than one maze per utterance, review the sample for complex sentence use. Note the number of propositions attempted and the syntactic forms used by the speaker. If syntax is limited to simple sentence forms and more than one proposition is attempted per utterance, then teaching complex syntax is your target. You can test this conclusion by working on producing one proposition at a time and reviewing the maze frequency. If this is the correct conclusion, then mazes will be significantly reduced. If not, work through the mazes from a word-level perspective. It should be noted that frequent abandoned utterances point to utterance-level issues. You may consider an abandoned utterance to be a failed maze in the sense that the speaker was not able to resolve the maze and gave up. Use the *Analyze menu: Standard Utterance Lists* to examine each abandoned utterance carefully to determine similarity of form and content used. You might look at the use of complex subordination by applying the SI (see Appendix O). The SI has been coded in most of the database samples and is available for comparison with an individual sample.

<u>Pauses</u>: Frequent pauses may be another indication of word retrieval or utterance formulation problems. Some individuals use repetition, revision, or filled pauses to find the right word or utterance form. Others just pause silently until the solution emerges. Only a few do both. The length of the silent pauses is an indication of the difficulty listeners will have in following the message. A pause of only 1 - 2 seconds signals an opportunity for speaking turn change. This discourse rule leaves listeners hanging when long pauses occur within the speaker's turn. The *Analyze menu: Rate and Pause Summary* (Figure 6-9) provides detailed measures of pause time and frequency within and between utterances. It also provides information on speaking rate (words and utterances per minute) for both speakers. In our experience, pauses within utterances are associated with word retrieval problems and pauses between utterances are linked to utterance formulation issues. You can get a list of all the utterances with pauses in the *Analyze menu: Standard Utterance Lists* option.

RATE SUMMARY		
Elapsed Time: 5 minutes		
	Child	Examiner
Words per Minute	43.40	80.20
Utterances per Minute	9.20	17.40

PAUSE SUMMARY			
	No. of Pauses	Total Pause Time	Average Pause Time
Within Child Utterances			
Main body	2	0:04	
Mazes	1	0:03	
Total	3	0:07	0:02
Between Child Utterances			
Within Turn	0	0:00	
Preceding Turn	7	0:24	
Total	7	0:24	0:03
Within Examiner Utterances			
Main body	0	0:00	
Mazes	0	0:00	
Total	0	0:00	0:00
Between Examiner Utterances			
Within Turn	3	0:11	
Preceding Turn	2	0:09	
Total	5	0:20	0:04

Figure 6-9

Whether the issue is frequent mazes or frequent pauses you should review vocabulary diversity. Review the number of different words (NDW) produced in the sample as well as the type token ratio (TTR) and moving average type token ratio (MATTR). If these measures are below 1 SD, then re-read the sample to identify circumlocutions and examine pronoun use. Pronoun use can also be examined in the *Database menu: Word Lists, Bound Morphemes, & Utterance Distribution* table which provides personal pronoun use compared to peers. The *Analyze menu: Standard Word Lists* option gives you frequencies of pronoun use for several types of pronouns.

Finally, in the pursuit to diagnose utterance formulation versus word retrieval difficulties, if you began with a conversational sample you should collect an additional narrative sample. Narrative samples put more pressure on the speaker to produce specific content which is usually familiar to the examiner. Select the type of narrative relative to age or ability level; story retell for younger individuals and expository or persuasion samples for those who are older. The narrative should elicit more examples of complex syntax from the speaker if he or she is capable. It also provides an opportunity to examine specific word use.

NARRATIVE ORGANIZATION

Problems with narrative organization are often the only issues arising from the language sample. You should collect a narrative sample, of course, but the SMR may not show any specific deficits. When you listen to the sample and re-read the transcript, however, it is clear that the speaker doesn't fluidly tell the story. Characters may not be introduced, plots may be ignored, conflicts and/or resolutions may be omitted or included at odd times, and so on. These speakers typically have difficulty with written language as well as with oral reports in school. Their language at the word and utterance level is usually fine, but be aware of possible issues with complex syntax. This is a profile that is often identified initially by teachers and SLPs when listening to oral language or reviewing written language assignments. The crux of the problem in production is taking the listener through the introduction, characters, conflicts, resolutions, character mental states, and conclusion in an orderly manner.

Narrative Scoring Scheme: We adapted a scoring procedure to document narrative organization; the Narrative Scoring Scheme (NSS). It is based on the work of Stein and Glenn, 1979; 1982 (see Appendix P). The NSS involves assigning scores for each of seven categories and then typing the scores into the transcript on plus lines inserted at the end of the transcript. SALT has utilities for inserting the scoring template (*Edit menu: Insert NSS Template*) and reports for summarizing the results (*Analyze menu: Narrative Scoring Scheme* and *Database menu: Narrative Scoring Scheme* (Figure 6-10)). The NSS measure was developed for our bilingual research project and was one of the best predictors of reading achievement in both Spanish and English (Miller, et al., 2006).

NARRATIVE SCORING SCHEME							
NSS Category			**DATABASE**				
	Score	**+/-SD**	**Mean**	**Min**	**Max**	**SD**	**%SD**
Introduction	4	0.12	3.90	1	5	0.83	21%
CharacterDev	3	-0.02	3.02	1	5	0.99	33%
MentalStates	1 **	-2.10	2.66	1	5	0.79	30%
Referencing	2 *	-1.98	3.32	2	5	0.66	20%
ConflictRes	3	-0.49	3.39	1	5	0.80	24%
Cohesion	2 *	-1.75	3.26	1	5	0.72	22%
Conclusion	4	0.59	3.34	1	5	1.11	33%
NSS Score	19	-0.94	22.89	12	32	4.13	18%

* At least 1 SD (** 2 SD) from the database mean

Figure 6-10

Expository Scoring Scheme: The Expository Scoring Scheme (ESS), based on the NSS measure, was developed to document narrative organization and content for expository samples (see Appendix Q). The ESS is scored for ten different features. Use the *Edit menu: Insert ESS Template* utility to insert the scoring template at the end of the transcript. Then assign the scores and summarize the results with the *Analyze menu: Expository Scoring Scheme* and *Database menu: Expository Scoring Scheme* reports (Figure 6-11).

EXPOSITORY SCORING SCHEME							
ESS Category			**DATABASE**				
	Score	**+/-SD**	**Mean**	**Min**	**Max**	**SD**	**%SD**
ObjectOfContest	2 *	-1.49	3.39	1	5	0.93	27%
Preparations	1 **	-3.15	3.30	1	5	0.73	22%
StartOfPlay	2 *	-1.44	3.34	1	5	0.93	28%
CourseOfPlay	2 *	-1.83	3.47	1	5	0.80	23%
Rules	2 *	-1.56	3.30	1	5	0.83	25%
Scoring	1 **	-2.57	3.24	1	5	0.87	27%
Duration	2 *	-1.03	3.14	0	5	1.11	35%
Strategy	1 **	-2.41	3.27	1	5	0.94	29%
Terminology	1 **	-2.49	3.19	1	5	0.88	28%
Cohesion	1 **	-3.11	3.17	2	4	0.70	22%
ESS Score	15 **	-3.21	32.80	13	44	5.54	17%
* At least 1 SD (** 2 SD) from the database mean							

Figure 6-11

Persuasion Scoring Scheme: The Persuasion Scoring Scheme (PSS) was also based on the NSS measure as well as the ESS. This scoring scheme was developed to document narrative organization and content for persuasion samples (see Appendix R). The PSS is scored for seven different features. The *Edit menu: Insert PSS Template* utility is used to insert the scoring template at the end of the transcript. Once the scores have been assigned, the results can be summarized with the *Analyze menu: Persuasion Scoring Scheme* and *Database menu: Persuasion Scoring Scheme* reports (Figure 6-12).

PERSUASION SCORING SCHEME							
PSS Category	**Child**		**DATABASE**				
	Score	**+/-SD**	**Mean**	**Min**	**Max**	**SD**	**%SD**
Issue and Change	4	0.14	3.89	2	5	0.83	21%
Supporting Reasons	4	0.28	3.77	2	5	0.81	21%
Other Point of View	2 *	-1.54	3.26	1	5	0.82	25%
Compromises	3	0.14	2.86	1	5	1.03	36%
Conclusion	2	-0.66	2.80	1	5	1.21	43%
Cohesion	3	-0.55	3.43	2	5	0.78	23%
Effectiveness	3	0.04	2.97	2	4	0.71	24%
PSS Composite Score	21	-0.52	22.97	16	31	3.76	16%
*At least 1 SD (** 2 SD) from the database mean							

Figure 6-12

DISCOURSE DEFICITS

Discourse deficits are best identified from conversational samples where there are multiple speaker turns. There are several measures pertaining to discourse included on the SMR which SALT calculates automatically. These include Percent Responses to Questions, Mean Turn Length (in words), Utterances with Overlapping Speech, and Interrupted Other Speaker. Percent Responses to Questions provides an index of number of examiner questions followed by an utterance, or response, from the target speaker. The utterances need to be reviewed to make sure that the target speaker's utterance was, in fact, a response to the question. For speakers with discourse problems we often see inappropriate responses or no response when a question is asked. When the percentage is low, examiner questions and target speaker responses should be looked at clinically. SALT provides an easy way to construct the list of questions using the *Analyze menu: Standard Utterance Lists* option. Select the 2nd speaker's (*examiner's*) utterances ending with a question mark and display them in context with several following entries - usually 2 or 3 will catch the response if it's available. You will then be presented with a list you can analyze for form and content. *Did the examiner allow sufficient opportunity for the response? Was the question answered appropriately? Was the right syntax used?* In Figure 6-13, the target speaker answered all three questions. But in two of the three responses the speaker produced one or more abandoned utterances. Perhaps the facts were not available to the speaker. Otherwise, we have evidence of word retrieval or utterance formulation problems.

STANDARD UTTERANCE LISTS Total Utterances 2nd Speaker		
Questions		
9	E	Do you ever eat Mexican food?
10	C	(Um) no not that>
11	C	Well I ate taco/s (one) one time.
23	E	Which one do you like best?
24	C	I like burrito/s.
25	C	They have a little pizazz in them.
26	E	What do they put in it to make it pizazzy?
27	C	(Um) green pepper/s and pepper/s (um)>
28	C	I/'ve never>

Figure 6-13

DISCOURSE SUMMARY
Based on Total Utterances

LANGUAGE MEASURE	CHILD		DATABASE				
	Score	+/-SD	Mean	Min	Max	SD	%SD
RESPONSES TO QUESTIONS							
Other Speaker Questions	6	-0.93	15.34	1	53	10.04	65%
Responses to Questions	4 *	-1.05	12.10	1	42	7.69	64%
Y/N Responses to Questions	0 *	-1.14	4.21	0	21	3.69	88%
% Responses to Questions	67%	-0.97	81.00	33	133	14.72	18%
TURN LENGTH SUMMARY							
Mean Turn Len (utts)	2.67	0.35	2.16	1.19	14.50	1.46	68%
Median Turn Len (utts)	2.00	0.28	1.57	1.00	14.50	1.51	97%
Mean Turn Len (words)	16.00	0.14	14.20	3.36	123.50	13.13	92%
Median Turn Len (words)	9.00	-0.08	10.14	1.00	123.50	13.62	134%
OTHER							
% Words Mentioned First	33%	-0.78	36.86	25	48	4.40	12%
Utts. with Overlapping Speech	2	-0.65	4.24	0	24	3.45	81%
Interrupted Other Speaker	0	-0.42	0.21	0	2	0.51	237%

* At least 1 SD (** 2 SD) from the database mean

NUMBER OF SPEAKER TURNS BY TURN LENGTH
Turn Length in Number of Utterances

	1	2	3	4	5	6+	Total
CHILD	5	4	3	1	0	2	15
DB Mean	14	5	2	1	0	1	23

Turn Length in Number of Words

	0	1	2	3	4	5	6	7	8	9	10	11	12	13	14	15+	Total
CHILD	1	3	1	0	1	0	0	1	0	1	0	0	0	1	0	6	15
DB Mean	0	5	1	1	1	1	1	1	1	1	1	1	1	1	0	6	23

Figure 6-14

If the discourse measures in the SMR are questionable then generate the *Database menu: Discourse Summary* (Figure 6-14) (or *Analyze menu: Discourse Summary* if the database comparison set is not available) to produce a summary of the number of examiner questions asked, the number answered, the number of yes/no responses, and the percentage of questions answered. Other indicators of whether or not the speaker is following discourse rules include the number of utterances with overlapping speech and the number of times the target speaker interrupted the other speaker. The *Turn Length Summary* section provides several measures of the speaker's turn taking. A turn is the number of speaker utterances or words while they hold the floor. As speakers become more language proficient their turn length increases. Turn length is also an indication of whether or not the speaker is following discourse rules, allowing the speaking partner turns for sharing information. The turn length distribution tables enable you to review turns by number of words and number of utterances. Look for a distribution of turn lengths, not just short responses or long responses. It is important to re-read and listen to the transcript focusing on how well the speaker follows discourse rules. We are concerned with individuals who are un-responsive to the speaking partner, or who seem to have their own topic of conversation, never attending to the partner's speech at all.

A follow-up measure to the turn length analysis is to code topic maintenance and change. This can be done by creating customized codes, e.g., [Topic_Initiate] and [Topic_Continue], and inserting the appropriate code at the end of each utterance (Figure 6-15). Check that "continuations" don't just dwell on detail but provide new information on the general topic, as in a typical fluid conversation.

```
E Do you have any brother/s or sister/s [Topic_Initiate]?
C I got[EW:have] three brother/s [Topic_Continue].
C But they don't live with us [Topic_Continue].
C They live with Grandma_Dale [Topic_Continue].
E Oh, ok [Topic_Continue].
C Grandma_Dale has got two dog/s [Topic_Initiate].
E She has two dog/s [Topic_Continue]?
C Yeah [Topic_Continue].
```

Figure 6-15

Use *Explore menu: Word and Code List* (Figure 6-16) to summarize the codes. The summary will tell you who initiated the topics in the conversation and who maintained them over the course of time. This will document responsiveness to the speaking partner from a content perspective.

Explore Words and Codes Total Utterances		
	Child	Examiner
[Topic_Initiate]	10	18
[Topic_Continue]	25	12
Total Frequency	35	30

Figure 6-16

FAST SPEAKING RATE

There are individuals who speak very fast yet have difficulty making specific references. This is often associated with reduced semantic content. Their speaking rate (WPM) is higher than their peers by more than one SD and their sample is longer. Their NDW is usually within one SD from the mean, but MLU is often higher. Calculating a Subordination Index often reveals appropriate syntax. A careful reading of the transcript reveals that the speakers hold the floor at all costs (*very long turn lengths*) and continue to speak until the content to be conveyed has been produced. This may be an adaptation to a word retrieval or utterance formulation problem where the problem focus seems to be the content. Evidence for this comes from the frequent circumlocutions within speaking turns. Fortunately these are not frequent cases as they seem very resistant to therapies. This suggests that we have not identified the basic problem. The follow-up analyses should focus on reading and coding the transcript for content errors and circumlocutions that suggest a word or utterance-level problem.

Coding More Detail of Specific Clinical Problems

SALT allows you to create customized codes to mark individual words and utterances for any feature that may be of special interest. Once coded, the program counts each code and lists the words or utterances containing them. This was illustrated previously with the example of topic initiation and continuation. Measures of specific features like Developmental Sentence Scoring (Lee & Canter, 1971) can also be coded and summarized. Lexical or syntactic forms targeted in therapy can be coded in spontaneous samples to document carry-over into everyday language use. This is perhaps the most powerful, yet under-used, feature of SALT. Although it requires you to hand code each feature, SALT has utilities to facilitate the task (see *Edit menu: Insert Code*). The *Explore menu: Word and Code List* can be used to identify and list utterances containing specific words, morphemes, phrases, and codes. If you are working on a set of vocabulary, for example, create a list of the words of interest. SALT will count the number of times each word occurs in the transcript and pull up the utterances containing them. If you are interested in discourse, you might code the examiner questions for their form, Y/N, what, where, why, etc. to determine the types of questions the speaker is able to answer and those that cause difficulty. If you want to mark phonological problems, for example, create codes and SALT will count them and show you where they occurred. You can easily look for patterns of occurrence from this analysis.

Linking Transcripts for Side-by-Side Comparison

The Link menu in SALT allows you to select any two transcripts for comparison. Once selected, you can generate reports for side-by-side comparisons. This facilitates, 1) monitoring change over time to document therapy progress or to observe for generalization, 2) comparing performance in different speaking contexts, 3) assessing proficiency across languages, 4) documenting RtI with naturalistic language use data, and 5) providing the necessary data to discontinue services.

Comparing transcripts is an important part of the clinical process. Evaluating time-1/time-2 language samples for growth or change can effectively show whether or not therapy targets have generalized to functional speaking tasks, not simply to drill and practice scenarios. Comparisons across speaking contexts can be invaluable to a diagnostic. For example, narratives may present more of a linguistic challenge than conversations for a particular speaker. Collecting samples in both contexts provides the opportunity for direct comparison of the SMR results using the linking tool. Bilingual speakers present a unique challenge because, in order to evaluate their total language proficiency, it is important to collect comparable samples in each language. Collecting samples in more than one language from the same speaker provides the opportunity to compare performance across languages. This helps us to distinguish speakers who are language disordered from those who need more English (or second language) instruction. (See Chapter 7 for a discussion pertaining to evaluating language performance of bilingual Spanish/English speakers.) RtI can be documented using the linking function. It facilitates the comparison of the speaker's performance at various points throughout the intervention phase of the process. SALT analysis of language samples provides thorough and detailed analysis of "real talk", generating functional data to make the case for dismissing a student from caseload. Language sample analysis is the only assessment that can prove the speaker does or does not have a "functional and effective communication system" which is often a requirement for dismissal.

Summary

SALT offers many ways to characterize oral language deficits. Your task is to make use of the tools to better describe oral language. SALT saves you time in analysis and provides clear direction on where to focus further diagnostic effort. At the end of the day, trust your clinical judgment as to the general problems the speaker exhibits. Then use SALT to document those areas to bring together a compelling case for enrolling for services, outlining an intervention plan, or dismissing from therapy.

Assessing the Bilingual (Spanish/English) Population

Raúl Rojas
Aquiles Iglesias

This chapter focuses on how to use language sample analysis (LSA) with bilingual (Spanish/English) children. Chapters 1 through 6 provided you with valuable information on the importance of using LSA, the advantages of the various elicitation procedures, transcription conventions, the different reports available in SALT, and assessing language production using SALT. In order to effectively use SALT with bilingual (Spanish/English) populations, you need to learn some additional transcription and segmentation conventions that are specific to transcripts elicited from bilingual children. The decision making process will also be slightly different since we are now dealing with two languages rather than one. We begin by providing a brief background on the bilingual (Spanish/English) population in the United States. This is followed by some additional conventions that are specific to the bilingual transcripts. Finally, we discuss the decision making process that should be followed in order to adequately assess bilingual children.

Background

Twenty percent of the population of the United States speaks a language other than, or in addition to, English. The vast majority of these individuals will speak Spanish, although many communities have very large numbers of speakers of languages other than English and Spanish (Shin & Kominski, 2010). All demographic predictors indicate that the size of the Spanish-speaking population is going to increase substantially in the coming decade; and the increases will not be limited to the southwestern states. Furthermore, the fastest growing segment of the U.S. student population are children who are in the process of learning English as a second language and lack sufficient mastery of English to successfully achieve in an English-language classroom without additional support (Swanson, 2009). These children are referred to as English Language Learners (ELLs). ELLs presently account for 10 percent of the elementary school population in the United States; with approximately half of the children enrolled in grades K-3 (National Center for Education Statistics, 2006) and 75 percent of these children are Spanish-speakers.

Regardless of your geographical location, there is a strong possibility that you will be faced with a linguistically diverse caseload. Some of your clients will be monolingual speakers of English, some will be monolingual speakers of a language other than English, and some will show various proficiency levels in their native language and in English. This last group presents a challenge since both the first or native language (L1) and the second language (L2) of a bilingual child will differ from the language of a monolingual child, and the two language systems will influence each other. In addition, the children will exhibit various levels of proficiency in each of their languages. As a result of these differences between monolinguals and bilinguals, the assessment process of bilinguals requires that we: (1) examine each of their languages independently, and (2) compare their performance in each language to the performance of children who are also speakers of the two languages.

The specific linguistic skills bilingual children demonstrate in each language at a particular point in time will vary as a function of numerous factors including the task and the interactors. For example, while playing with one of their siblings at home, a child may use English or Spanish with comparable proficiency. In a more cognitive and linguistically demanding situation, e.g., an oral presentation on how to play Monopoly in front of his school peers, the same child might show different levels of proficiency in each language. The child may have the ability to make the presentation in both languages, but there may be an obvious struggle in the less proficient language. This struggle might be characterized by an increase in mazes, a decrease in speaking rate, a decrease in mean length of utterance in words (MLUw) and number of different words (NDW), and/or an increase in grammatical errors. Making a clinical decision solely on their performance on an expository narration in the child's least proficient language would be inappropriate. It would also be inappropriate to base a clinical decision on a conversational task that did not challenge the child to use complex language. Our clinical decisions must be based on tasks that provide examples of the child's optimal linguistic ability. In addition, the child's linguistic skills in each of the two languages must also be taken into consideration when making this decision.

Before discussing the clinical decision making process, let's consider some additional SALT conventions we will need in order to ensure that our transcripts will be comparable to the transcripts in the Bilingual Spanish/English Reference databases (Appendices G & H) that we will be using to compare bilingual children's performance.

Bilingual (Spanish/English) Transcription Conventions and Segmentation

A growing body of research (Bedore, et al., 2006; Gutiérrez-Clellen, et al., 2000; Heilmann, Nockerts, & Miller, 2010; Kohnert, Kan, & Conboy, 2010; Miller et al., 2006; Rojas & Iglesias, 2009, 2010) establishes the importance of conducting LSA with bilingual populations. Thorough and accurate transcription is necessary to get the best results from SALT. This section focuses on four modifications to standard SALT conventions that were developed in order to address the unique characteristics of Spanish and bilingual transcripts.

Special Characters
ISSUE: Accent marks in Spanish serve two distinct purposes. One purpose is to assist in the pronunciation of words that do not follow basic stress rules such as, *words ending in a vowel, -n, or –s are stressed in the penultimate syllable*, e.g., *za-pa-to* "shoe". Thus, a word like *comí* "I ate" requires an accent mark because it is pronounced with stress in the last syllable and this stress pattern violates the basic stress rule of penultimate stress on words ending in vowels. The other purpose of accent marks is to disambiguate words that otherwise are written the same but have different syntactic roles or meanings, e.g., *el* "the" as definite article vs. *él* "he" as personal pronoun. Failure to account for lexical stress and

grammatical category by not marking accents would negatively impact several SALT measures and reports, especially NDW and the *Analyze menu: Standard Word Lists* report.

SOLUTION: SALT accepts accent characters and considers homophones differentiated by accented letters as distinct words. Thus, words such as *que* "that" (conjunction) and *qué* "what" (pronoun; adjective) are counted as different words and are reflected correctly in the *Analyze menu: Standard Word Lists* report. Figure 7-1 lists some of the most common homophones in Spanish that are distinguished by the accent mark.

Non-accented	Meaning		Accented	Meaning
adonde	(to) where		adónde	(to) where?
aquel	this (adjective)		aquél	this one (pronoun)
como	as; like; I eat		cómo	how?
cual	which		cuál	what?; which one?
cuando	when		cuándo	when?
de	of; from		dé	to give (subjunctive present)
donde	where		dónde	where?
el	the (article)		él	he; him (pronoun)
ese	that (adjective)		ése	that one (pronoun)
este	this (adjective)		éste	this one (pronoun)
mas	but		más	more
mi	my		mí	me; myself
porque	because		por qué	why?
se	himself; herself		sé	I know
si	if		sí	yes
te	yourself (clitic)		té	tea
tu	your		tú	you
que	that		qué	what?
quien	who		quién	who?; whom?

Figure 7-1

Similar to the issue of accented Spanish characters, reflexive and non-reflexive pronouns in Spanish use overlapping word forms. To distinguish between these words, reflexive pronouns are marked in SALT with the special word code "[X]", e.g., *se[X]*.

Bound Morphemes in Spanish and the Calculation of MLU (in words)

ISSUE: The calculation of MLU in morphemes (MLUm) requires that specific bound morphemes (-s plural; -ed past tense; -ing present progressive; -s 3rd person regular tense; -'s possessives) be counted. Although it is possible to mark all bound morphemes in Spanish, the process is not as easy as it is for English. In English, the SALT convention is to mark the morpheme using the bound morphemes "*/*" convention (walk/ed; walk/3s; walk/ing; dog/s; dog/z; dog/s/z). Although there are consistent morphological markers for the different tenses in regular Spanish verbs, marking verb morphology using the bound morphemes "*/*" convention would be somewhat difficult and cumbersome since the infinitive forms (roots) of the regular verbs are not always maintained across their conjugations. In addition, Spanish has a large number of irregular verbs that according to Brown's rules for calculating MLUm should not be counted as two separate morphemes. A number of regular (*hablar* "to speak"; *pensar* "to think"; *dormir* "to sleep") and irregular (*ser* "to be"; *ir* "to go") verbs in Spanish are conjugated across number and tense in Figure 7-2 for illustration purposes.

		HABLAR	PENSAR	DORMIR	SER	IR
Present Indicative	1st singular	hablo	pienso	duermo	soy	voy
	2nd singular	hablas	piensas	duermes	eres	vas
	3rd singular	habla	piensa	duerme	es	va
	1st plural	hablamos	pensamos	dormimos	somos	vamos
	3rd plural	hablan	piensan	duermen	son	van
Preterit Indicative	1st singular	hablé	pensé	dormí	fui	fui
	2nd singular	hablaste	pensaste	dormiste	fuiste	fuiste
	3rd singular	habló	pensó	durmío	fue	fue
	1st plural	hablamos	pensamos	dormimos	fuimos	fuimos
	3rd plural	hablaron	pensaron	durmieron	fueron	fueron

Figure 7-2

Over the years, some individuals have unsuccessfully attempted to establish rules for calculating MLUm in Spanish. These attempts have met strong resistance from the research community for various reasons. To many, the

Spanish MLUm calculation appeared to be arbitrary and sometimes inconsistent. It is important to remember that the specific bound morphemes selected by Brown to calculate MLUm were morphemes in English that had multiple phonological variants, received only slight stress, and developed gradually. *To what extent are these morphemes relevant to Spanish? For example, clitics in Spanish also fit Brown's criteria, should they also be included?* Instead of developing a new way of calculating MLUm in Spanish, the majority of researchers examining language acquisition in Spanish have opted to use MLU in words (MLUw); a measure that appears to be equally valuable (Parker & Brorson, 2005). Thus, the need to code verb morphology in Spanish becomes unnecessary.

However, not accounting for inflected word forms, including verb conjugations, would inflate NDW since inflected variants having the same root would be counted as different words. Using the verbs in Figure 7-2, *soy, eres, es, somos,* and *son,* all inflected conjugations of *ser* "to be", would be incorrectly considered as different words in the calculation of NDW.

SOLUTION: The decision to focus on MLUw, rather than MLUm, eliminated the need to develop conventions for marking verb morphology in Spanish. The root identification "|" convention was developed to ensure that the rich inflectional variation in Spanish was not lost for subsequent SALT measures and reports, and to prevent inflation of lexical measures like NDW. The vertical bar character "|", is used to identify verb root forms in any language, e.g., *la manzana es|ser roja,* "the apple is|be red". The word located to the left of the "|" (actual word) is included in the count of total words; the word located on the right of the "|" (root word) is included in the count of different words. The root identification "|" convention simultaneously (a) captures multiple inflected verb forms in Spanish and irregular verb forms in English; (b) credits the speaker for using distinct inflections; and (c) maintains the infinitive root form for each of these conjugations. It is important to note that using the root identification convention is required for Spanish samples and optional for English samples.

Identifying the word root of verbs in Spanish is a rather time consuming task, especially when transcribing multiple transcripts. In order to further reduce the time required to transcribe the language samples, the *Edit menu: Identify Roots* command is built into SALT. This command, which requires just a few steps, automates the process of marking word roots and their inflected words forms. The *Edit menu: Identify Roots* command instructs SALT to automatically check over 450,000 inflected verb conjugations in Spanish; SALT then automatically inserts the appropriate verb root into the transcript. In cases where there is more than one root option, e.g., identical inflectional variants such as *fui*, which can be either *fui/ser* "I was" or *fui/ir* "I went", SALT provides you with a list of choices to select from.

If you're interested in knowing the specific tenses or moods children are using, you could create special word or utterance codes to mark this. For example, to mark the frequency of particular tenses, you could create a code for each tense of interest and attach a code to the verb, e.g., *El niño agarró/agarrar[PRT] la pelota y se la llevó/llevar[PRT] para la casa* "the boy grabbed the ball and took it home"; [PRT] codes for preterit. The *Analyze menu: Code Summary* can be used to count these codes and list the verbs associated with them.

Marking plurals in Spanish, however, is rather easy to do when number is marked in nouns, adjectives, and adverbs. In order to obtain an accurate NDW, the "/" convention should be used with all plural nouns, adjectives, and adverbs, e.g., *los perro/s grande/s* "the big dogs". It should be noted that articles are not marked for number, as they are considered stand-alone morphemes in Spanish.

Pronominal Clitics

ISSUE: In Spanish, direct and indirect object pronouns can be either independent words or bound affixes. These pronominal clitics can be located before or after the verb, and they can be free standing or bound to the verb. Regardless of where the clitic is located relative to the verb, the meaning of the utterance typically remains the same. For instance, an imperative statement such as, *give it to me*, can be stated in Spanish as follows: ***me lo** das* "give it to me", or *dá**melo*** "giveittome". Orthographic convention dictates ***me lo** das* written as three separate words and *dá**melo*** written as one word. Both of these phrases, however, contain two clitics (*me* "me"; *lo* "it") and one verb (*dar* "to give").

SOLUTION: The bound pronominal clitics "+" convention was developed in SALT to (a) maintain orthographic integrity; (b) credit equal morphological weight; (c) control for dialectal variation in Spanish; and (d) to increase the precision of certain length-based measures such as MLUw and NDW. For instance, the three words (two clitics + one verb) in *dámelo* would be marked with the bound pronominal clitic convention as follows: *dá+me+lo*.

SALT automatically marks bound pronominal clitics in Spanish via the *Edit menu: Identify Roots* command. It is important to note that the *Spanish Nouns and Clitics* RIF is an incomplete list, based on the most frequent words used to retell *Frog, Where Are You?* (Mayer, 1969).

Utterance Segmentation: Modified Communication Units (MC-units)

ISSUE: The basic unit for segmenting utterances used in SALT is the Communication Unit (C-unit; an independent clause and its modifiers, including subordinate clauses). Thus, a sentence like, *the boy went running and grabbed the frog*, would be segmented as one utterance. Although the equivalent of this sentence in Spanish, *el niño estaba corriendo y agarró la rana*, could also be segmented as one utterance, doing so would ignore the pro-drop nature of Spanish. Whereas omitting subject nouns or pronouns is ungrammatical in English, these can be grammatically dropped in Spanish as the null subject information is encoded in the verb (Bedore, 1999). For instance, the English phrase *he jumped*, can be grammatically stated in Spanish as: (a) *él brincó* ("he jumped") including the pronoun *él* ("he"); or (b) as *brincó* ("[he] jumped") since the Spanish verb encodes for person and gender, in this case singular and male.

SOLUTION: Modified C-units (MC-units), based on rules originally proposed by Gutiérrez-Clellen and Hofstetter (1994) for Terminable Units in Spanish, were used to segment the language transcripts contained in the Bilingual Spanish/English Reference databases in order to (a) account for the pro-drop nature of Spanish, and (b) facilitate consistency when transcribing language samples in Spanish and English from the same bilingual speaker. Therefore, segmenting utterances as MC-units is recommended in SALT for bilingual (Spanish-English) samples.

MC-units follow two rules. The first rule, like standard C-unit segmentation, states that an utterance consists of an independent clause and its modifiers, including subordinated clauses. The second rule states that independent clauses joined by a coordinating conjunction are segmented as two separate utterances when there is co-referential subject deletion in the second clause. MC-unit segmentation is illustrated in Figure 7-3. The first row illustrates subordinated clauses in Spanish and English, which are not segmented as two separate utterances. The subordinating conjunction *cuando*, is used in Spanish; the subordinating conjunction *when*, is used in English. The second row illustrates coordinated clauses in Spanish and English, which are therefore segmented into two utterances in each language. The coordinating conjunction *y*, is used in Spanish; the coordinating conjunction *and*, is used in English. Further, pro-drop in used in the segmented utterance in Spanish, *y olvidó sus llaves* ("and [he] forgot his keys").

Spanish subordinated clause (1 utt) "C Marcelo se fue **cuando** se acabó la comida."	English subordinated clause (1 utt) "C Marcelo left **when** he finished the food."
Spanish coordinated clause (2 utts) "C Marcelo se fue." "C **y** olvidó sus llaves."	English coordinated clause (2 utts) "C Marcelo left." "C **and** forgot his keys."

Figure 7-3

Making Clinical Decisions

Sometimes, bilingual children perform poorly on a particular battery of tests. One question we should always ask is, *was the poor performance due to the language in which the assessment was conducted or is the child truly language impaired?* To illustrate this issue, let's look at Figure 7-4 which is a two-dimensional graph where performance in one language (Language A) is on the x-axis and performance in the other language (Language B) is on the y-axis. The two dotted lines represent the average performance in each language. The intersection of the two lines divides the space into four unique quadrants (Quadrants I-IV).

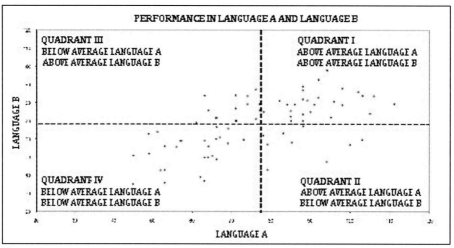

Figure 7-4

Children in Quadrant I (above average in Language A and B) will perform like (or above) their typically developing peers regardless of whether they are assessed in Language A or Language B. Children in Quadrants II and III will be perform like their typically developing peers if we take into consideration the language in which they are most proficient (Language A for children in Quadrant II; Language B for children in Quadrant III). Children in Quadrant IV are below the average in both languages. The decision as to whether children in Quadrant IV are typically developing or language impaired will be dependent on the cut-off score used to make this clinical decision. SALT contains the Bilingual Spanish/English reference databases (Appendices G & H). These databases consist of narratives produced in English and Spanish by over 4,600 typically developing bilingual (English-Spanish) children enrolled in transitional ELL classrooms (kindergarten through third grade) in Texas and California. The narrative retell language samples were elicited using a series of Mercer Mayer's wordless picture books; *Frog, Where Are You?* (Mayer, 1969), *Frog Goes To Dinner* (Mayer, 1974), and *Frog On His Own* (Mayer, 1973), following a standardized elicitation protocol. The unique story samples were elicited using wordless picture book, *One Frog Too Many* (Meyer & Meyer, 1975). These databases allow users to compare a speaker's performance in either language to age and/or grade-matched bilingual peers retelling the same story using the same language.

As should be clear by now, children's performance can vary as a function of the language in which they are assessed. The clinical decision making process involves: (1) deciding to which of the four quadrants the child belongs to; and (2) determining whether the child's performance is significantly below the performance of his or her peers in both languages, particularly if the child's performance falls within Quadrant IV. Ideally, we should first assess the child in his or her native language. However, we are clearly aware that for many speech-language pathologists, assessing the child in his native language will be impossible since the majority of clinicians do not speak a language other than English. This can also be the case for clinicians who may be bilingual, but do not speak the native language of the client. Thus, we suggest that clinicians first assess the child in the language in which the clinician is the most comfortable. Figure 7-5 graphically illustrates the decision making process we recommend for bilingual children.

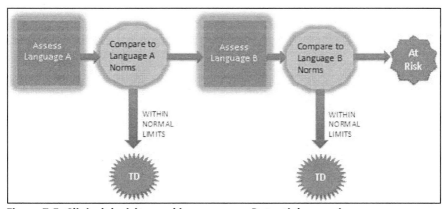

Figure 7-5: Clinical decision-making process – Potential scenarios

In some cases, clinicians will only need to assess one language. In other cases, they will not be able to make a diagnosis until both languages are assessed. First, assess the speaker's language in English or in Spanish and compare the performance to the English or Spanish of typical bilinguals. If the performance is within normal limits, then stop. However, if the performance in the first language assessed is below what is expected based on bilingual norms, then assess in the other language. If the performance in either language is within normal limits, then there should be no clinical concern. However, if testing in English and testing in the native language both reveal areas of concern, then the speaker is at risk for a language disorder and intervention plans should be developed.

To illustrate the decision-making process, let's look at the performance of four children, illustrated in Figure 7-6. Four children (Alex, Betty, Carlos, and Daniel) were asked to narrate *Frog, Where Are You?* (Mayer, 1969) following the protocol from the Bilingual Spanish/English Story Retell databases. The *Database menu: Standard Measures Report* was obtained from the children's narration compared to grade-matched peers. Their performance on MLUw and NDW can be seen in Figure 7-6.

		ALEX *Grade 1st* *Age 7;4*	**BETTY** *Grade 1st* *Age 6;10*	**CARLOS** *Grade K* *Age 5;10*	**DANIEL** *Grade 3rd* *Age 10;1*
ENGLISH	**MLUw**	6.57 (0.19)	5.53 (-0.86)	5.52 (-0.22)	4.69 (-2.52)
	NDW	94 (0.80)	72 (-0.07)	55 (-0.15)	53 (-1.71)
SPANISH	**MLUw**	5.19 (-1.33)	5.86 (-0.56)	5.43 (-0.33)	4.67 (-2.52)
	NDW	41 (-1.87)	85 (0.27)	72 (0.42)	72 (-1.52)

Figure 7-6

Alex: Alex's performance was within the normal range in English (0.19 and 0.80 *SD* for MLUw and NDW, respectively). His performance in Spanish was significantly below that of his peers (-1.33, and -1.87 *SD* for MLUw and NDW). Based on the fact that his performance was within the normal range in one language (in this case English), he is functioning as a typically developing child.

Betty and Carlos: Although Betty and Carlos demonstrated low-level performance in several of the measures in English and in Spanish, these results do not indicate language impairment since the performance was never significantly below the normal range in either language.

<u>Daniel</u>: Daniel's performance in English and in Spanish is consistently below the normal range (below -1. 5 SD). His overall below average performance in both languages indicates that he is likely to be language impaired.

Summary

LSA should be used as a fundamental component of clinical practice with bilingual children who speak Spanish. A series of articles by Rojas and Iglesias (2009; 2010) discuss LSA methods and approaches with bilingual language samples, including (a) how to implement LSA for purposes of assessment and intervention with Spanish-speaking children who are learning English as a second language, and (b) how to use LSA to measure language growth.

For an example of how LSA is used to assess the language production of a bilingual (Spanish/English) student, refer to Case Study 6 in Chapter 10.

The Dialect Features of AAE and Their Importance in LSA

Julie Washington

Introduction

Historically, it has been difficult to distinguish the linguistic features of African American English (AAE) from linguistic forms characterizing language disorders. Further, many of the earliest reports of AAE focused on children from impoverished backgrounds, fueling beliefs that AAE was an impoverished language system. These shortcomings in the literature and ultimately in our understanding, fueled reports by educational psychologists and others that African American children growing up in poverty were significantly behind their middle-class White peers in their language development (Bereiter & Englemann, 1966).

A paucity of language assessment measures appropriate for use with AAE speakers has contributed to over-diagnosis of language disorders in the African American school-aged population. In the last decade tremendous growth has been made in the development of language evaluation instruments appropriate for students speaking AAE. This research and development has provided practitioners with a growing number of language evaluation instruments that are non-discriminatory when used with this population. In particular, Language Sample Analysis (LSA) has proven to be one of the most non-biased measures of oral language production across English speaking populations. However, this is only true if the examiner has knowledge of the specific linguistic features of the language being assessed. The goal of this chapter is to instruct readers on the dialect features of AAE, support the use of LSA for use with AAE-speaking children, and ensure a non-biased component to the language evaluation process. After reading this chapter you should be able to recognize dialect when you see it in African American children. Our hope is that you apply this knowledge to the LSA process.

What is African American English?

The most neutral definition of "dialect" defines it simply as a language variety shared by a group of speakers (Wolfram & Schilling-Estes, 1998). Dialects are systematic, rule-governed variants of a parent language. African American English (AAE) is a dialect used by most, but not all, African Americans in the United States. AAE is developmental. Some of the forms used when children are young fade out with age, whereas others develop and become more sophisticated as speakers get older. AAE is the most studied dialect of English in the United States.

Earlier in its history, it was believed that AAE was simply a poor variation of English, not rule-governed, not predictable, and not systematic in any way, but that it developed from poverty and from poor knowledge of English. That belief, which was called The Deficit Hypothesis, has been disproven. Many linguists in the late sixties and early seventies put forth great efforts documenting the use of the dialect and defining what makes AAE a dialect. At this point in history, it is well accepted that AAE is a dialect of English.

It is important to remember that AAE is used by most, but not all, African Americans. It would be a mistake to assume, because a person is African American, that person is a dialect speaker. When talking about children in the United States, it is the case that approximately ninety-five percent of children entering school are dialect speakers. Consider the importance of the other five percent. If the belief were that *all* African American children used dialect, those five percent who don't, but who show some difference in oral and/or written language may, in fact, be language impaired. Thus, one must be careful not to over-generalize this dialect to those approximately five percent who do not speak it

When thinking about AAE as a dialect in children, it is important to recognize that AAE is used almost exclusively by children in the United States who are referred to as "African American," and are descended from slavery. AAE is considered a creolization of English that arose during slavery when slaves from different African countries needed to develop a common language to allow them to communicate both with each other and with slaveholders. In contrast, children whose families are immigrants from Africa or the Caribbean are not typically AAE speakers. These children are more likely to use dialectal variations derived from their native countries and languages.

All children typically enter school bringing with them the language of their homes and their communities. AAE is highly variable in the amount of dialect used by a given child or community. The way this is described is called "density of dialect". We know that some kids are low density users, some are moderate users, and some are very high users. Those that are the highest users of the dialect are the ones that sound the most "non-standard". A high user of AAE might have 50% of their words or 35-50% of their utterances marked with one or more features of the dialect, and they would sound very different from a low density user. Interesting to note is that these two speakers may not have to come from different regions or geographic areas. They may come from the same neighborhood or live on the same street.

Considering AAE in Language Assessment

The two most common or frequently used forms in AAE, deletion of the copula and subject verb agreement, happen to be the most common markers of a disorder among Standard American English (SAE) speakers. This makes it very difficult to diagnose language impairment in the AAE population. There appears to be considerable overlap between the forms that are used by impaired SAE speaking children and typically developing AAE speaking children. Despite the fact that some of the forms and features are the same in these two groups, the overall quality of the talk is not the same. This coupled with the high variability of density of dialect is of concern to the SLP as this may influence language assessment and the diagnosis of language impairment in this population. Today, many more of the morphosyntactic forms used in AAE are included in some language assessment instruments used by SLPs. In the past, only the most common features, more easily recognizable to SAE speakers, were included in assessments. Although improvements in standardized measures are flourishing, familiarity with the features of AAE is of the utmost importance when conducting a language assessment.

AAE and the Written Form

AAE has developed as an oral dialect with no well-developed written counterpart. Because we write like we talk, however, you will notice African American children write using dialect features. It is not that the dialect has a written form. It is instead that children perceive language the way they use it. If a child is using some AAE features in their oral language, you may see those features are also used in their writing. In addition, African American children who speak SAE may write using AAE dialect features. Children who come to school speaking SAE have an advantage when text is presented to them. That text is similar to what they speak and probably hear. This often will not be the case for African American children who use AAE.

Writing is both a bridge and a mirror into code switching with African American students. So if you are an AAE speaker, you will also write using AAE. Teachers in public schools often say, "These kids write just like they talk." That is absolutely true. The way that you speak syntactically, phonologically, is also the way you will write. Thus, African American students who can write in SAE can also speak in SAE. When you encounter an AAE child who is writing standard classroom English, he or she is a child who is probably able to code switch to the use of standard classroom English. So for educators and clinicians, writing is both a bridge to SAE and a mirror into the African American child's code switching ability. This bridge means that if we can teach children to write in SAE, we can also assist in the generalization of that writing to oral language. And it's a mirror because, sometimes with a child who is reticent to talk, or from whom we cannot hear those features orally, if you ask them to generate something in writing, you will see the use of AAE features. The interesting thing about writing, however, is that unlike oral language, where we do have some tolerance for non-standard forms or for variety, we do not have the kind of tolerance in the written domain. It is expected that when you write you will use the conventions of writing without deviation. The exception is when writing dialogue. If a child is trying to write in the voice of the speaker often you will see dialect used. We see "voice" put in quotation marks and we allow variety within those quotation marks.

It's important to identify AAE features in writing samples for a number of reasons, but probably the most important reason is that these are not simply errors. If a child has spelling or grammatical errors, they are just mistakes which you can point out and the child can fix. What we are talking about here is a child's linguistic system. This is their dialect which is not as easily amendable to being changed through editing. This doesn't mean that you don't target them but, what it means for the teacher, typically, is that these will take more time for the child to understand because you're not just asking them to make grammatical changes, you're asking them to switch linguistic codes from AAE to standard classroom English. Thus, when you see dialect forms in writing, recognize that it likely will take more time, more effort, and more attention to change them.

The Features

The features discussed below are those primarily used by children in northern dialect regions or the Midwestern states. These are the most common features and might be thought of as a core set of features generalized across regions. Children from other regions, like the south, will use many of these features. However, they also use other features that characterize the regional area. For example, children from Georgia or Alabama will use AAE as well as Southern English, and they will also speak a form of AAE that is spoken by children in the south.

The morphosyntactic features, or those that can be seen from the written grammar of the transcript, are best defined by example. These are the features we are most interested in when taking a language sample as they affect the vocabulary and syntax of the sample. They are explained below in order of frequency of use, from most frequently used to least frequently used.

1. **Deletion of the Copula & Auxiliary** is the first feature defined. The copula is a form of the verb "to be". It is the form of the verb that is *not* a helping

form. The form of "be" stands alone as the only verb. Examples include the deletion of the copula "is" as in, "This a dog", "She hungry", or, "I happy". Also frequently noted in AAE is the deletion of the auxiliary, which is deletion of the form of the verb "to be" as in "They catchin' a bus". Here the deletion is of the helping form "are" from the phrase "They are catchin' a bus". The deletion of the copula and auxiliary forms are the most common features seen in AAE. If a child or adult is a speaker of AAE, they will be deleting the copula and auxiliary forms. This is seen 100% of the time in AAE.

2. **Subject-Verb Agreement** is also very common in AAE. This form is seen in 85-90% of AAE speakers. For example, the speaker might say, "*they was* eatin' cookies", rather than "*they were* eatin' cookies".

3. **"Fitna/Sposeta/Bouta"** are forms that code imminent action, or something that's getting ready to happen, or that is going to happen immediately. "Fitna" is a form of "fixin to", often used in the south, as in "I'm fixin to do something". In the case of children, it is a catenative form similar to "gonna", "wanna", or "hafta". Instead of saying "fixin' to", the speaker says "fitna", e.g., "Is she fitna drink some?", "Is she fitna go to the store? This particular form derives from the south. Historically, African American people migrated from the south, so AAE has several features that overlap with Southern English. There are forms that African American people learned to use when they were in the south that are now considered part of the dialect because, when those speakers left the south, they took those forms with them and they became part of the language of the community. You may encounter African American people who speak AAE in California, Florida, Maine, or New York, for example, who use features that came from the south. Other catenative forms include, "He was *bouta* get in the car." which derives from "about to", and, "We sposta go to the store." which derives from "supposed to".

4. **Undifferentiated Pronoun Case** is used more frequently by African American children than by African American adults. Nominative, objective, and demonstrative cases of pronouns occur interchangeably. Examples

include, "*Them* pullin' up the hill.", "My uncle forgot *they* lunch", or, "*Him* did it".

5. **Multiple Negation**, such as, "I *don't* got *none*" is a form that many people are familiar with and often equate with AAE. Typically we think of *double* negation, or the use of two negatives in one sentence. But the negative is used for the purpose of emphasis, so you may see many multiple negatives in one sentence. An example of Multiple Negation is "Why you don't want nobody to put none too close to your mouth?". This can be interpreted to mean "Why don't you want anybody to put any too close to your mouth?".

6. **Zero Possessive** can be used by children in a number of ways. Typically we see the deletion of the apostrophe ('s) in possessive forms such as "That the dog ('s) food", or "They're goin' to her brother ('s) house". Also seen with younger children is the deletion of the possessive form of a pronoun, such as, "They waitin' for they car" rather than "their car", or "you house", instead of "your house". AAE is developmental, thus some forms are used by young children, but change or fade as language develops.

7. **Zero Past Tense**, such as, "he *dig* a hole" or "she *jump* over the puddle", is common in AAE. The past tense marker is deleted. In AAE we often see elements deleted that would be redundant in Standard English, however the speaker will be sure to leave no ambiguity. Both the zero possessive and the zero past tense forms are good examples of this. The language will include some form of tense marking such as the use of words like "yesterday", "last week", or "this morning" to ensure the tense is clear. So, if a conversation is being held in past tense, for example, in AAE there is no reason to include the past tense marker –ed. When working with a typically developing African American child, the deletion of the past tense creates no ambiguity about whether what is being spoken about is in the past or in the present. But, in the case of a child who is not typically developing, for example, a child with language impairment, ambiguity is possible.

8. **Invariant *Be*** is frequently associated with AAE, however, is it not as commonly used as people believe it to be. It is not used frequently by young children, but rather, if it is used, we tend to see it in teenagers or adults. It is

also regionally dependent in that it is more prominent in the south. Invariant "be" is the infinitive form of the verb "be" regardless of the subject. You might see "he be", "she be", "we be", "Sally be". The "be" verb is not conjugated. More examples include, "They *be* getting' some ice cream", or "He *be* goin' down the hill".

9. **Zero *To*** is the deletion of the "to" infinitive marker in front of an infinitive verb. An example of this is, "And he waitin' for the train go". In SAE, the infinitive would be stated, such as, "And he [is] waitin' for the train *to* go".

10. **Zero Plural** is where the plural marker is removed from a noun. The plural is usually marked somewhere in the speech context so there is no ambiguity that the word which is missing the plural marker is in its plural form, e.g., "A girl puttin' some *glass* out on the table to drink". The word "some" indicates to the listener there that there are multiple glasses.

11. **Double Modal** is most often seen in the southern regions by speakers of all ages. It overlaps with Southern English. It is typically heard in adolescent and adult speech in forms such as "might could". "I *might could* help you." Younger children's use of the double modal is less mature, or more child-like, such as, "Why *didn't* the boy *didn't* stop?". Here the child used two modal auxiliary forms. Also frequently heard in young African American children are the double modal forms "I'm am" and "I'm is". An example includes, "I'm am goin' to the store."

12. **Regularized Reflexive**, such as, "He stands by *hisself*" or "They goin' by *theyself*", is characterized by changing the irregular reflexive pronoun patterns to a regularized form. The speaker is, in a sense, smoothing out irregular patterning of forming reflexive pronouns by applying the same rule to all forms in the set.

13. **Indefinite Article** is characterized by the use of the indefinite article "a" even when the following word begins with a vowel. The use of "an" prior to a noun starting with a vowel is absent. Examples include "He saw *a* elephant." or "They're building *a* apartment."

14. **Appositive Pronoun** is where both the pronoun and the noun, or the noun phrase that it refers to, are included in the utterance, rather than one or the other. In SAE, either the noun or pronoun is used. In AAE in young children it is very common to hear examples such as, "My mamma *she* said I could go." My daddy, *he* gave me that." or "My auntie, *she* bought me my coat." A more adult form might include "And the other ones *they* didn't have nothin'."

15. **Remote Past "been"** is an interesting form. It is typically used by older children because the verb phrase is more sophisticated. The speaker is talking about something that happened in the remote past that is habitual or continuous. "I *been* knowin' how to swim" can be paraphrased as "I have known how to swim for a long time".

The following six forms are not typically heard from children in the early elementary grades such as preschool through grade two. However, they are used by children in the upper elementary, middle, or high school grades.

16. **Preterite *Had*** is the past tense use of had followed by a past tense verb, either regular –ed, or irregular such as "had went". Examples include "You *had got* his toes stuck before.", "He *had went* home.", "And then she *had called* the house."

17. **Completive *Done*** in AAE means it's over; it's completed. It is one of the forms that overlaps with Southern English. Examples include "I think we done ate enough.", and, "I think we done finished."

18. **Existential *It*** is a form in AAE heard in children and adult's oral language, but seen significantly more in their writing. Instead of saying or writing, for example, "There's a lot more to do now", an African American speaker would say or write, "It's a lot more to do now". The word "it's" is used in place of "there's". Another example might be, "It seems like *it's* a lot more on here that you haven't shown me."

19. **Resultative *Be Done*:** Unlike the Completive *Done* that tells you something is over, Resultative *Be Done* tells you what is going to happen if you keep doing something. It is the result. "We be done dropped these and broke 'em." means "if we keep doing this, we're going to drop these and break them". Another example might be, "We be done got a ticket if we keep speedin'."

20. **Double Marked –S** is a feature, that, if used in the home by adults, we are likely to hear children use as well. We do not often hear it with very young children. It is heard more in the south. It is the double marking of –S in a possessive case such as "mines", "mens", and sometimes in plural cases where the plural is double marked. For example, "This one is like *mines*."

21. **Non-inverted Question** is a feature that we frequently hear adults using with their children. What is spoken is a statement with rising intonation rather than asking a "wh" question. So, rather than "Where is she going?", the question would be formed with rising intonation, "She going to the store?". "How does it go?" would be stated with question intonation, "That's how it go?".

These 21 morphosyntactic AAE features are summarized in Figure 8-1.

The phonological features of AAE, those which can be heard when listening to a speaker, are defined in Figure 8-2. It is important to have some familiarity with these features when using LSA. Presence or absence of these features help to discern the density of dialect and can indicate the possible presence of morphosyntactic features within a language sample.

When transcribing phonological features using SALT, we transcribe the words used but not the pronunciation used by the speaker. For example, if the speaker drops the "g" and says "waitin" for "waiting", this would be transcribed as "waiting".

Morphosyntactic AAE Features Used by Children in Northern Dialect Regions		
Feature	**Example**	**Code**
1. Deletion of Copula & Aux	they__ catchin' a bus	[COP]
2. Subject-Verb Agreement	*they was* sittin' down at the table	[SVA]
3. Fitna/Sposeta/Bouta code *imminent action*	is she *fitna* drink some? he was *bouta* get in the car	[FSB]
4. Undiff. Pronoun Case	*Them* pullin' them up the hill	[UPC]
5. Multiple Negation	why you *don't* want *nobody* to put *none* too close to your mouth?	[NEG]
6. Zero Possessive	they waitin' for *they* car	[POS]
7. Zero Past Tense	and then he *fix__* the food yesterday we *take* the long way home	[ZPT]
8. Invariant "be"	they *be* gettin' some ice cream	[IBE]
9. Zero "to"	and he waitin' for the train __ go	[ZTO]
10. Zero plural	a girl puttin' some *glass__* out on the table to drink	[ZPL]
11. Double Modal	why *did* the boy *didn't* stop?	[MOD]
12. Regularized Reflexive	he stands by *hisself*	[REF]
13. Indefinite Article	they buildin' *a* apartment	[ART]
14. Appositive Pronoun	and the other ones *they* didn't have nothin	[PRO]
15. Remote Past "been"	I *been* knowin' how to swim	[BEN]
Morphosyntactic AAE Features Used by Older Children and Adults		
16. Preterite *had*	he *had* got his toes stuck before	[HAD]
17. Completive *done*	I think we *done* ate enough	[DON]
18. Existential *it*	it seems like *it's* a lot more on here that you haven't shown me	[EIT]
19. Resultative *be done*	we *be done* dropped these and broke 'em	[BED]
20. Double marked –*s*	this one is like *mines*	[DMK]
21. Non-inverted Questions	that's how it go?	[NIQ]

Figure 8-1

Phonological AAE Features		
Feature	**Example**	**Code**
1. Postvocalic consonant reduction	mouth /maU/ for /maUθ/	[PCR]
2. "g" dropping	waitin', jumpin'	[G]
3. f /θ , v/ð and t/θ in intervocalic and postvocalic positions	/wif/with/, bave/bathe, wit/with	[STH]
4. d/ð in prevocalic positions	dis/this	[STH]
5. Consonant cluster reduction	col-/cold	[CCR]
6. Consonant cluster movement	aks/ask; ekscape/escape	[CCM]
7. Syllable deletion	--came/became	[SDL]
8. Monophtongization of dipthongs	ar/our	[VOW]
9. Voiceless final consonants replace voiced	hiss/hiz (his)	[FCV]

Figure 8-2

Transcription Codes

The codes listed with each AAE feature in Figures 8-1 and 8-2 have been used in SALT to flag the occurrences of those features in samples from dialect speakers.

To see an example of how LSA is implemented with an AAE speaker, refer to Case Study 7 in Chapter 10.

Additional Applications of SALT

Joyelle DiVall-Rayan
Jon F. Miller
Karen Andriacchi
Ann Nockerts

Introduction

While we traditionally think of SALT Software as an assessment tool to evaluate and analyze oral language skills, there are other non-traditional applications for which SALT can be useful as well. Due to the flexibility of the software and ability to customize codes, SALT can be used for almost any language production task. In this chapter we highlight two alternative uses of SALT; to assess expressive language in written form, and to assess disfluent motor speech production.

Using Salt to Assess Written Language

In our technology-driven society, brevity seems to be appreciated when we are texting or typing out 140-character tweets. However, strong written language skills are still a vital part of the language arts curriculum starting in kindergarten and extending through 12th grade. Students are expected to write opinion pieces, informative/explanatory texts, narratives, and research texts. The Common Core State Standards suggest that, starting in second grade, students should, "Use knowledge of language and its conventions when writing, speaking, reading, or listening" (CCSS:L.2.3). Students in second grade are required to, "Write opinion pieces in which they introduce the topic or book they are writing about, state an opinion, supply reasons that support the opinion, use linking words to connect opinion and reason, and provide a concluding statement or section" (CCSS: W.2.1). By their senior year, students are required to "Write narratives to develop real or imagined experiences or events using effective technique, well-chosen details, and well-structured event sequences" (CCSS: W.11-12.3). Based on the standards, developing proficient writing skills is no small feat. SALT can be used to analyze written language samples to provide an abundance of information about developing written language skills.

Nickola Nelson, of Western Michigan University, says the following about the usefulness of using SALT software when analyzing written language samples (personal communication, August 7, 2015).

> We have used SALT extensively in our research and clinical work on written language with school-age children and adolescents. (See Nelson, 2014a, 2014b, for information about this work and about a story probe technique for gathering baseline samples for a classroom-based writing lab approach.) SALT is beautifully suited to conducting some forms of analysis that are difficult to manage by hand, such as counting the number of words and more particularly, the number of different words. Both of these can be helpful repeated measures for written language samples gathered under similar conditions. SALT facilitates the process of coding (you can make up your own as well as using standard SALT conventions) and counting of codes. SALT features allow you to count the child's use of specific conjunctions and pronouns, which can be quite useful as well, in establishing baseline levels and marking progress. When transcribing written language samples, it is important to follow the special rules for transcribing spelling errors in order to make accurate word counts. When dividing utterances into C-units (also called T-units within written language samples) it is best to treat them as if they were oral language samples (i.e., ignoring student punctuation). By transcribing each C unit as a separate utterance, you can use SALT's calculation of Mean Length of C-unit to compare your student's samples across time or writing contexts. Not to be missed are the

advantages of working on language samples that do not have to be transcribed from an audio recording and the delights of experiencing how children and adolescents express their ideas in writing.

How the text was generated should also be considered when assessing written language. *Was it hand written? Or was it created by a word processing program or a speech-to-text software application such as Dragon Dictate?* The question must be considered, *does the text generation method contribute to the end result?* Hand writing can be difficult to decipher making it challenging to identify words and word boundaries. Certainly, spelling can be a challenge, particularly when consistent forms are not used. Broadening definitions of words to accommodate "invented" spelling will require using a "rich interpretation" strategy where credit is given if the word form is consistent but not correctly spelled.

SALT can be used to assess written samples and to track progress on features of written language performance from writing conventions such as capitalization, punctuation, and spelling to use of specific vocabulary such as linking words. Written samples can be coded to capture any feature of writing an evaluator is interested in tracking. By applying SALT's standard transcription conventions and codes to the written sample, analysis will also yield measures of linguistic performance such as MLU, NDW, and more. The types and extent of coding, as is always the case in SALT, is left to the discretion of the user. By marking more features within the sample, more information can be yielded from the analysis.

Procedure

The procedure developed to analyze written language in SALT requires typing the written language into the SALT editor using SALT transcription conventions and then applying the suggested written language coding scheme to the sample. Once the sample is entered and coded, SALT can generate reports from the Analyze menu with information on specific vocabulary, length of sentences, errors, e.g., coded spelling errors, or punctuation errors, and grammar. There are no comparison databases with the SALT program for comparing written samples. However, samples can be compared time 1/time 2 to track progress in writing skills. The following coding scheme is recommended to capture written language performance.

Written Sample Coding Scheme

Misspellings [S] Mark misspellings for analysis of vocabulary, language and spelling skills.	[S]- spelling error Misspelling|correct spelling[S] Example: *Forg|frog*[S] [S] [EW:__] spelling and word form error Example: *Baite|bite*[S][EW:bit] Spelling error and omitted bound morpheme Example: *Lok|look/*ed*[S] Spelling error with correct morpheme Example: *Cyring|cry/ing*[S] Spelling and overgeneralization error Example: *Teled|tell*[S][EO:told] Non-grapheme symbol (unidentifiable) Example: *frXg|frog*[S] Code switch with (Spanish) misspellings Example: *The abehas|abeja/s*[S] *chase/ed the boy* [CS].
Upper/lower case errors [IC] Incorrect use of upper case or lower case letters [IC]	Obligatory capitalization, e.g., proper pronouns or beginning of utterances Wrote: *the frog was gone.* Transcribed: *the*[IC] *frog was gone.* Use of capital letters in middle of word. Wrote: *He rAn home.* Transcribed: *He rAn*[IC] *home.*
Letter reversals	Type correct grapheme assuming they are developmentally appropriate. Create custom code to analyze this feature, if desired.

Punctuation [PN] Mark missing, incorrect, and/or extraneous punctuation. Do not insert commas and quotations even if obligatory.	[PN] – punctuation error Missing end of utterance punctuation Insert code at end of utterance followed by appropriate punctuation. Wrote: *The frog jumped* Transcribed: *The frog jump/ed [PN].* Incorrect punctuation Type the writer's punctuation in the code followed by correct punctuation outside of bracket. Wrote: *Where are they.* Transcribed: *Where are they [PN.]?* Extraneous punctuation mark Insert the [PN] code, including punctuation produced, at location of extra punctuation. Wrote: *He said. to go away.* Transcribed: *He said [PN.] to go away.*
Word Punctuation [WPN]	[WPN]- word punctuation error Missing word-level punctuation Wrote: *The girls coat was red.* Transcribed: *The girl[WPN']s|girl/z coat was red.*
Numbers	Type numbers as they were written. Example: *8 or eight*
Sound effects	Type as they were written
Extra Space [XSP]	Extra space within written word. Wrote: *honey moon* Transcribed: *honey[XSP]moon*
Space Required [SPR]	Space required within written word. Wrote: *theyare* Transcribed: *they [SPR] are*

Case Study: Using SALT for written language sample analysis

The following is an example of a written narrative collected from a first grade student writing about the wordless picture book, *One Frog Too Many* (Mayer & Mayer, 1975).

Written Sample

wone day the litte boy had a geft
the litte boy was exited and he saw a
cord and ti had hes name and then he
open the box and he saw a litte frog
and the big frog dieret like it and
then the big frog bit hes leg and the
boy was mad and then they went for
a walk and then the littl frog and
the big frog got on the tres back
and then the big frog puch the
litte frog and he begen to cri
and then they went on a log
and they left the big frog and then
the big frog jump and puch the
littl frog in the water and then
the tril saw it and then the boy
saw it and then they look for
hem evry wer and then the boy
went home and then they hred
a nois and it was the litte frog
and he jump in the wendoor and
he jump on top of his had and
then the dig frog lik hem.

Figure 9-1

SALT Transcript

```
$ Child
+ Grade: 1
+ Context: WNar
+ Subgroup: OFTM
= case was not coded as it was not of interest to the examiner

C wone|one[S] day the litte|little[S] boy had a geft|gift[S] [PN].
C the litte|little[S] boy was exited|excited[S] [PN].
C and he saw a card [PN].
C and ti|it[S] had hes|his[S] name [PN].
C and then he open/*ed the box [PN].
C and he saw a litte|little[S] frog [PN].
C and the big frog dieret|did/n't[S] like it [PN].
C and then the big frog bit hes|his[S] leg [PN].
C and the boy was mad [PN].
C and then they went for a walk [PN].
C and then the littl|little[S] frog and the big frog got on the tres|tree/z[S][WPN']
back[EW:branch] [PN].
C and then the big frog puch|push/*ed[S] the litte|little[S] frog [PN].
C and he begen|began[S] to cri|cry[S] [PN].
C and then they went on a log [PN].
C and they left the big frog [PN].
C and then the big frog jump/*ed and puch|push/*ed[S] the littl|little[s] frog in the
water [PN].
C and then the tril|turtle[S] saw it [PN].
C and then the boy saw it [PN].
C and then they look/*ed for hem|him[S] evry[XSP]wer|everywhere[S]  [PN].
C and then the boy went home [PN].
C and then they hred|heard[S] a nois|noise[S] [PN].
C and it was the litte|little[S] frog [PN].
C and he jump/*ed in the wendoor|window[S] [PN].
C and he jump/*ed on top of his had|head[S] [PN].
C and then the big frog lik|like/*ed[S] hem|him[S].
```

Figure 9-2

The written narrative (Figure 9-1) shows that the student's handwriting is legible. Other features to note are the lack of capitalization and ending punctuation. The transcript (Figure 9-2) shows the missing end punctuation marked with the [PN] code. The lack of capitalization could have been coded using the [IC] code but was instead just indicated with a comment at the beginning of the transcript. Also note the production of multiple spelling errors. The student is using emerging sequencing as noted by her use of "and then" to begin most sentences.

STANDARD MEASURES REPORT		
	Child	*******
TRANSCRIPT LENGTH		
Total Utterances	25	0
# Analysis Set (C&I Verbal Utts)	25	0
All Words Including Mazes	175	0
Elapsed Time		---
INTELLIGIBILITY		
% Intelligible Utterances	100%	---
% Intelligible Words	100%	---
SYNTAX/MORPHOLOGY		
# MLU in Words	7.00	---
# MLU in Morphemes	7.08	---
SEMANTICS		
# Number Total Words	175	0
# Number Different Words	55	0
# Type Token Ratio	0.31	---
# Moving-Average TTR (100)	0.38	---
ERRORS		
# % Utterances with Errors	32.0%	---
Number of Omissions	8	0
Number of Error Codes	1	0
# Calculations based on C&I Verbal Utts		

Figure 9-3

The Analyze menu contains a number of reports which can be used to analyze this sample. The *Standard Measures Report* (Figure 9-3) provides a summary of the sample. The student wrote 25 utterances (sentences) using, on average, seven words per sentence. The intelligibility measure indicates that all words were legible. A total of 175 words were written with 55 of those being different words. Note that the student had errors in 32% of her sentences. There were eight omissions (words and/or bound morphemes) and one word or utterance marked as an error. The next step is to analyze the codes to further explore the written sample.

	CODE SUMMARY							
	WORD CODES							
	Child				***			
	Main Body		Mazes		Main Body		Mazes	
	Anal Set	Total Utts	Anal Set	Total Utts	Anal Set	Total Utts	Anal Set	Total Utts
[EW:BRANCH]	1	1	0	0	0	0	0	0
[S]	28	28	0	0	0	0	0	0
[WPN']	1	1	0	0	0	0	0	0
[XSP]	1	1	0	0	0	0	0	0
	UTTERANCE CODES							
	Child				***			
	Main Body		Mazes		Main Body		Mazes	
	Anal Set	Total Utts	Anal Set	Total Utts	Anal Set	Total Utts	Anal Set	Total Utts
[PN]	24	24	0	0	0	0	0	0

Figure 9-4

The *Code Summary* (Figure 9-4) reveals that the student wrote one erroneous word, made 28 spelling errors, wrote one word without word-level punctuation, and wrote one word with an extra space within the word. Note there were 24 utterance codes [PN] where the student did not use punctuation. Recall from the sample that there were 25 total sentences and ending punctuation was only used on the last sentence.

In addition to the frequency and location of the written errors in a language sample, it may be valuable to look at the lexicon produced in the writing. The *Grammatical Categories* report (Figure 9-5) lists the parts of speech and the number of times each part of speech occurred in the sample. As reported, the student used mostly nouns (57) and determiners (28), e.g., *a, the, his*. Note that the student produced 25 coordinators, which seems high.

GRAMMATICAL CATEGORIES		
	Child	✱✱✱
TOTAL UTTERANCES		
Initiators	0	0
Determiners	28	0
Adjectives	8	0
Nouns	57	0
Personal Pronouns	15	0
Other Pronouns	0	0
Auxiliary Modals	0	0
Auxiliary Operators	0	0
Verbs	16	0
Copula Forms	3	0
Verb Particles	0	0
Adverbs	14	0
Intensifiers	0	0
Prepositions	9	0
Existential	0	0
Question Words	0	0
Coordinators	25	0
Subordinators	0	0
Infinitives	0	0
Possessives	1	0
Negation Words	1	0
Lets Words	0	0
Interjections	0	0

Figure 9-5

The *Grammatical Categories List* (Figure 9-6) produces lists of the specific words identified in any of the grammatical categories. After selecting coordinators, the report details which coordinators were used. In this sample there were 25 uses of the word *and*. Although there was a high frequency of coordinators, the student actually only used this one coordinating form.

GRAMMATICAL CATEGORY LISTS Total Utterances		
Coordinators		
	Child	***
AND	25	0
Total Frequency	25	0

Figure 9-6

WORD CODE TABLE Table Expanded by Words and Codes Total Utterances - Main body 1st Speaker			
	Child		***
	Total	Expanded	Total
[EW:BRANCH]	1		0
BACK[EW:BRANCH]		1	
[S]	28		0
BEGEN|BEGAN[S]		1	
CRI|CRY[S]		1	
DIERET|DID/N'T[S]		1	
EVRY[XSP]WER|EVERYWHERE[S]		1	
EXITED|EXCITED[S]		1	
GEFT|GIFT[S]		1	
HAD|HEAD[S]		1	
HEM|HIM[S]		2	
HES|HIS[S]		2	
HRED|HEARD[S]		1	
LIK|LIKE/*ED[S]		1	
LITTE|LITTLE[S]		5	
LITTL|LITTLE[S]		2	
NOIS|NOISE[S]		1	
PUCH|PUSH/*ED[S]		2	
TI|IT[S]		1	
TRE[WPN']S|TREE/Z[S]		1	
TRIL|TURTLE[S]		1	
WENDOOR|WINDOW[S]		1	
WONE|ONE[S]		1	
[WPN']	1		0
TRE[WPN']S|TREE/Z[S]		1	
[XSP]	1		0
EVRY[XSP]WER|EVERYWHERE[S]		1	

Figure 9-7

The *Word Code Table* (Figure 9-7) lists each word code expanded to show the words that were coded. The clinician can then analyze these words for patterns in errors. The [S] code marked spelling errors. Spelling information can be shared with other professionals on the education team and, if needed, interventions can be implemented. In the student's language sample, she consistently misspelled *little* and substituted "e" for "i" in *gift, him, his,* and *window*.

Case Study Summary

In the written narrative sample we ascertained that the student had very legible writing. She met the core standard, "Write narrative in which they recount two or more appropriately sequenced events, include some details regarding what happened, use temporal words to signal even order, and provide some sense of closure" (CCSS W.1.3). The analyses revealed that the student did not begin sentences with upper case letters nor did she use ending punctuation. Temporal words produced in the narrative lacked variety as she only used *and then* to sequence her narrative. Finally, it might be beneficial to monitor the student's progress on spelling comparing to subsequent samples to see if the number of spelling errors decreases. For children with severely impacted spelling skills, computer software for apps may offer support for spelling through spell-checking, word prediction, or speech-to-text capabilities.

Other Considerations for Written Language

It may be informative to explore various modalities for written language for students with and without language disorders. When pulling together an initial work-up of strengths and weaknesses, the production method must be taken into consideration in order to get an accurate assessment. Comparing performance of written language across hand written, word processed, or speech-to-text productions may help to discern how the production method helps or hinders text creation. It is also the case that software may mask difficulties where word choices and spelling help is automatic. It may be sufficient to help students work out the best technology-based supports possible to enhance their written language production.

Using Salt to Assess Fluency

The coding scheme described in this section was specifically designed to mark speech disfluencies. The coding can be applied to an existing transcript, previously coded for oral language production, or a speech sample can be elicited for the sole purpose of assessing fluency. These fluency codes are flexible in nature. They can be general, just marking the occurrence of a disfluency, or further defined to add more detail. The *Analysis menu: Fluency Codes and Behaviors* report provides detailed information on the number and types of disfluent productions within the connected speech sample. This fluency report is useful, not only for initial evaluations, but additionally to track therapy progress or changes in fluency behaviors over time and/or contexts.

Differentiating typical disfluencies from stuttering is imperative to a fluency assessment in order to determine whether there is a need for intervention. The American Speech Language Hearing Association (ASHA) provides the information below, which demonstrates how a language sample might help differentiate what are language vs. fluency production difficulties.

> *Fluency Disorders/Language Difficulties*
> Children with language difficulties at the sentence, narrative, or conversational discourse level may exhibit increased speech disfluencies, particularly interjections, revisions, and phrase repetitions. However, their disfluencies are not likely to involve prolongations, blocks, physical tension, or secondary behaviors that are more typical for children who stutter (Boscolo, Bernstein Ratner, & Rescorla, 2002).
>
> Word-finding issues can create increased non-stutter like disfluencies that are similar to those observed in cluttering; specific standardized tests can be used to rule out word-finding difficulties. Assessing organization of discourse also can help rule out verbal organization issues that might be mistaken for cluttering (van Zaalen-Op't Hof, Wijnen, & De Jonckere, 2009).

Coleman (2013) states that typical speech disfluencies are made up of multisyllabic whole-word and phrase repetitions, interjections, and revisions. Conversely, stuttering contains sound or syllable repetitions, prolongations, and/or blocks. Other differential behaviors seen in speakers who stutter may include physical tension and/or concomitant behaviors such as eye blinks, facial grimacing, and changes in pitch or loudness. Negative reaction or frustration may be noted. Avoidance behaviors such as reduced verbal output may also be present. These behaviors are not seen in speakers with typical disfluencies. A family history of stuttering may be also an important differential.

Understanding the difference between typical disfluencies and stuttering helps clinicians make decisions about the coding scheme(s) they may want to apply during the transcription step of speech sampling. *Will the sample be analyzed only for fluency, or are there features of oral language that will add to the assessment outcomes?*

Fluency treatment programs focus on increasing fluent speech production and effective communication. A desired outcome is to help the speaker participate more fully in social, educational, civic, and/or professional activities. The achievement of optimal communication in naturalistic, everyday communication contexts, such as in conversation or narration, make speech sampling a preferred practice for fluency evaluation since it can assess everyday use of oral language as well as speech production in these contexts.

As mentioned previously, SALT's fluency coding scheme can be applied to any transcript from any sample of spoken language. A clinician may collect a typical conversational or narrative sample. Or a sample from a specific speaking context such as a telephone conversation, ordering at a restaurant, a debate, or a mock interview may best capture the speaker's difficulties with fluent speech production. It may be prudent to assess fluency in multiple linguistic contexts to determine the impact of each context on oral fluency. For example, a conversation, which taps into discourse and pragmatics, may yield different results than a narrative sample, where discourse is not interposed. Or, a conversational sample could be compared in analysis to a sample of oral reading where the opportunity to use alternate vocabulary is not present. The analysis results can be compared side-by-side using SALT's linking feature.

Recommended codes to mark disfluent speech production

SALT contains a default list of fluency codes which may be edited to suit your purposes. They include:

[FL] used to mark any unspecified type of disfluency
[FLR] used to mark repetitions
[FLP] used to mark prolongations
[FLB] used to mark silent blocks

Coding Unspecified Types of Disfluencies - [FL]

The insertion of the [FL] code can be used to highlight any type of disfluent production and will be tallied in analysis to provide the frequency of occurrence.

- [FL] used to mark disfluent *utterances*. Insert the code [FL] at the end of any utterance containing one or more disfluencies. The fluency report will count and display the coded utterances.
- [FL] used to mark disfluent *words*. Insert the [FL] code at the end of each disfluent word. When the [FL] code is attached to a word, with no space between the word and the code, the code indicates the presence of some type of disfluent behavior associated with that word. The fluency report will count and display the coded words with the option of also including the utterances.

Applying the code [FL] at the word or utterance level provides only the number of words or number of utterances in the sample that contained disfluencies. Using further defined codes will generate more specific results in analysis.

Coding the Type of Disfluency – [FLR], [FLP], [FLB]

The default set of codes for SALT's fluency analysis were developed to mark repetitions, prolongations, and silent blocks. These speech disfluencies occur at the sound, syllable, or whole-word level and are marked in the transcript using word codes, i.e., codes the disfluent words.

Select *Edit menu: Insert Code* to bring up the dialogue box "Code Lists Used to Facilitate Inserting Codes in a Transcript" (Figure 9-8).

At the bottom left of the dialogue box, check the "Fluency Codes" option. The default codes are listed. The code list can be changed, or customized, and saved for future use if desired.

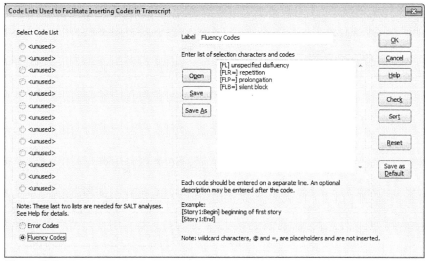

Figure 9-8

After accepting the default list of codes, or customizing your own set of codes, click OK in the upper right corner of the dialogue box. The "Select code to be inserted" dialogue box is displayed (Figure 9-9).

Figure 9-9

You are provided with options for the position of the fluency codes. The codes can be inserted at the point of the cursor in the transcript, at the beginning of a word, at the end of a word, or at the end of an utterance.

Basic Coding

Basic coding involves inserting one or more codes at the end of each disfluent word within the SALT transcript. This coding option is a fast method of tallying the number and types of disfluencies produced in the language sample.

Examples:

C *My[FLR] mom was really angry.*	Repeated some or all of the word
C *She like/3s banana/s[FLP].*	Prolonged some part of the word
C *She is funny[FLB].*	Silent block at the beginning or in middle of the word
C The boy woke**[FLR][FLP]** up.	Sound or whole word repetition followed by prolongation.

This *basic* level, inserting codes at the end of each word, does not distinguish the position of the disfluency within the word in analysis. Nor does this level of coding indicate the number of repetitions produced or the length of a prolongation or block.

The fluency report, using the *basic* level of coding, will count the total number of [FLR], [FLP], and [FLB] codes (and/or customized codes) that were inserted in the sample. Selecting the *Analyze menu: Fluency Codes and Behaviors* report (Figure 9-10), you specify the speaker, utterance base, and whether counts are given for disfluencies within and outside mazes. You have the option of displaying the coded words, or you can expand the report to additionally display the utterances containing the codes.

Figure 9-10

Should a more detailed description be of interest, these codes can be positioned and/or expanded to provide further information as described in the following sections.

Indicating Position within the Word

Inserting fluency codes at the position of the disfluency provides additional documentation. The fluency report will count the codes and display the specific words with their positional codes.

- **Repetitions**: insert the code immediately <u>before</u> the repeated sound or syllable. If the entire word is repeated, insert the code at the end of the word. For example,

*C She like/3s **[FLR]**banana/s.*	Repeated the initial sound /b/ or syllable /ba/
*C She like/3s ba**[FLR]**nana/s.*	Repeated the medial sound /n/ or syllable /na/
*C She is funny**[FLR]**.*	Repeated the whole word

Distinguishing between repeated sounds and syllables

Notice, in the first two examples, that it may not be evident whether the positional code is marking a sound or a syllable. If you wish to distinguish between sounds and syllables for repetitions, expand the fluency codes by adding "Snd" for sound and "Syl" for syllable, i.e., [FLRSnd], [FLRSyl]. For example,

C *She like/3s ba[**FLRSnd**]nana/s.*   Repeated the sound /n/
C *She like/3s ba[**FLRSyl**]nana/s.*   Repeated the syllable /na/

- **Prolongations**: insert the code immediately <u>before</u> the prolonged sound or syllable. For example,

C *She is [**FLP**]funny.*   Prolonged the initial sound /f/
C *She like/3s ba[**FLP**]nana/s.*   Prolonged the sound /n/
C *She like/3s ban[**FLP**]ana/s.*   Prolonged the sound /a/
C *She like/3s banana/[**FLP**]s.*   Prolonged the final sound /s/

- **Silent blocks**: insert the code at the position of the block. For example,

C *She is [**FLB**]funny.*   Silent block at beginning of sound/word
C *She is fun[**FLB**]ny.*   Silent block in middle of the word, between the syllables

Adding Number of Repetitions

When coding repetitions, you may want to indicate the number of repetitions. To do this, expand the repetition code by adding a colon followed by a number representing the number of extra repetitions. For example,

C *The [**FLR:4**]boy is chase/ing the dog.*   Repeated the initial sound /b/ four extra times
C *The boy[**FLR:2**] is chase/ing the dog.*   Repeated the word "boy" two extra times

C *She like/3s ba[**FLR:4**]nana/s.*   Repeated the sound /n/ or the second syllable /na/ four extra times

Note, in this last example, that you could differentiate between sounds and syllables by adding "Snd" for sound and "Syl" for syllable, i.e., [FLRSnd:4], [FLRSyl:4].

Adding Length of Prolongations and Blocks

When coding prolongations and silent blocks, you may want to indicate their duration. Note that the duration may be measured in a variety of ways, e.g., seconds, milliseconds, numeric scale. The duration doesn't have to be numeric. You may want to use a scale such as L=long, M=medium, and S=short. If you choose to include duration, just be consistent in how you measure it within and across your data sets. In the examples which follow, duration of prolongation is measured in number of seconds.

C *There are [**FLP:04**]many people.*   Initial sound/syllable was prolonged for 4 seconds

C *The kangar[**FLP:05**]oo was funny.*   Final sound was prolonged for 5 seconds

C *He like/3s [**FLB:03**]banana/s.*   3-second silent block at beginning of word

Coding Concomitant Behaviors

Concomitant behaviors are secondary, or accessory, behaviors that can accompany disfluency in speech production. They vary from person to person. These characteristics are best rated at the time of elicitation, directly after, or from a video recording of the speech-language sample. Rather than code concomitant behaviors in the transcript at the point(s) where they occur, these behaviors are marked using plus lines inserted at the end of the transcript. The suggested coding is divided into the following five categories:

- **Vocal quality** such as pitch rise, vocal tic, change in volume (louder/softer), change in rate (faster/slower)
- **Grimace (*facial*)** such as jaw jerk, tongue protrusion, lip press, squinting, tremor of lips or face

- **Eye movement** such as avert eye gaze, close eyes, blink eyes
- **Distracting sound** such as fast or shallow breathing, sigh, whistle, blow (*air*), click, laugh, clear throat
- **Movement of extremities** such as arm movement, hand movement, hands around face, finger movement, shrug shoulders, clap, nod, shake, jerk

Select *Edit menu: Insert Fluency Template* to insert the following plus lines used to rate these five concomitant behavior categories:
+ Vocal Quality:
+ Grimace:
+ Eye Movement:
+ Distracting Sound:
+ Movement of Extremities:

Each category is rated on a 0-3 scale as follows:
0 = does not occur
1 = LOW frequency of occurrence
2 = MEDIUM frequency of occurrence
3 = HIGH frequency of occurrence

Example of using SALT to code disfluencies

Figure 9-11 contains an excerpt from a SALT transcript showing the *basic* level of coding for disfluency as well as the rating of concomitant behaviors. The child in this sample is retelling the story *Frog, Where Are You?* (Mayer, 1969). The [FLR], [FLP], and [FLB] codes were inserted at the end of words. , indicating type of disfluency but not position within the word, number of repetitions, or length of prolongations and blocks. The concomitant, or secondary, behaviors were assessed on a scale of 0-3 and the rating values inserted on plus lines at the end of the transcript.

The *Analyze menu: Fluency Codes and Behaviors* report (Figure 9-12) produces a list of the disfluent words. The child repeated words 16 times and prolonged words 18 times. No silent blocks were coded. At the bottom of the report are the severity rating scores applied to concomitant behaviors.

$ Child
+ Context: Nar
+ Subgroup: FWAY
+ [FLR]: repetition
+ [FLP]: prolongation
+ [FLB]: silent block
+ [EW:] error at the word level

C Once there[FLR] was a boy that[FLR][EW:who] had a frog.
C He like/ed it very much[FLP].
C And the dog did[FLR] too.
C (Um) one night when the[FLP] boy and the dog were sleep/ing the[FLP] frog crept out : 02 of the (um) container.
C Then (w*) right when[FLP] the boy and dog woke[FLR][FLP] up, (he was) he was miss/ing.
C He look/ed everywhere (from hi*) from his boot/s (to hi* his) to inside the bowl[EW:jar].
C And then[FLR] he call/ed out his name from[FLP] the window[FLP].
C Then his dog jump/ed out the[FLP] window[FLP].
C Still the container (was[FLR] in his) was on his head.
C And the[FLR] boy got up with his boot/s and got him.
C He went[FLP] look/ing for him.
C They[FLR] went into the woods[FLR][FLP].
; :02
C He found[FLP] a hole.
C And the dog found[FLP] a[FLR] beehive.
C And then a[FLR] gopher came[FLR] out of the hole.
C (And the[FLP]) and the[FLP] bee/s start/ed chasing[FLR] the dog[FLR].
C Then the gopher was[FLP] stare/ing at the[FLR] boy while[FLP] he was climb/ing up the tree[FLR] branch and look/ing[FLP] through a hole.
....
= Concomitant Behaviors
+ Vocal Quality: 0
+ Grimace: 0
+ Eye Movement: 3
+ Distracting Sound: 0
+ Movement of Extremities: 2

Figure 9-11

Fluency sample for book Analysis Set: C&I Verbal Utts		
FLUENCY CODES **Total Utterances - Main body & Mazes** **1st Speaker**		
	Child	
	Total	Expanded
Word-level Fluency Codes		
[FLR=]	16	
A[FLR]		2
CAME[FLR]		1
CHASING[FLR]		1
DID[FLR]		1
DOG[FLR]		1
THAT[FLR][EW:WHO]		1
THE[FLR]		2
THEN[FLR]		1
THERE[FLR]		1
THEY[FLR]		1
TREE[FLR]		1
WAS[FLR]		1
WOKE[FLR][FLP]		1
WOODS[FLR][FLP]		1
[FLP=]	18	
FOUND[FLP]		2
FROM[FLP]		1
LOOK/ING[FLP]		1
MUCH[FLP]		1
THE[FLP]		5
WAS[FLP]		1
WENT[FLP]		1
WHEN[FLP]		1
WHILE[FLP]		1
WINDOW[FLP]		2
WOKE[FLR][FLP]		1
WOODS[FLR][FLP]		1
Utterance-level Fluency Codes		
CONCOMITANT BEHAVIORS		
Vocal Quality	0	
Grimace	0	
Eye Movement	3	
Distracting Sound	0	
Movement of Extremities	2	

Figure 9-12

Benefits of Coding Disfluencies

There are numerous benefits of coding disfluencies in samples of everyday communication. The analyses are taken from the very behavior we are addressing, frequent social or text-based communication contexts. Taken together, verbal fluency and language analyses provide a powerful tool to document speech and language performance individually and how they interact for the target speaker. These tools provide the information necessary to pinpoint specific deficits which can guide the clinician in developing and implementing effective intervention programs.

Other Applications of SALT

Over the years, SALT Services has provided consultation and transcription services for projects covering a wide array of assessment aims. These projects have shed light on just how flexible and valuable coding language samples is to the processes of diagnostics, measuring gains or changes in performance, and discovering outcomes that may not have been expected. Below are just a few of these projects.

- Building local norms
  - o SALT has been used by researchers and school districts to build reference databases of local norms from samples they collected.
- Language from AAC devices
  - o Alzheimer's and Primary Progressive Aphasia: Speakers used spoken language augmented with low tech AAC (communication boards). Both spoken language and use of AAC were captured in transcription, providing data to assess the speaker's combined productive language.
  - o The output of AAC devices were transcribed to assess the speaker's vocabulary and discourse.
  - o AAC and the conversational partner: The output of the AAC devices was transcribed along with the spoken responses of the conversation partners to assess the quantity and quality of partner responses to generated speech.

- Language from LENA™ recordings (LENA™ Research Foundation, 2015)
  - A number of projects have been undertaken to evaluate the quality of the language spoken in the home or classroom setting in addition to the quantity of spoken language that LENA recordings provide.
- Language of speakers with hearing impairment
  - Language samples of children with hearing loss were analyzed to track the amount of code switching between spoken and signed language.
  - Language samples were collected over time to track the spoken performance of children with cochlear implants.
- Classroom intervention projects
  - Teacher language was recorded and transcribed to assess pre and post instruction when teaching language/reading.
  - Classroom language was analyzed to assess student performance pre and post direct vocabulary instruction, and pre and post shared story intervention.
- Adult assessment of pragmatics
  - Mock job interviews of college students were custom coded for specific pragmatic features.
  - *Positive language* pre and post intervention was assessed for increased use of positive words and phrases.
- Customer support calls
  - Support calls from a large business were recorded, transcribed, and analyzed to track the types of calls and the quality of the responses.
- Interviews
  - Research interviews were transcribed and coded to quantify responses to specific questions.
  - Interview task; SALT transcripts were coded for various pragmatic skills of adolescent children with Autism Spectrum Disorder (ASD)
- Gorilla sign language
  - SALT was used to track the vocabulary of a sign-language speaking gorilla.

SALT's flexible transcription and coding options make it a great tool for analyzing any type of language sample.

10

Pulling It All Together: Examples from our case study files

Joyelle DiVall-Rayan
Jon F. Miller

Incorporating language sample analysis into your practice can best be illustrated by working through a series of case studies. These cases are from our clinical collaborations with SLPs who have graciously granted permission to present their work. We have taken some liberty with commentary to explain why certain measures contribute to the overall picture of the oral language skills presented by each case. The focus is on the description and diagnostic value of the measures with only general consideration of intervention plans.

A main theme of this book is that language disorders take a variety of forms. In each case, LSA provides insight into the overall picture of oral language skill in naturalistic, everyday communication demands. As you read through these cases, focus on the story that the test scores and language sample measures tell us about overall communication effectiveness. The challenging part of our work as SLPs is figuring out what it means once the information is collected. Enjoy the cases as they capture a range of oral language problems.

Case Study 1: CARTER

SALT Transcript: Carter PGHW.slt[7]

BACKGROUND

Carter is 8;1 and is in the second grade. He is diagnosed with Autism Spectrum Disorder (ASD) and Attention Deficit Hyperactivity Disorder (ADHD). He has a normal IQ according to neuro-psychological testing. He is receiving speech/language services for speech articulation, which has improved his speech intelligibility. Carter also received therapy services as a preschooler that focused on expressive/receptive language and social skills. He is being assessed for language skills following teacher concerns and SLP observations of difficulty with utterance formulation in both speaking and writing. Carter was attentive to assessment tasks and followed directions well throughout the evaluation.

ASSESSMENT MEASURE

A story retell narrative task was the best choice to assess Carter's presenting language issues. It challenged his word, utterance, and text-level proficiency, and the skills required for the narrative closely mirror the demands of the school curriculum. Carter listened to the story *Pookins Gets Her Way* (Lester, 1987) and then retold the story using the book with the text covered. He listened carefully to the instructions and gave his best effort retelling the story. The results are considered to be representative of his oral language skills. The recorded sample was transcribed and then coded for sentence complexity (SI, see Appendix O) and narrative structure (NSS, see Appendix P). It took Carter 5½ minutes to retell the story and his sample contained 480 words and 46 utterances. Carter's sample was compared to samples selected from the Narrative Story Retell database (see Appendix D).

Selected database samples:
    82 samples matched by age: 7;7 - 8;7
    39 samples matched by age and same number of total words (NTW)

---

[7] *Carter PGHW* is one of the sample transcripts included with the software.

SALT ANALYSIS

Carter PGHW
Word base: Exclude ((parenthetical remarks))

TRANSCRIPT INFORMATION	DATABASE INFORMATION
Speaker: Carter (Child)	Database: Narrative Story Retell
Sample Date:	82 Samples Matched by Age
Current Age: 8;1, Grade: 2	39 Samples Cut at 312 Number Total Words
Context: Narration (PGHW)	Context: Narration (PGHW)

STANDARD MEASURES REPORT

	LANGUAGE MEASURE	Child		DATABASE				
		Score	+/-SD	Mean	Min	Max	SD	%SD
	Current Age (8;1)	8.08	-0.06	8.10	7.58	8.58	0.29	4%
	Compared to 82 Samples Matched by Age (ENTIRE TRANSCRIPT)							
	TRANSCRIPT LENGTH							
	Total Utterances	46	0.36	41.51	22	85	12.46	30%
#	C&I Verbal Utts	40	0.09	38.95	21	76	11.66	30%
	All Words Including Mazes	480	0.86	375.39	186	923	121.37	32%
	Elapsed Time (5:32)	5.53	0.83	4.26	1.47	10.57	1.52	36%
	INTELLIGIBILITY							
	% Intelligible Utterances	90.9%	-0.80	96.18	63.41	100.00	6.62	7%
	% Intelligible Words	98.9%	-0.71	99.53	94.93	100.00	0.85	1%
	NARRATIVE STRUCTURE							
	NSS Composite Score	19	-0.94	22.89	12	32	4.13	18%
	Compared to 39 Samples Equated by Same Number of Total Words (CUT AT 312 NTW)							
	SYNTAX/MORPHOLOGY							
#	MLU in Words	7.80	-0.73	8.55	5.85	10.83	1.03	12%
#	MLU in Morphemes	8.85	-0.66	9.62	6.65	12.34	1.17	12%
#	SI Composite Score	1.13 *	-1.80	1.30	1.00	1.52	0.10	7%
	SEMANTICS							
#	Number Total Words (NTW)	312	0.00	312.00	312	312	0.00	0%
#	Number Different Words (NDW)	145 *	1.78	126.26	105	148	10.50	8%
#	Type Token Ratio (TTR)	0.46 *	1.78	0.40	0.34	0.47	0.03	8%
#	Moving-Average TTR (100)	0.66 **	2.50	0.57	0.51	0.65	0.04	6%
	VERBAL FACILITY							
	Words/Minute	86.75	-0.39	94.63	59.22	143.92	20.29	21%
#	Maze Words as % of Total Words	25.4% **	3.05	11.56	2.50	19.17	4.53	39%
	Pauses Within Utterances	8 *	1.80	2.36	0	13	3.14	133%
	Pauses Between Utterances	9	0.16	8.08	0	22	5.60	69%
	Abandoned Utterances	0	-0.41	0.74	0	11	1.83	246%
	ERRORS							
#	% Utterances with Errors	17.5%	0.30	14.64	0.00	48.57	9.66	66%
	Number of Omissions	2	-0.34	3.05	0	16	3.09	101%
	Number of Error Codes	8 **	2.02	3.36	0	10	2.30	68%

 # Calculations based on C&I Verbal Utts
* At least 1 SD (** 2 SD) from the database mean
Database selection criteria: age +/- 6 months (7;7 - 8;7)

Figure 10-1

Database Menu: Standard Measures Report (Figure 10-1)

- *Transcript Length*: The sample was age appropriate in length for the number of utterances and words, as well as elapsed time.
- *Intelligibility*: Intelligibility did not impact the sample.
- *NSS Composite Score*: Macrostructure analysis of the Carter's story revealed NSS scores, although low, were within the normal range of performance.
- *Syntax/Morphology*: MLU in words and morphemes were also within normal limits. However, Carter's utterances, while of appropriate length, did not include the more complex structure typical for his age and grade. This was evidenced by the SI Composite Score, a measure of clausal density.
- *Semantics*: Number of Different Words (NDW), Type Token Ratio (TTR) and the Moving Average Type Token Ratio (MATTR) were all more than one standard deviation above the database mean. These are measures of vocabulary diversity and the positive SDs indicate strengths.
- *Verbal Facility*: Carter's rate of speech was comparable to his peers at 86.75 Words per Minute (WPM). Also noted were a high number of pauses within utterances at 1.80 SD above the database mean. Slightly over 25% of Carter's words were maze words. This is just over three standard deviations higher than the database mean and warrants a more in-depth look at mazes.
- *Errors*: The percent of utterances containing errors was within normal limits. However, Carter's sample contained 2 omissions and 8 errors which should be examined for patterns.

Additional information is provided in subsequent reports.

Database Menu: Narrative Scoring Scheme (Figure 10-2)

Carter's sample was scored using the Narrative Scoring Scheme (NSS) to specify age-appropriate narrative ability. The NSS is a tool to assess the structure and content of a narrative (see Appendix P). The narrative is scored on seven features of storytelling such as introduction, character development, mental states, referencing, and cohesion. Carter's NSS scores were compared to the database samples. His composite score on the NSS was 19 out of 35, which is within normal limits for his age. However, his individual category scores were low in the categories of mental states, referencing, and cohesion.

NARRATIVE SCORING SCHEME Compared to 82 Samples Matched by Age							
NSS Category	Child		DATABASE				
	Score	+/-SD	Mean	Min	Max	SD	%SD
Introduction	4	0.12	3.90	1	5	0.83	21%
Character Development	3	-0.02	3.02	1	5	0.99	33%
Mental States	1**	-2.10	2.66	1	5	0.79	30%
Referencing	2*	-1.98	3.32	2	5	0.66	20%
Conflict Resolution	3	-0.49	3.39	1	5	0.80	24%
Cohesion	2*	-1.75	3.26	1	5	0.72	22%
Conclusion	4	0.59	3.34	1	5	1.11	33%
NSS Composite Score	19	-0.94	22.89	12	32	4.13	18%

*At least 1 SD (** 2 SD) from the database mean*
Database selection criteria: age +/- 6 months (7;7 - 8;7)

Figure 10-2

Database Menu: Subordination Index (Figure 10-3)

The Subordination Index (SI) is a relatively fast way to document the use of complex syntax (see Appendix O). This is an important measure from Carter's sample to confirm the SLP's observation of infrequent use of complex syntax and the frequent mazes which may be associated with utterance formulation problems, i.e., limited command of complex syntax. SI is a measure of clausal density, calculated by dividing the number of clauses by total number of utterances. SALT calculated the score and compared it to the matched database samples. Carter's SI composite score was 1.13, which is 1.8 SD below the database mean of 1.30. Most of his utterances contained one clause.

SUBORDINATION INDEX Calculations Based on C&I Verbal Utts, Transcripts Cut at 312 Number Total Words (39 samples)							
LANGUAGE MEASURE	Child		DATABASE				
	Score	+/-SD	Mean	Min	Max	SD	%SD
[SI-0]	0	-0.51	0.46	0	4	0.91	198%
[SI-1]	34*	1.57	26.18	16	38	4.99	19%
[SI-2]	5*	-1.36	8.72	2	14	2.74	31%
[SI-3]	0*	-1.07	1.13	0	4	1.06	94%
[SI-4]	0	-0.23	0.05	0	1	0.22	436%
[SI-5]	0	-0.16	0.03	0	1	0.16	624%
SI Composite Score	1.13*	-1.80	1.30	1.00	1.52	0.10	7%

*At least 1 SD (** 2 SD) from the database mean*
Database selection criteria: age +/- 6 months (7;7 - 8;7)

Figure 10-3

Database Menu: Maze Summary (Figure 10-4)

The *Maze Summary* report shows that Carter produced mazes at the word and phrase level. The word-level mazes were mostly repetitions while the revisions were more prominent at the phrase level. These data provide support for both word retrieval as well as utterance formulation problems.

	MAZE SUMMARY						
Calculations Based on C&I Verbal Utts, Transcripts Cut at 312 Number Total Words (39 samples)							
LANGUAGE MEASURE	Child		DATABASE				
	Score	+/-SD	Mean	Min	Max	SD	%SD
Total Verbal Utterances	40	0.50	37.67	29	54	4.69	12%
Utterances with Mazes	25 **	2.11	15.33	5	25	4.58	30%
Average Mazes per Utterance	0.93 **	3.14	0.08	0.00	1.00	0.27	351%
Total Number of Mazes	37 **	2.08	20.38	5	40	7.99	39%
Number Total Words	312	0.00	312.00	312	312	0.00	0%
Total Maze Words	106 **	3.57	41.67	8	74	18.04	43%
% Maze Words/Total Words	25.4% **	3.05	11.56	2.50	19.17	4.53	39%
Average Words per Maze	2.86 **	2.32	1.59	1.00	3.00	0.55	35%
Revisions							
Part Word	2	-0.27	2.54	0	8	1.97	78%
Word	8 **	2.88	2.67	0	8	1.85	70%
Phrase	14 **	2.22	6.59	0	14	3.34	51%
Repetitions							
Part Word	7 **	2.72	2.23	0	9	1.75	79%
Word	24 **	6.37	3.62	0	13	3.20	89%
Phrase	8 **	2.30	2.28	0	9	2.48	109%
Filled Pauses							
Single Word	7	0.42	4.69	0	24	5.55	118%
Multiple Words	0	-0.29	0.26	0	5	0.88	343%

*At least 1 SD (** 2 SD) from the database mean*

Figure 10-4

Analyze Menu: Utterances with pauses (Figure 10-5)

Carter's frequent pauses within utterances prompt a review of these utterances directly. The majority of the within-utterance pauses were in mazes which supports the utterance formulation/word retrieval profile. In these instances, Carter used pausing, rather than just repeating and revising, to work out a solution to the utterance.

Utterances with Pauses	
26	C And she (:03 made whatever <>) made uh XX <X scary> monster face/s [SI-X].
30	C (Um :04) Pookins alway/3s ate icecream at lunch or dinner or anything [SI-1].
53	C (The the of* the :06 the) the troll[REF] said :05, "(I/'ll set him are you really) do you really want that wish" [SI-2]?
67	C Finally, when she is[EW:was] big, (the) the elf[EW:troll][REF] (ask/ed :02) ask/3s[EW:said], "(are y*) you (made a w* not wise choice :05) made a not wise choice" [EU].
70	C (And then and then and and then) and then (the the um :03 the flowe* th* the :02) (((what) what is she call/ed again[REF])) <> (oh Pookins uh Pook*) Pookins cover/ed (uh that the elf[REF]) the troll[REF] [SI-1].

Figure 10-5

Explore Menu: Utterances without mazes (Figure 10-6)

To better understand Carter's frequent use of mazes, let's examine his utterances which don't contain any mazes.

Selected Utterances	15
20	C She sticked|stick[EO:stuck] her tongue out [SI-1].
24	C She threw apple/s [SI-1].
25	C She yell/ed [SI-1].
32	C So she gave it[EW:them] to her cat [SI-1].
34	C She had all the toy/s she want/ed which was no fair ((maybe)) [SI-1].
44	C She brought her apple/s just in case [SI-1].
46	C The troll[REF] rub/ed his hat [SI-1].
47	C And she had cowboy boots [SI-1].
50	C The troll[REF] rub/ed her[EW:his] hat [SI-1].
51	C It came true [SI-1].
52	C Next she want/ed to be a flower [SI-1].
59	C He rub/ed his hat, %poof [SI-1].
61	C She turn/ed into a flower [SI-1].
66	C She grew and grew_and_grew_and_grew_and_grew [SI-1].
73	C "First you have to give me all your temper tantrum/s stuff to me [SI-1].

Figure 10-6

Notice that all of the fluent utterances had simple syntax (grammatical form). *Was he attempting to produce more than one proposition at a time without command of complex syntax to accomplish the task?* Further analysis of complex syntax is warranted. Also notice that the code [REF] was applied during transcription to mark referencing difficulty, which may be contributing to word retrieval impairment. The [REF] code was applied to the *troll* character because Carter referred to this character previously as an *elf*.

Analyze Menu: Standard Utterance Lists (Figure 10-7)

Selecting "Utterances with Error Codes" from the *Standard Utterance Lists* displays all the words and utterances coded as errors. This follow-up report should be used to look for patterns of errors. Carter made several pronoun errors, e.g., *it* for *them*, *her* for *his*, and several word choice errors, e.g., *before* for *after*, and *elf* and *troll* both used to refer to the same character.

STANDARD UTTERANCE LISTS
Total Utterances
1st Speaker

Utterances with Error Codes

20	C She sticked|stick[EO:stuck] her tongue out [SI-1].
22	C She made (fu*) goofy face/s, sticked|stick[EO:stuck] her tongue out [SI-1].
32	C So she gave it[EW:them] to her cat [SI-1].
39	C And she rollerskate/*ed in the living room which made the cat jump up on the couch and then make[EW:made] the lamp fall over and then made (the pot) the pot crack and X [SI-X].
40	C Then (all) she stay/ed *up all night (before the) before[EW:after] the owl/s went to bed [SI-2].
50	C The troll[REF] rub/ed her[EW:his] hat [SI-1].
67	C Finally, when she is big, (the) the elf[REF] (ask/ed :02) ask/3s, "(are y*) you (made a w* not wise choice :05) made a not wise choice" [EU].
69	C (The the) the elf[EW:troll][REF] cry/ed, "Oh, I/'m go/ing to lose my power/s in the rain" [SI-2]!

Figure 10-7

STANDARDIZED TEST INFORMATION

Clinical Evaluation of Language Fundamentals-4th Edition

Language Domain with Composite Score:

Core Language: 76

Receptive Language: 59

Expressive Language: 80

Language Structure: 73

Language Content: 78

Peabody Picture Vocabulary Test-4 (PPVT-4)

Standard Score: 116

Percentile: 86

Age Equivalent: 8;9

Expressive Vocabulary Test: 2 (EVT-2)
Standard Score: 117
Percentile: 87
Age Equivalent: 8;1

INTERPRETATION

Performance Profile
Carter's language sample results are consistent with the word retrieval and utterance formulation profile. His simple sentence attempts are produced without mazes, consistent with limited complex syntax use and confirmed by the SI measure. The Maze Summary table provides evidence for both word retrieval as well as utterance formulation issues. The phrase level mazes are revisions for the most part, while repetitions are at the word level. His pauses within utterances fit these observations as his repetitions and revisions did not create enough time to find the right word or the syntax to combine more than one idea into one utterance.

Strengths
Carter was enthusiastic and enjoyed listening to and retelling the story. He used adequate vocabulary with number of different words (NDW) being 145, which is slightly higher than the database mean. He also had adequate mean length of utterance at 7.8. These results are substantiated by his score on the Expressive Vocabulary Test, where he scored well above average on single word expression. Another area of relative strength is the length of his story. Carter told the story in average time and his story contained an average number of words and utterances.

Challenges
Carter's sample contained an abundance of mazes (repetitions, revisions, and filled pauses) with 25% of his words being maze words. His mazes consisted of part-word, word, and phrase repetitions as well as word and phrase revisions. The prevalence of pauses within utterances, at 1.80 standard deviations above the mean, indicates that he spent more time pausing within an utterance than age-matched peers. This might indicate difficulty with word retrieval as well as overall utterance organization. Word-level errors were also common

throughout Carter's sample. Errors included overgeneralization, e.g., *sticked* for *stuck*, and pronoun errors, e.g., *it* for *them* and *her* for *his*. Of note, Carter was inconsistent when referring to one of the main characters in the story; the gnome. He referred to the gnome as *elf*, and *troll* but not *gnome*. Carter requested from the clinician the name of the main character, Pookins, saying that he forgot her name. Some of these errors suggest delays in specific areas of language, overgeneralization of past tense, and lack of complex sentence use. The frequent mazes suggest that his self-monitoring of language production results in numerous changes to get the utterance that he has in mind produced correctly. Improving verbal fluency will require both direct instruction on complex syntax and strategies to find the right word.

Clinical Impressions

Carter performs in the average range on standardized tests. With the exception of his receptive language on the CELF-4, all other language domains are in low-average range. His receptive language score may be due to reduced attention to the task versus actual issues with auditory comprehension. When looking at his score on the PPVT-4 and EVT-2, Carter presents as though he has very high expressive and receptive language skills, which is true in some aspects as he has a normal MLU and NDW. However, these tasks are decontextualized and isolate language in a way that does not assess functional language. When Carter has to use the whole language system simultaneously, i.e., comprehend picture book, organize thoughts, formulate utterances, his language system breaks down and he demonstrates utterance and word retrieval difficulties along with pauses. This can be frustrating as he has complex ideas as well as vocabulary but cannot always get his intended message across to the listener. He also uses gestures and non-specific vocabulary to convey his ideas.

Ideas for Intervention

Recommendations include:

- Working on references so the listener clearly knows who/what Carter is talking about
- Word retrieval strategies, e.g., description, synonyms, etc.
- Taking time to formulate and organize thoughts before talking
- Direct instruction on complex syntax within a narrative context
- Fluency practice producing only simple sentences, one proposition at a time

Case Study 2: MAX

SALT Transcript: Max Expo.slt[8]

BACKGROUND

Max is 11;2 and is in the 5th grade. He began receiving speech/language services when he was four years old. He was identified with a learning disability in the first grade. Teacher concerns include difficulty expressing himself in a clear and concise manner. In speech-language therapy Max has been working on word retrieval, thought organization, and staying on topic. Max's conversational skills are very good. It is unlikely that someone would realize he has a language delay from a casual conversation with him. He asks appropriate questions, makes appropriate comments, stays on topic (most of the time), and listens to his partner.

ASSESSMENT MEASURE

Max completed an expository language sample where he was asked to tell how to play his favorite game or sport. The expository task began with a planning phase of 3-5 minutes where Max was asked to make notes on a template addressing ten required categories for a complete exposition. Max chose to explain how to play the board game Monopoly. He was compliant during the task and appeared to give his best effort. The recorded sample was transcribed and then coded for sentence complexity (SI, see Appendix O) and expository structure (ESS, see Appendix Q). Max's sample was compared to samples selected from the Expository database (see Appendix E).

Selected database samples:
    88 samples matched by age: 10;8 - 11;8
    83 samples matched by age and same number of total words (NTW)

---

[8] *Max Expo* is one of the sample transcripts included with the software.

SALT ANALYSIS

Max EXPO							
TRANSCRIPT INFORMATION Speaker: Max (Child) Sample Date: Current Age: 11;2, Grade: 5 Context: Exposition			DATABASE INFORMATION Database: Expository 88 Samples Matched by Age 83 Samples Cut at 247 Number Total Words Context: Exposition				

STANDARD MEASURES REPORT

LANGUAGE MEASURE	Child		DATABASE				
	Score	+/-SD	Mean	Min	Max	SD	%SD
Current Age (11;2)	11.17	-0.07	11.19	10.67	11.67	0.32	3%
Compared to 88 Samples Matched by Age (ENTIRE TRANSCRIPT)							
TRANSCRIPT LENGTH							
Total Utterances	34	-0.90	55.76	13	180	24.24	43%
# C&I Verbal Utts	31	-0.99	53.86	13	170	23.09	43%
All Words Including Mazes	376 *	-1.00	695.51	172	2422	320.45	46%
Elapsed Time (4:02)	4.03	-0.73	5.45	1.30	15.32	1.95	36%
INTELLIGIBILITY							
% Intelligible Utterances	97.1% *	-1.62	99.17	95.45	100.00	1.30	1%
% Intelligible Words	99.7% *	-1.54	99.93	99.52	100.00	0.12	0%
EXPOSITORY STRUCTURE							
ESS Composite Score	15 **	-3.21	32.80	13	44	5.54	17%
Compared to 83 Samples Equated by Same Number of Total Words (CUT AT 247 NTW)							
SYNTAX/MORPHOLOGY							
# MLU in Words	7.97 *	-1.74	11.87	7.78	22.64	2.25	19%
# MLU in Morphemes	8.58 *	-1.82	12.99	8.72	24.45	2.43	19%
# SI Composite Score	1.33 *	-1.16	1.65	1.00	2.45	0.27	17%
SEMANTICS							
# Number Total Words (NTW)	247	0.00	247.00	247	247	0.00	0%
# Number Different Words (NDW)	91	-0.96	102.53	67	139	11.97	12%
# Type Token Ratio (TTR)	0.37	-0.96	0.42	0.27	0.56	0.05	12%
# Moving-Average TTR (100)	0.53	-0.58	0.56	0.42	0.70	0.05	9%
VERBAL FACILITY							
Words/Minute	93.22 *	-1.47	130.98	57.80	201.04	25.64	20%
# Maze Words as % of Total Words	32.0% **	3.89	10.24	0.80	31.96	5.58	54%
Pauses Within Utterances	10 **	6.09	0.83	0	7	1.50	181%
Pauses Between Utterances	5 *	1.31	1.51	0	15	2.66	177%
Abandoned Utterances	2 **	3.34	0.27	0	2	0.52	196%
ERRORS							
# % Utterances with Errors	16.1%	0.58	11.03	0.00	47.06	8.77	80%
Number of Omissions	3 *	1.51	0.89	0	10	1.40	157%
Number of Error Codes	2	0.10	1.82	0	8	1.73	95%

Calculations based on C&I Verbal Utts
* At least 1 SD (** 2 SD) from the database mean
Database selection criteria: age +/- 6 months (10;8 - 11;8)

Figure 10-8

Database Menu: Standard Measures Report (Figure 10-8)

- *Transcript Length*: Max's expository sample was somewhat shorter in terms of number of utterances, number of words, and time than what was produced by his age-matched peers.
- *Intelligibility*: Although highlighted as significant, the measures of intelligibility are reasonable at 97.1% and 99.7%.
- *Expository Structure*: Max's ESS Composite Score, which measures the structure and content of the exposition, was more than 3 SDs below the database mean.
- *Syntax/Morphology*: Max's average utterance length was shorter than expected with MLUw at 1.74 SD and MLUm at 1.82 SD below the database mean. His SI Composite Score, which measures clausal density, was low.
- *Semantics*: Number of different words (NDW) and type token ratio (TTR), indicators of vocabulary diversity, were nearly one standard deviation below the database mean. Perhaps eliciting a language sample from another context would provide evidence to determine whether or not this is of significance.
- *Verbal Facility*: All measures were one or more standard deviations from the database means. Max's rate of speech, measured in words per minute, was 1.47 SD below the database mean. The low rate of speech was a result, at least in part, of the high number of silent pauses. 32% of Max's words were in mazes and he abandoned 2 utterances.
- *Errors*: There were 3 omissions in Max's sample which was 1.51 SD above the database mean.

Additional information is provided in subsequent reports.

Database Menu: Expository Scoring Scheme (Figure 10-9)

The Expository Scoring Scheme (ESS, see Appendix Q) was used to score the structure and content of Max's expository sample. His sample was scored on ten categories such as preparations, rules, and terminology. Most of these categories are based on the planning sheet that Max used to complete his expository sample. Max's composite score was 15 out of 50 compared to an average composite score of 32.8 for age-matched peers. The structure and content of Max's expository language sample was in the minimal/emerging range for his age.

EXPOSITORY SCORING SCHEME Compared to 88 Samples Matched by Age							
ESS Category	**Child**		**DATABASE**				
	Score	+/-SD	Mean	Min	Max	SD	%SD
Object of Contest	2*	-1.49	3.39	1	5	0.93	27%
Preparations	1**	-3.15	3.30	1	5	0.73	22%
Start of Play	2*	-1.44	3.34	1	5	0.93	28%
Course of Play	2*	-1.83	3.47	1	5	0.80	23%
Rules	2*	-1.56	3.30	1	5	0.83	25%
Scoring	1**	-2.57	3.24	1	5	0.87	27%
Duration	2*	-1.03	3.14	0	5	1.11	35%
Strategy	1**	-2.41	3.27	1	5	0.94	29%
Terminology	1**	-2.49	3.19	1	5	0.88	28%
Cohesion	1**	-3.11	3.17	2	4	0.70	22%
ESS Composite Score	15**	-3.21	32.80	13	44	5.54	17%

*At least 1 SD (** 2 SD) from the database mean
Database selection criteria: age +/- 6 months (10;8 - 11;8)

Figure 10-9

Database Menu: Subordination Index (Figure 10-10)

The Subordination Index (SI, see Appendix O) was applied to Max's sample. The SI measures clausal density and is computed by dividing the total number of clauses by total number of C-units. Max yielded a composite score of 1.33 whereas the database mean for age-matched peers is 1.65. Max's score was 1.16 SD below the database mean. He used mostly one-clause utterances (14 total) and 9 two-clause utterances.

SUBORDINATION INDEX Calculations Based on C&I Verbal Utts, Transcripts Cut at 247 Number Total Words (83 samples)							
LANGUAGE MEASURE	**Child**		**DATABASE**				
	Score	+/-SD	Mean	Min	Max	SD	%SD
[SI-0]	1*	1.62	0.13	0	3	0.54	404%
[SI-1]	14	0.57	11.64	4	22	4.16	36%
[SI-2]	9	0.95	6.61	1	14	2.50	38%
[SI-3]	0*	-1.41	1.89	0	5	1.34	71%
[SI-4]	0	-0.75	0.54	0	3	0.72	133%
[SI-5]	0	-0.46	0.22	0	2	0.47	217%
[SI-6]	0	-0.11	0.01	0	1	0.11	911%
[SI-7]	0	-0.19	0.04	0	1	0.19	520%
[SI-8]	0	-0.11	0.01	0	1	0.11	911%
[SI-9]	0	-0.11	0.01	0	1	0.11	911%
SI Composite Score	1.33*	-1.16	1.65	1.00	2.45	0.27	17%

*At least 1 SD (** 2 SD) from the database mean
Database selection criteria: age +/- 6 months (10;8 - 11;8)

Figure 10-10

Database Menu: Maze Summary (Figure 10-11)

The *Maze Summary* report gives detailed information about mazes and compares this information to the database. 32% of Max's total words were in mazes. This is 3.89 standard deviations higher than the database mean. The number of total mazes was also high as was the average words per maze, indicating that he produced frequent and relatively long mazes. Max's mazes were made up of primarily phrase revisions and word repetitions, with a significant number of filled pauses. The maze distribution tables revealed that a high percentage of utterances, even utterances that were relatively short, contained mazes. In fact, Max had mazes in most of his utterances that were longer than 2 morphemes. Compare Max's values with the much lower database mean values provided in this distribution table. As the length of his utterances increased, mazes continued to be present.

MAZE SUMMARY
Calculations Based on C&I Verbal Utts, Transcripts Cut at 247 Number Total Words (83 samples)

LANGUAGE MEASURE	Child		DATABASE				
	Score	+/-SD	Mean	Min	Max	SD	%SD
Total Verbal Utterances	31 **	2.30	22.20	11	32	3.82	17%
Utterances with Mazes	25 **	3.97	9.77	2	20	3.84	39%
Average Mazes per Utterance	1.23 **	2.69	0.13	0.00	2.00	0.41	307%
Total Number of Mazes	38 **	3.31	13.86	2	51	7.30	53%
Number Total Words	247	0.00	247.00	247	247	0.00	0%
Total Maze Words	116 **	4.60	29.34	2	116	18.84	64%
% Maze Words/Total Words	32.0% **	3.89	10.24	0.80	31.96	5.58	54%
Average Words per Maze	3.05 **	2.02	1.61	0.00	4.00	0.71	44%
Revisions							
Part Word	1	-0.10	1.13	0	6	1.27	112%
Word	6 **	2.11	2.20	0	9	1.80	82%
Phrase	16 **	3.77	4.86	0	12	2.96	61%
Repetitions							
Part Word	3	0.89	1.27	0	15	1.94	154%
Word	9 **	3.43	1.33	0	13	2.24	169%
Phrase	3 *	1.39	0.99	0	8	1.44	146%
Filled Pauses							
Single Word	29 **	4.74	5.31	0	26	4.99	94%
Multiple Words	1 **	2.55	0.11	0	2	0.35	322%

*At least 1 SD (** 2 SD) from the database mean*

MAZE DISTRIBUTION TABLES
% of Utterances with Mazes by Utterance Length in Morphemes

	1	2	3	4	5	6	7	8	9	10	11	12	13	14	15+	Total
Child	0%	0%	100%	100%	100%	50%	100%	60%	100%	100%	100%	67%	100%	100%	100%	81%
DB Mean	0%	1%	5%	11%	17%	22%	26%	27%	30%	27%	29%	38%	36%	26%	60%	32%

Figure 10-11

Analyze Menu: Rate and Pause Summary (Figure 10-12)

Max's sample was 4 minutes, 2 seconds in length which, according to the *Standard Measures Report* (see Figure 10-8), was within normal limits for the expository task. His speaking rate was slower than age-matched peers and his sample contained a larger number of pauses. The *Rate and Pause Summary* provides more detail about Max's verbal facility. His sample contained 10 within-utterance pauses, all occurring in mazes. These pauses totaled 38 seconds and lasted, on average, 4 seconds. Max also had a few between-utterance pauses, totaling 8 seconds, lasting 2 seconds on average.

RATE SUMMARY		
Elapsed Time: 4 minutes 2 seconds		
	Child	Examiner
Words per Minute	93.22	3.47
Utterances per Minute	8.43	0.74

PAUSE SUMMARY			
	No. of Pauses	Total Pause Time	Average Pause Time
Within Child Utterances			
Main body	0	0:00	
Mazes	10	0:38	
Total	10	0:38	0:04
Between Child Utterances			
Within Turn	3	0:06	
Preceding Turn	1	0:02	
Total	4	0:08	0:02
Within Examiner Utterances			
Main body	0	0:00	
Mazes	0	0:00	
Total	0	0:00	0:00
Between Examiner Utterances			
Within Turn	0	0:00	
Preceding Turn	1	0:04	
Total	1	0:04	0:04

Figure 10-12

Analyze Menu: Omissions and Error Codes (Figure 10-13)

The *Standard Measures Report* (see Figure 10-8) revealed that Max produced three omission errors in his sample which was 1.51 SD above the database mean. Omission errors are not common at this age level, with most speakers producing less than one omission error. The *Omissions and Error Codes* report displays omitted words and/or bound morphemes as well as their context within the utterance. This report also displays utterances containing error codes. Max's language contained three omitted words, one word-level error, and one utterance-level error.

	Child		
OMISSIONS AND ERROR CODES **Total Utterances** **1st Speaker**	**Total**	**Expanded**	
Omitted Words	3		
*GET		1	
*ON		1	
*SAY		1	
29 C (Like how do) you like try to (not the other team like not really team but) like *get other player/s (to win) not to win [SI-1].			
32 C And other way/s to win. (you have to get) you can give people card/s that *say you have to give them money (or like yeah yeah) [SI-2].			
47 C And then you like put your piece/s *on [SI-1].			
Omitted Bound Morphemes	0		
Word-level Error Codes			
=[EW:=]	1		
RULE/S[EW:RULE]		1	
23 C Like the basic rule/s[EW:rule] for this game is (you have to like if you like) you can/'t steal from the banker [SI-2].			
Utterance-level Error Codes			
[EU]	1		
33 C And other good thing/s. (you) you can get (a a j*) a free jail out of card if you/'re in jail [EU].			

Figure 10-13

INTERPRETATION

Performance Profile

The delayed language profile is characterized by low mean length of utterance, low number of different words, slow speaking rate, and word and utterance-level errors. Max's language production fits into this profile. His syntax was limited to simple sentences with few attempts at complex sentence forms as evidenced by his low SI scores. All of Max's language sample scores contribute to his low scores on the ESS in that his sample is short and syntactic forms do not allow him to express complex relationships.

Strengths
As mentioned earlier, Max has good conversational skills. He was a willing participant in the assessment process and made only a few word or utterance errors.

Challenges
Max demonstrated limited lexical diversity with low MLU and NDW. His low SI score indicates that he uses simple syntax with limited use of subordination. Verbal fluency was decreased as evidenced by increased mazes and pause times. This could be related in part to utterance formulation difficulty. Max's ESS scores indicated problems with cohesion, e.g., overall flow of the sample, organization, sequencing, etc., and terminology, e.g., adequately defining new terms. Max also scored lower on the content of his expository sample in areas such as explaining how the game is scored, strategies used, and preparations for the game.

Clinical Impressions
Max's performance could be related in part to formulation difficulties as seen by the length of his mazes and the fact that mazes were present even in short, simple utterances. The expository task is challenging but revealing of his oral language issues. Comparing his conversational skills with his expository skills may suggest opportunities to improve his overall verbal output.

Ideas for Intervention
- Foster vocabulary enrichment, such as pre-teaching content words related to specific areas of the curriculum
- Organize thoughts before speaking by practicing with the ESS matrix to fulfill expectations for detail
- Practice narrative retell to improve sequencing of events and story structure
- Teach complex sentence forms beginning with conjunctions to expand utterances

Case Study 3: TIMMY

SALT Transcript: Timmy FWAY.slt[9]

BACKGROUND

Timmy is a 5-year, 8-month old boy who was in early childhood when he first received therapy for language delay. He is now in kindergarten and his therapist wants to assess his language production using a story retell as it relates directly to the kindergarten curriculum.

ASSESSMENT MEASURE

Timmy completed a narrative story retell using the wordless picture book *Frog, Where are You?* (Mayer, 1969). First, the clinician told the story using a script, and then Timmy retold the story using the pictures from the book. Timmy completed the task without prompting and the therapist thought the sample was a valid indicator of his current level of oral language. The recorded sample was transcribed and then coded for sentence complexity (SI, see Appendix O) and narrative structure (NSS, see Appendix P). Timmy's sample was compared to samples selected from the Narrative Story Retell database (see Appendix D).

Selected database samples:
    69 samples matched by age: 10;8 - 11;8
    66 samples matched by age and same number of total words (NTW)

SALT ANALYSIS

Database Menu: Standard Measures Report (Figure 10-14)
- *Transcript Length*: Timmy used significantly fewer utterances, words, and time to retell the story than his age-matched peers.
- *Narrative Structure*: Timmy's NSS Composite Score, which measures the structure and content of the narrative, was 1.83 SD below the database mean.

---

[9] *Timmy FWAY* is one of the sample transcripts included with the software.

Timmy FWAY							
TRANSCRIPT INFORMATION Speaker: Timmy (Child) Sample Date: Current Age: 5;8, Grade: K Context: Narration (FWAY)				DATABASE INFORMATION Database: Narrative Story Retell 69 Samples Matched by Age 66 Samples Cut at 139 Number Total Words Context: Narration (FWAY)			

STANDARD MEASURES REPORT

	LANGUAGE MEASURE	Child		DATABASE				
		Score	+/-SD	Mean	Min	Max	SD	%SD
	Current Age (5;8)	5.67	-0.10	5.69	5.17	6.17	0.29	5%
	Compared to 69 Samples Matched by Age (ENTIRE TRANSCRIPT)							
	TRANSCRIPT LENGTH							
	Total Utterances	26 *	-1.35	38.59	22	60	9.30	24%
#	C&I Verbal Utts	24 *	-1.34	34.84	20	56	8.08	23%
	All Words Including Mazes	154 *	-1.72	285.57	150	458	76.58	27%
	Elapsed Time (1:54)	1.90 *	-1.71	3.52	1.72	7.03	0.95	27%
	INTELLIGIBILITY							
	% Intelligible Utterances	96.2%	0.21	94.75	70.59	100.00	6.77	7%
	% Intelligible Words	99.4%	0.12	99.23	94.92	100.00	1.04	1%
	NARRATIVE STRUCTURE							
	NSS Composite Score	13 *	-1.83	18.83	11	26	3.18	17%
	Compared to 66 Samples Equated by Same Number of Total Words (CUT AT 139 NTW)							
	SYNTAX/MORPHOLOGY							
#	MLU in Words	5.79 *	-1.25	7.16	4.93	9.33	1.09	15%
#	MLU in Morphemes	6.54 *	-1.19	7.95	5.21	10.47	1.18	15%
#	SI Composite Score	1.05	-0.74	1.13	0.94	1.47	0.11	10%
	SEMANTICS							
#	Number Total Words (NTW)	139	0.00	139.00	139	139	0.00	0%
#	Number Different Words (NDW)	62	0.53	59.02	47	70	5.60	9%
#	Type Token Ratio (TTR)	0.45	0.53	0.42	0.34	0.50	0.04	9%
#	Moving-Average TTR (100)	0.49	0.53	0.47	0.39	0.54	0.04	8%
	VERBAL FACILITY							
	Words/Minute	81.05	-0.17	84.38	44.58	129.17	20.12	24%
#	Maze Words as % of Total Words	4.1%	-0.93	9.87	0.00	24.46	6.14	62%
	Pauses Within Utterances	1	-0.16	1.27	0	10	1.76	138%
	Pauses Between Utterances	9	0.86	5.26	0	18	4.33	82%
	Abandoned Utterances	1	0.65	0.50	0	3	0.77	154%
	ERRORS							
#	% Utterances with Errors	20.8%	0.59	15.83	0.00	38.89	8.45	53%
	Number of Omissions	2	0.71	1.12	0	5	1.23	110%
	Number of Error Codes	3	0.31	2.50	0	6	1.64	66%

Calculations based on C&I Verbal Utts
* At least 1 SD (** 2 SD) from the database mean
Database selection criteria: age +/- 6 months (5;2 - 6;2)

Figure 10-14

- *Syntax/Morphology*: Timmy's MLU in words and morphemes was lower than his age-matched peers though his SI Composite Score, a measure of sentence complexity, was within the normal range for his age.
- *Semantics*: Number of different words (NDW) and type token ratio (TTR and MATTR), which are measures of vocabulary diversity, were also within the normal range.
- *Verbal Facility*: Timmy's words per minute (WPM) score was within the normal range for his age. His sample contained very few mazes or a significant number of silent pauses.
- *Errors*: Although 20% of Timmy's utterances contained errors, this was not significantly more than his age-matched peers.

Additional information is provided in subsequent reports.

Database Menu: Narrative Scoring Scheme (Figure 10-15)

Timmy's sample was scored using the Narrative Scoring Scheme (NSS), a tool to assess the structure and content of a narrative (see Appendix P). Timmy's composite score on the NSS was 13 out of 35, which is -1.83 SDs below the mean compared to age-matched peers. Timmy had lower scores on the categories of introduction, mental states, and cohesion. He appeared to have difficulty grasping the structure of the narrative task.

	NARRATIVE SCORING SCHEME Compared to 69 Samples Matched by Age						
NSS Category	Child		DATABASE				
	Score	+/-SD	Mean	Min	Max	SD	%SD
Introduction	1 *	-1.43	2.33	0	4	0.93	40%
Character Development	2	-1.13	2.72	1	4	0.64	23%
Mental States	1 *	-1.31	2.01	1	4	0.78	39%
Referencing	3	0.03	2.97	1	5	0.89	30%
Conflict Resolution	2	-1.52	2.88	1	4	0.58	20%
Cohesion	2 *	-1.79	3.06	2	5	0.59	19%
Conclusion	2	-0.95	2.84	0	5	0.88	31%
NSS Composite Score	13 *	-1.83	18.83	11	26	3.18	17%

*At least 1 SD (** 2 SD) from the database mean*
Database selection criteria: age +/- 6 months (5;2 - 6;2)

Figure 10-15

WORD LISTS, BOUND MORPHEMES, & UTTERANCE DISTRIBUTION
Calculations Based on C&I Verbal Utts, Transcripts Cut at 139 Number Total Words (66 samples)

LANGUAGE MEASURE	Child		DATABASE				
	Score	+/-SD	Mean	Min	Max	SD	%SD
WORD LISTS							
Question Words							
Total	0	-0.24	0.15	0	4	0.64	421%
Type	0	-0.28	0.08	0	1	0.27	352%
Negatives							
Total	2	0.71	1.11	0	6	1.27	115%
Type	2 *	1.44	0.82	0	3	0.82	100%
Conjunctions							
Total	21	0.36	18.38	5	36	7.25	39%
Type	3	-0.48	3.55	2	6	1.14	32%
Modal Auxiliary Verbs							
Total	0	-0.46	0.30	0	3	0.66	216%
Type	0	-0.51	0.21	0	1	0.41	194%
Personal Pronouns							
Total	14	0.37	12.17	0	23	4.94	41%
Type	2 *	-1.37	3.39	0	6	1.02	30%
BOUND MORPHEMES							
/3S	0	-0.25	0.25	0	6	0.99	402%
/ED	10	0.74	7.57	0	13	3.30	44%
/ING	1	-0.87	3.09	0	12	2.39	77%
/S	5 **	2.13	1.90	0	6	1.46	77%
/Z	1 *	1.34	0.28	0	2	0.54	196%

*At least 1 SD (** 2 SD) from the database mean*

NUMBER OF UTTERANCES BY UTTERANCE LENGTH

Utterance Length in Words

	0	1	2	3	4	5	6	7	8	9	10	11	12	13	14	15+	Total
Child	0	2	1	3	2	2	5	4	2	0	1	0	2	0	0	0	24
DB Mean	0	0	0	1	3	4	3	3	2	1	1	1	1	0	0	1	21

Utterance Length in Morphemes

	0	1	2	3	4	5	6	7	8	9	10	11	12	13	14	15+	Total
Child	0	2	1	1	3	1	3	3	6	1	1	0	1	0	0	1	24
DB Mean	0	0	0	0	2	3	3	3	2	2	1	1	1	0	0	1	19

Database selection criteria: age +/- 6 months (5;2 - 6;2)

Figure 10-16

Database Menu: Word Lists, Bound Morphemes, & Utt. Distribution Report (Figure 10-16)

Timmy's MLU in words and morphemes was lower than his age-matched peers. The *Word Lists, Bound Morphemes, & Utterance Distribution report from the* Database menu was produced to try and gain further information about words and utterances produced in his sample. This report can often assist in determining if there are particular forms that may be the primary contributor to low MLU. Timmy's use of personal pronouns was less diverse that the database comparison set (-1.37 SDs) for this task. No other forms were significantly low when compared to the database comparison set. Timmy produced more plural and possessive bound morphemes than his age-matched peers retelling the same story.

The low MLU can be validated by looking at the *Number of Utterances by Utterance Length* distribution table. His utterances primarily clustered in length between three and eight words. This seems reasonable since his MLU in words was 5.79 (see Figure 10-14).

Database Menu: Subordination Index (Figure 10-17)
The Subordination Index (SI) was applied to Timmy's sample. The SI is a fast measure of complex syntax, computed by dividing the total number of clauses by total number of C-units (see Appendix N). Timmy yielded a composite score of 1.05 which is within normal limits compared to the database mean. This means that most of his utterances contained one clause.

SUBORDINATION INDEX							
Calculations Based on C&I Verbal Utts, Transcripts Cut at 139 Number Total Words (66 samples)							
LANGUAGE MEASURE	Child		DATABASE				
	Score	+/-SD	Mean	Min	Max	SD	%SD
[SI-0]	0	-0.47	0.21	0	2	0.45	211%
[SI-1]	21*	1.00	17.14	8	26	3.88	23%
[SI-2]	1	-0.75	2.26	0	7	1.69	75%
[SI-3]	0	-0.39	0.14	0	1	0.35	254%
SI Composite Score	1.05	-0.74	1.13	0.94	1.47	0.11	10%

*At least 1 SD (** 2 SD) from the database mean*
Database selection criteria: age +/- 6 months (5;2 - 6;2)

Figure 10-17

Analyze Menu: Omissions and Error Codes (Figure 10-18)

The *Omissions and Error Codes* report lists all of the omissions and error codes marked in the transcript. In this transcript, there were two omitted words and three word-level errors. According to the *Standard Measures Report* (Figure 10-14), omissions and errors are within normal limits when compared to peers. However, they should be looked at in case there are patterns of errors that could be identified. Notice that all three error codes marked problems with verbs, including two instances of over-generalized past tense verbs.

OMISSIONS AND ERROR CODES Total Utterances 1st Speaker		
	Child	
	Total	Expanded
Omitted Words	2	
*BRANCHES		1
*WERE		1
36 C And they *were look/ing over tree branch/s [SI-1].		
37 C But they were/n't *branches [SI-1].		
Word-level Error Codes	3	
LIKEDED|LIKE/ED[EO:LIKED]		1
ROLLEDED|ROLL/ED[EO:ROLLED]		1
WERE[EW:WAS]		1
14 C {C sighs} Well the boy likeded|like/ed[EO:liked] the frog [SI-1].		
26 C And he rolleded|roll/ed[EO:rolled] [SI-1].		
48 C And then there were[EW:was] one still down there [SI-1].		

Figure 10-18

INTERPRETATION

Performance Profile

Timmy's language production is characterized by low MLU. His sample was far shorter than those of his age-matched peers and his narrative organization and structure scores revealed his story was less mature and effective. This fits the profile of delayed language which is often associated with low MLU and shorter samples.

Challenges

Timmy produced a short narrative with short utterances. His vocabulary use, albeit not significantly lower than his peers, did lack some diversity. Timmy simply did not talk very much. His short sample contained several errors and he had difficulty with the narrative task. It would be beneficial to elicit another sample, possibly a conversation, to determine if MLU and vocabulary diversity increase.

Strengths

Timmy's sample contained very few mazes and the number of errors produced were not significant compared with his database peers.

Clinical Impressions

Overall, Timmy's sample reveals a reticent talker, possibly because he has not been a successful communicator. His limited verbal output may account for his low scores for syntax and limited ability with narrative structure. He is a fluent speaker with slightly limited lexical diversity, using mostly simple syntax.

Ideas for Intervention

- Set up language-facilitating games to encourage more verbal output
- Provide vocabulary enrichment related to curriculum phrases with increased length and mature forms
- Practice story retell using the NSS scoring categories to teach story structure

---

Case Study 4: ALEX

SALT Transcript: Alex 16;7 Con.slt[10]

BACKGROUND

Alex is a 16;7 year old high school sophomore who has received special education services since age seven for speech and language. In addition, he currently receives support services for math and language arts. His productive language skills are being assessed as part of his three-year Individualized Education Plan (IEP) re-evaluation.

ASSESSMENT MEASURE

A conversational sample was collected as part of an assessment of Alex's spoken language skills. Alex was cooperative throughout the elicitation process. The results are considered to be an accurate representation of his oral language ability. The sample was transcribed using SALT software and SALT transcription conventions. There is no age-matched database comparison for Alex's conversational sample since the Conversational database contains samples from participants in the age range 2;9 to 13;3 (see Appendix B). Two options are available to help interpret the language sample measures. An informal option is to compare his sample to the oldest age group from the Conversation database. It seems reasonable to assume that a 16-year-old should have at least the skills of a 13-year-old. However, there may be unknown factors which come into play suggesting that this might not be a valid comparison. The other option is to use the Analyze menu which produces language measures for Alex and the examiner. For this case study we will use the second option and look at his measures independent of the database.

Criteria: Measures produced from the Analyze menu

---

[10] *Alex 16;7 Con* is one of the sample transcripts included with the software.

SALT ANALYSIS

STANDARD MEASURES REPORT		
	Child	**Examiner**
TRANSCRIPT LENGTH		
Total Utterances	70	38
# Analysis Set (C&I Verbal Utts)	65	35
All Words Including Mazes	672	133
Elapsed Time	(4:05)	4.08
INTELLIGIBILITY		
% Intelligible Utterances	98.6%	100%
% Intelligible Words	99.9%	100%
SYNTAX/MORPHOLOGY		
# MLU in Words	8.78	3.63
# MLU in Morphemes	9.58	3.83
# SI Composite Score	1.33	---
SEMANTICS		
# Number Total Words	571	127
# Number Different Words	217	73
# Type Token Ratio	0.38	0.57
# Moving-Average TTR (100)	0.64	0.64
DISCOURSE		
% Responses to Questions	66.7%	---
Mean Turn Length (words)	25.87	6.29
Utterances with Overlapping Speech	8	9
Interrupted Other Speaker	1	1
VERBAL FACILITY		
Words/Minute	164.57	32.57
# Maze Words as % of Total Words	13.1%	0.8%
Pauses Within Utterances	0	0
Pauses Between Utterances		1
Abandoned Utterances	3	0
ERRORS		
# % Utterances with Errors	7.7%	0.0%
Number of Omissions	0	0
Number of Error Codes	5	0

Calculations based on C&I Verbal Utts

Figure 10-19

Analyze Menu: Standard Measures Report (Figure 10-19)

- *Transcript Length*: Alex produced a total of 70 utterances; twice as many as the examiner in his four minute sample.
- *Intelligibility*: There were no significant issues with intelligibility.
- *Syntax/Morphology*: Alex's MLUm was 9.58, which is likely within normal limits considering the context of the sample (conversations) and his age. His SI Composite Score indicates that his utterances contained an average of 1.33 clauses.
- *Semantics*: His ratio of number of different words (NDW) to number of total words (NTW) indicates that his vocabulary diversity was adequate.
- *Discourse*: Max's turn length in words was 25.87 compared to the examiner's 6.29 words. Alex responded to just 67% of questions posed by the examiner. His speaking rate, measured in words per minute, appeared elevated at 164.57.
- *Errors*: There were five error codes in the sample; 7.7 percent of Alex's utterances contained one or more errors.

Additional information is provided in subsequent reports.

Analyze Menu: Standard Utterance Lists (Figure 10-20)

Alex's low response to questions prompts a closer look. Using SALT to display the examiner's questions along with the two subsequent entries is revealing. After examining these utterances more closely and listening to the audio, Alex's low rate of responses to questions was likely due to the examiner asking consecutive questions. Alex did not have the opportunity to respond before the next question was asked. His failure to respond to questions was pragmatically appropriate.

Analyze Menu: Maze Summary (Figure 10-21)

Thirteen percent of Alex's total words were contained in mazes, which is higher than expected (8% is typical for 13-year-olds) and interferes with getting his intended message across. His mazes averaged 2.10 words in length. The mazes consisted primarily of phrase-level revisions. Filled pauses, e.g., *er* and *um*, were also frequent throughout Alex's sample.

STANDARD UTTERANCE LISTS
Total Utterances
2nd Speaker

Questions

11 E Can you tell me anything else about the Badger/s?
12 C (Um) they're my favorite team.
13 E Mhm.

28 E Anything else you wanna tell me about sport/s?
29 E What get/3s you really excited?
30 C (Um) mostly (uh) it get/3s me excited when (uh) I hear that I can go somewhere.

31 E <Like> where?
32 C <Like i*>>
33 E Like <tell me>, <tell me>^

36 E <Have you> ever had to do that?
37 C Yes, I have.
38 C (I d* I d*) I had the chance (w*) this year, in January, to go when the Minnesota game was, with Ms_Fifer.

59 E So your favorite part was kind of see/ing what the coach was gonna say?
60 E What <Bo_Ryan> said to the player/s.
61 C <Yeah>.

Figure 10-20

MAZE SUMMARY				
	Child		**Examiner**	
	Analysis Set	**Total Utterances**	**Analysis Set**	**Total Utterances**
Total Verbal Utterances	65	70	35	36
Utterances with Mazes	29	31	1	1
Average Mazes per Utterance	0.63	0.61	0.03	0.03
Total Number of Mazes	41	43	1	1
Number Total Words	571	595	127	132
Total Maze Words	86	89	1	1
Maze Words as % of Total Words	13%	13%	1%	1%
Average Words per Maze	2.10	2.07	1.00	1.00
Revisions				
Part Word	2	2	0	0
Word	7	7	1	1
Phrase	12	12	0	0
Repetitions				
Part Word	2	4	0	0
Word	1	1	0	0
Phrase	3	3	0	0
Filled Pauses				
Single Word	23	24	0	0
Multiple Words	1	1	0	0

Figure 10-21

Analyze Menu: Utterance Code Table (Figure 10-22)

There were three utterance-level errors in Alex's language sample. These utterances are shown in the *Utterance Code Table* for further investigation. Alex switched tenses within the same utterance. This occurred when he attempted longer (more complex) utterances as in the first utterance shown in the table. This tendency to switch tenses makes utterances awkward and difficult to comprehend.

	UTTERANCE CODE TABLE Error Codes Only Table Expanded by Utterances		
		Child	Examiner
[EU]		3	0
	C And we were sit/ing down right where they are, near the Coach_Ryan and Coach_Gard before they/'re done play/ing the game [EU].		
	C And what I was amazed about is that (he talk/3s about) at the end I/'ve never heard what he say/3s [EU].		
	C He last/ed until the sixth inning to do that with (nothing nothing) score nothing nothing [EU].		

Figure 10-22

Analyze Menu: Subordination Index (Figure 10-23)

The Subordination Index (SI) was completed on Alex's sample. The SI measures clausal density and is computed by dividing the total number of clauses by total number of C-units (see Appendix N). Alex scored a 1.3, meaning most of his utterances consisted of one clause (40 utterances with a score of SI-1). Alex had nine utterances with two clauses and five utterances with three clauses.

SUBORDINATION INDEX		
	Child	Examiner
[SI-0]	1	0
[SI-1]	40	0
[SI-2]	9	0
[SI-3]	5	0
SI Score	1.33	---

Figure 10-23

Explore Menu: Utterances Coded as [SI-3] (Figure 10-24)

The Explore menu was used to pull up the five utterances which contained three clauses (coded as [SI-3]). Four of the five utterances contained direct quotes which increased the number of clauses without, necessarily, increasing sentence complexity.

Alex 16;7 Con
Word base: Exclude ((parenthetical remarks))
Analysis Set: C&I Verbal Utts

	Explore Words and Codes C&I Verbal Utts - Main body	
	Child	
[SI-3]	5	
30 C (Um) mostly (uh) it get/3s me excited when (uh) I hear that I can go somewhere [SI-3].		
54 C I thought he/'d just say, "Nice job" and, "(Go in the locker) go into your (uh) locker and get changed" [SI-3].		
103 C And then I was like, "Oh, I don't think I wanna watch this anymore" [SI-3].		
107 C When I call/ed her, she was like, "Stop watching it" [SI-3].		
110 C And I/'m like, "Yeah, I guess you/'re right" [SI-3].		
Total Frequency	5	
Isolated codes are word and utterance codes		

Figure 10-24

INTERPRETATION

Performance Profile
Alex's sample showed a fast speaking rate with low semantic content. This profile of language disorder features accelerated speaking rate (high WPM), high turn length, high MLU, and less complex sentence use. It is supported by Alex's elevated turn length which was more than four times longer than the examiner's turns. His messages were not always effectively completed as indicated by frequent rephrasing, circumlocutions, and filled pauses. He also had limited content given his high MLU and NDW, and less mature clausal structure.

Strengths
Alex used a variety of words in his language sample as seen by the high NDW. He was friendly and completed the task with enthusiasm. He also stayed on topic during the conversation, and responded appropriately to questions.

Challenges
Alex's speaking rate was fast which made his language hard to follow at times. Alex talked more than twice as much as his conversational partner. He tended

to be verbose and didn't often allow his speaking partner to "chime in." He tended to rush to complete his thoughts as evidenced by revised word selection and sentence structure as well as utterance-level errors. Combined, these characteristics made his language relatively difficult to understand. Alex's SI score indicated that he used mostly one-clause utterances, a simplified sentence structure. His utterance-level errors occurred when he attempted longer, more complex utterances.

Clinical Impressions

This conversational sample allowed for careful examination of Alex's speaking rate in relation to a speaking partner, his responsiveness to that partner, and his ability to express coherent utterances syntactically and semantically. The sample showed overall thought organization problems since Alex's mazes consisted mostly of phrase-level revisions and filled pauses. With repeated samples, his progress on intervention goals can be tracked. It might also be beneficial to elicit an expository sample to monitor his progress. An expository sample might better provide an opportunity to examine semantic content, syntax, and overall text organization.

Ideas for Intervention
- Organization: language-based planning activities using the expository template or the narrative scoring categories as targets
- Generate utterances using various subordinating conjunctions to create more complex sentences
- Guided speaking rate practice using a metronome or digital counter
- Practice slower speaking rate with known content like story retelling or expository tasks

> **Case Study 5: SAM**
> **Response to Intervention**

SALT Transcripts: Sam DDS Pre.slt & Sam DDS Post.slt[11]

This case study was contributed by Maureen Gonter, M.S., CCC-SLP and Jane Morgan, M.S. Speech and Language/AVID Resource Teacher from Madison Metropolitan School District.

BACKGROUND: RtI PROGRAM

This case study is an example of how to use language sample analysis as part of assessing a Response to Intervention (RtI)[12] program. This RtI study was completed with 6th grade students who were selected based on:

- lower scores on 5th grade Wisconsin Knowledge and Concept Examination (WKCE), a state standardized test
- 6th grade Scholastic Reading Inventory score (fall semester)
- teacher recommendations based on moderate difficulty meeting 6th grade standards across academic areas
- outcomes of Assessment of Classroom Communication and Study Skills, a 6th grade whole class screener

Students in the RtI program were involved in a literacy intervention group and were seen for 15 sessions over 10 weeks during the course of one school quarter. The students received Tier 2 literacy instruction focusing on four areas: reading, writing, listening, and speaking. The focus of the intervention was to teach the students specific strategies and then give them opportunities to practice and apply the strategies to classroom activities and tasks. For example, the students were given a strategy to use in the classroom to signal to the teacher if they were having difficulty with vocabulary (make a "v" with two fingers) or understanding content/ideas (make a "w" for "what?" with three

---

[11] *Sam DDS Pre* and *Sam DDS Post* are sample transcripts included with the software.

[12] Response to Intervention is a variation of an old diagnostic method formerly known as Diagnostic Therapy (Miller, 1981) and later as Dynamic Assessment (Olswang, Bain, & Johnson, 1991).

fingers). In this case study we look at one specific student, Sam, and his response to intervention.

BACKGROUND

In the classroom, Sam struggles with staying focused and on task. He engages in off-task behaviors which distract others such as humming and singing. He particularly struggles with attention and focus during math. Teachers believe this is because math is a more challenging subject for him. If the task is more engaging, Sam is better able to focus. He sometimes does not attempt tasks if he feels he will not be successful. He tends to do better on tasks that allow him to be creative. His language sample scores seem to reflect his functioning in the classroom (as measured by the Assessment of Classroom Communication and Study Skills) better than the results of his standardized testing.

STANDARDIZED TEST INFORMATION

Peabody Picture Vocabulary Test-4th Edition (PPVT-4), Form A
Pre RtI Therapy Program:
- Standard Score: 104,
- Percentile: 61
- Age Equivalent: 13;5

Score on the on the PPVT-4 was within normal range. Sam used verbal mediation throughout this assessment. He would comment about word parts, rhymes, or other connections he could make as he tried to figure out the meaning of an unfamiliar word.

INFORMAL MEASURES

Assessment of Classroom Communication and Study Skills
- Reading Comprehension   1 of 4 points
- Following Directions   7 of 20 points
- Language Detective   2 of 5 points
- Vocabulary   8 of 10 points

- Total   18 of 39 points
- Percentage   46%   (> 70 % is considered passing)

Narrative Language Sample

Sam retold the story *Doctor De Soto* (Steig, 1982) using the book with the text covered as per the elicitation protocol (see Appendix D). A retell sample was collected at the beginning of the RtI program and then again after participating in the 8-10 week intervention.

The focus in this case study is on the differences seen between the pre and post intervention language samples. Using the Link menu in SALT, Sam's pre and post samples were linked for side-by-side analysis with the samples equated by the same number of total words (NTW = 530). Sam's linked samples were compared to age-matched peers retelling the same story selected from the Narrative Story Retell database (see Appendix D).

Selected database samples Pre-RtI:
    79 samples matched by age: 11;7 – 12;7
    34 samples matched by age and same number of total words (NTW)

Selected database samples Post-RtI:
    55 samples matched by age: 11;10 – 12;8
    27 samples matched by age and same number of total words (NTW)

SALT ANALYSIS

Database Menu: Standard Measures Report (Figure 10-25)
- The *Standard Measures Report* shows the results of the pre and post samples with the relevant standard scores for each of the standard measures.
- *Transcript Length*: In each story retell Sam used an adequate number of utterances and retold the narrative in average elapsed time.
- *Narrative Structure*: Sam's NSS Composite Score, which measures narrative structure and content, increased from 17 (1.79 SD below the database mean) to within normal limits at 26 (0.30 SD above the database mean).
- *Syntax/Morphology*: His mean length of utterance in morphemes (MLUm) was low in both retells. MLUm was 9.28 (1.13 SDs below the mean) on his first retell which but increased to 10.33 (0.73 SD below the database mean) on his second retell. His SI Composite Score, a measure of clausal density, was also low for both retells, but increased from 1.20 in the first retell to 1.42 in the second retell.

Sam DDS Pre & Sam DDS Post
Word base: Exclude ((parenthetical remarks))

| | PRE RTI
Sample Date: 1/11/2011
Current Age: 12;1, Grade: 6
Context: Narration (DDS)
Database: Narrative Story Retell
79/34 Database samples | POST RTI
Sample Date: 4/15/2011
Current Age: 12;4, Grade: 6
Context: Narration (DDS)
Database: Narrative Story Retell
55/27 Database samples |

STANDARD MEASURES REPORT

LANGUAGE MEASURE	Pre RtI		Post RtI	
	Score	+/-SD	Score	+/-SD
Current Age	(12;1) 12.08	0.11	(12;4) 12.33	0.37

Compared to 79/55 Samples Matched by Age (ENTIRE TRANSCRIPT)

TRANSCRIPT LENGTH				
Total Utterances	68	0.88	69	0.90
# C&I Verbal Utts	64	0.70	66	0.77
All Words Including Mazes	732	0.85	764	0.90
Elapsed Time (minutes)	(5:17) 5.28	-0.02	(6:39) 6.65	0.67
INTELLIGIBILITY				
% Intelligible Utterances	94.1% **	-2.42	100%	0.47
% Intelligible Words	99.4% **	-2.59	100%	0.47
NARRATIVE STRUCTURE				
NSS Composite Score	17 *	-1.79	26	0.30

Compared to 34/27 Samples Equated by Same Number of Total Words (CUT AT 530/530 NTW)

SYNTAX/MORPHOLOGY				
# MLU in Words	8.28 *	-1.25	8.93 *	-1.02
# MLU in Morphemes	9.28 *	-1.13	10.33	-0.73
# SI Composite Score	1.20 *	-1.91	1.42	-0.74
SEMANTICS				
# Number Total Words (NTW)	530	0.00	530	0.00
# Number Different Words (NDW)	174	-0.60	188	0.24
# Type Token Ratio (TTR)	0.33	-0.60	0.35	0.24
# Moving-Average TTR (100)	0.59	-0.40	0.57	-0.77
VERBAL FACILITY				
Words/Minute	138.55	0.72	114.76	-0.48
# Maze Words as % of Total Words	17.2% *	1.99	22.1% **	3.12
Pauses Within Utterances	0	-0.55	12 **	5.58
Pauses Between Utterances	3	-0.68	7	0.02
Abandoned Utterances	0	-0.56	0	-0.64
ERRORS				
# % Utterances with Errors	9.4%	0.49	10.0%	0.59
Number of Omissions	4 *	1.58	0	-0.69
Number of Error Codes	3	0.22	6 *	1.92

 # Calculations based on C&I Verbal Utts
* At least 1 SD (** 2 SD) from the database mean
Pre RtI: Database selection criteria: age +/- 6 months (11;7 - 12;7)
Post RtI: Database selection criteria: age +/- 6 months (11;10 - 12;8)

Figure 10-25

- *Semantics*: Sam used a higher number of different words (NDW) on his second sample.
- *Verbal Facility*: Areas of challenge included high number of mazes and increased pause times. Sam's number and length of mazes increased in the second sample. We also note that his within-utterance pauses increased significantly on the second sample.
- *Errors*: Sam's first retell contained 4 omissions while there were no omissions in his second retell. Error codes, however, increased from 3 in his first retell to 6 in his second retell.

Additional information is provided in subsequent reports.

Database Menu: Narrative Scoring Scheme (Figure 10-26)

Sam's sample was scored using the Narrative Scoring Scheme (NSS, see Appendix P) specific to the story *Doctor De Soto*. The NSS is a tool to assess the structure and content of a narrative. The narrative is scored on seven features of a narrative such as introduction, character development, mental states, and referencing, for a total of 35 possible points. Sam's composite score on the NSS was 17 (1.79 standard deviations *below* the mean) on the first assessment and increased to 26 (0.30 standard deviations *above* the mean) on the post-therapy assessment.

NARRATIVE SCORING SCHEME Compared to 79/55 Samples Matched by Age					
NSS Category	Pre RtI			Post RtI	
	Score	+/-SD		Score	+/-SD
Introduction	2 *	-1.90		4	0.45
Character Development	2 **	-2.10		3	-0.73
Mental States	2 *	-1.69		3	-0.48
Referencing	2 **	-2.15		3	-0.67
Conflict Resolution	3	-0.76		4	0.58
Cohesion	2 **	-2.01		4	0.66
Conclusion	4	0.43		.5 *	1.63
NSS Composite Score	17 *	-1.79		26	0.30

*At least 1 SD (** 2 SD) from the database mean*
Pre RtI: Database selection criteria: age +/- 6 months (11;7 - 12;7)
Post RtI: Database selection criteria: age +/- 6 months (11;10 - 12;8)

Figure 10-26

Database Menu: Subordination Index (Figure 10-27)

The Subordination Index (SI, see Appendix N) measures clausal density and is computed by dividing the total number of clauses by total number of C-units. The SI was calculated and compared to the database of peers for both pre and post intervention assessment. The pre-treatment score was 1.20 (1.91 standard deviations below the mean) and the post-treatment score was 1.42 (0.74 standard deviations below the mean) indicating that Sam used utterances with more clauses, i.e., increased syntactic complexity, in the post-intervention sample. He had more scores of [SI-2] and [SI-3] in the second sample. His scores showed a decrease in utterances marked as [SI-0].

SUBORDINATION INDEX Calculations Based on C&I Verbal Utts, Transcripts Cut at 530/530 Number Total Words (34/27 samples)				
LANGUAGE MEASURE	**Pre RtI**		**Post RtI**	
	Score	+/-SD	Score	+/-SD
[SI-0]	3 **	3.76	0	-0.32
[SI-1]	46 *	1.63	39	0.99
[SI-2]	14	-0.19	17	0.57
[SI-3]	1 *	-1.50	4	-0.15
[SI-4]	0	-0.86	0	-0.74
[SI-5]	0	-0.50	0	-0.58
SI Composite Score	1.20 *	-1.91	1.42	-0.74

*At least 1 SD (** 2 SD) from the database mean
Database selection criteria: age +/- 6 months (11;7 - 12;7)

Figure 10-27

Database Menu: Maze Summary (Figure 10-28)

The *Maze Summary* indicated that Sam used more mazes in his second sample than his first. His percent maze words to total words increased from 17.2% to 21.1%. His mazes were mostly phrase revisions which may indicate utterance formulation difficulty.

MAZE SUMMARY Calculations Based on C&I Verbal Utts, Transcripts Cut at 530/530 Number Total Words (34/27 samples)					
LANGUAGE MEASURE	Pre RtI			Post RtI	
	Score	+/-SD		Score	+/-SD
Total Verbal Utterances	64 *	1.31		60 *	1.01
Utterances with Mazes	28 *	1.11		34 **	2.08
Average Mazes per Utterance	0.72	0.00		0.82	0.00
Total Number of Mazes	46 *	1.92		49 **	2.22
Number Total Words	530	0.00		530	0.00
Total Maze Words	110 **	2.06		150 **	3.45
% Maze Words/Total Words	17.2% *	1.99		22.1% **	3.12
Average Words per Maze	2.39 *	1.96		3.06 **	3.19
Revisions					
Part Word	5	0.75		7 *	1.67
Word	7	0.74		6	0.44
Phrase	23 **	2.27		29 **	3.16
Repetitions					
Part Word	0	-0.96		3	0.81
Word	2	-0.40		7 *	1.69
Phrase	2	0.05		5 **	2.00
Filled Pauses					
Single Word	15 *	1.14		19 *	1.76
Multiple Words	1 **	2.41		1 **	2.10

* At least 1 SD (** 2 SD) from the database mean

Figure 10-28

Analyze Menu: Rate and Pause Summary (Figure 10-29)

Sam used an abundance of pauses during his second story retell as compared to his first story retell. Most of his pauses occurred within mazes. Sam paused for a total of 8 seconds in the main body of his narrative and 23 seconds within mazes on his second story retell.

PAUSE SUMMARY Comparison Based on Same Number Total Words			
	No. of Pauses	Total Pause Time	Average Pause Time
Within PRE Utterances			
Main body	0	0:00	
Mazes	0	0:00	
Total	0	0:00	0:00
Between PRE Utterances			
Within Turn	3	0:11	
Preceding Turn	0	0:00	
Total	3	0:11	0:04
Within POST Utterances			
Main body	2	0:08	
Mazes	10	0:23	
Total	12	0:31	0:03
Between POST Utterances			
Within Turn	7	0:16	
Preceding Turn	0	0:00	
Total	7	0:16	0:02

Figure 10-29

Analyze Menu: Standard Utterance Lists → Utterances with Error Codes (Figure 10-30)

There were more word-level errors in the second sample than the first with an increase from three errors to six. The errors that Sam made seemed to be varied with no specific pattern. His language sample included errors in overgeneralization, word choice, conjunctions, and tense markers.

Utterances with Error Codes
Pre RtI
50	C Then he was say/ing (stuff like) delicious and stuff and (the fox I mean) the mouses[EO:mice] (knew what they were talk/ing) knew (he) what he was dream/ing about [SI-2].
64	C (The wife come/3s) the mouse come/3s[EW:Go/3s] into the mouth [SI-1].
65	C And the fox close/3s and saying[EW:says] "I/'m just kidding" [SI-2].
Post RtI
17	C And (he work/ed um) he work/ed with patient/s that are[EW:were] (a*) other animal/s [SI-2].
19	C And in this picture (he/'s stand/ing on) he use/3s a ladder on[EW:for] (um) tall animal/s or bigger animal/s [SI-1].
25	C (And s*) and he has (rubber um rubber um ((what are they called)) :03 these rubber) these[EW:this] rubber (glove thing/s) stuff that go/3s over his feet so he does/n't get his feet wet [SI-3].
28	C They look down[EW:out] the window [SI-1].
63	C Over here they/'re talk/ing about (how he) if[EW:whether] he might eat them [SI-2].
86	C And the fox[EW:mouse] climb/3s up into the fox/z mouth and start/3s painting all the teeth with the formula [SI-1].

Figure 10-30

Analyze Menu: Standard Utterance Lists → Utterances with Parenthetical Remarks (Figure 10-31)

Parenthetical remarks are comments that to do not contribute to the story. They are excluded from analysis and marked in ((double parentheses)). Sam used an abundance of parentheticals that mostly related to word retrieval or perhaps working memory difficulty. He specifically stated, "What's his name?", "I'm just going to say doctor", "I don't remember", and "I don't know." There were significantly less parenthetical remarks in the second sample than in the first sample.

Utterances with Parenthetical Remarks	
Pre RtI	
14	C (Um Dr_Sukodo) ((wait, what/'s his name)) < > (De_soto) Dr_De_Soto, (um he was being) he/'s just a really nice doctor in this page.
30	C And then the (dr_sudo*) ((I/'m just going to say doctor)) < > (um) doctor saw this fox he said he did/n't want to *treat.
40	C (He was wash/ing) ((I don/'t remember this page)) he was wash/ing his hand/s get/ing all ready.
44	C They saw that tooth ((I don't remember the name something with a v, I think)).
59	C And on this page they/'re just talk/ing about stuff ((I don't remember)).
74	C And (they/'re say/ing and he was think/ing) ((I think it was on this page)) he was thinking um sure he did/n't want any tooth pain/s anymore.
77	C And ((ugh I don/'t remember)) (she/'s) the fox (is just think/ing xx oh yeah he) was think/ing yeah, I/'m going to eat them.
86	C And (then the fox is I mean the doctor is say/ing um) ((x be on the page)) the doctor was say/ing "yeah you won't be able to open you mouth for one (to or) to two days".
89	C And (the two the two mouse doctor/s) ((I missed this one part)) (the two doc*) the two (doctor/s were) dentist/s (um) were happy.
Post RtI	
25	C (And s*) and he has (rubber um rubber um ((what are they called)) :03 these rubber) these[EW:this] rubber (glove thing/s) stuff that go/3s over his feet so he does/n't get his feet wet.
30	C ((I don't know what/'s go/ing on here)).
42	C (He/'s) ((I don't know)) he/'s wash/ing his hand/s.
47	C ((I think)).
62	C ((I think)).

Figure 10-31

INTERPRETATION

Performance Profile

Sam's oral language skills best fit with the word retrieval and utterance formulation profile. His language samples are characterized by increased mazes and frequent utterances where Sam stated he "can't remember" words. Additionally, Sam's samples were marked by pauses that occurred within utterances, usually within mazes, which indicates utterance formulation difficulty.

Strengths

Subsequent to the intervention phase, Sam's MLU in words increased as did his syntactic complexity and vocabulary diversity. He had a decrease in word omissions. He improved his Subordination Index score indicating that he used more complex utterances after completing the intervention. He also increased his narrative structure and content score demonstrating improved organization and content of his narrative. He also increased the structural components of his narrative in the areas of cohesion, introduction, and conclusion.

Challenges

Sam was responsive to intervention as seen by the many areas of improvement. However, he continues to demonstrate difficulty with organization, word retrieval, and utterance formulation. He also had significant amount of pausing. Difficulty in these areas was highlighted in his second narrative retell. As many of his syntactic and semantic features improved, he demonstrated increased difficulty with mazes and pauses. He used more complex syntax with richer vocabulary but with more difficulty.

Clinical Impressions

Sam's attempts at longer and more complex utterances support that he is generalizing his increase in MLU and NDW, the strategies learned, and the general language learning from the intervention program. As he attempted the longer and more complex utterances, his mazes, pauses, and utterance-level errors increased. These increases likely reflect the production challenges to Sam's language system and his struggle to put what was learned into practice. Sam's improved NSS and SI scores also support these impressions.

Sam would most likely not be a candidate for speech and language programming within a special education program since he was responsive to intervention and many of his language measures are now within functional limits. As Sam begins 7th grade the following suggestions might help him be more successful in his academic classes:

Ideas for Intervention
- Consult with parents at the start of the school year to provide word retrieval and language formulation strategies.
- Encourage Sam to take his time to formulate and organize thoughts before speaking.
- Consult with teachers to provide reminders and cues to use with Sam during classroom discussions and/or presentations.
- Suggest placement in a supported Social Studies classroom where large group vocabulary instruction and language activities occur once per month. Keep monthly data to monitor his progress.
- Provide Sam with a visual reminder of the RtI strategies to be kept in his planner.

| Case Study 6: MARÍA |
| Bilingual (Spanish/English) |

SALT Transcripts: María English FWAY.slt & María Spanish FWAY.slt[13]

BACKGROUND

María is 7 years and 3 months old. She is a native Spanish speaker who was placed in a transitional bilingual first grade classroom. Her classroom instruction is 20% Spanish and 80% English. Although Spanish is the only language spoken in her home, María attended a monolingual English daycare prior to starting school. She has an older sibling with speech and language needs who received services in the school. María was referred for a speech and language evaluation by her classroom teacher because of difficulty acquiring English. The clinician responsible for the evaluation is a native English speaker with minimal Spanish proficiency.

ASSESSMENT MEASURE IN ENGLISH

The clinician first elicited an English sample. María was seated next to the clinician who told the story *Frog, Where Are You?* (Mayer, 1969) in English following the provided script. They looked at the story together as it was told. The clinician then asked Maria to retell the same story in English. Her sample was transcribed and compared to age and grade-matched bilingual peers retelling the same story in English. Comparison samples were selected from the Bilingual English Story Retell reference database (see Appendix G).

Selected database samples:
    123 samples matched by age (7;1 – 7;5) and grade (1st)
    112 samples matched by age, grade, and same number of total words (NTW)

---

[13] *María English FWAY* and *María Spanish FWAY* are two of the sample transcripts included with the software.

SALT ANALYSIS OF ENGLISH SAMPLE

Maria FWAY English

TRANSCRIPT INFORMATION	DATABASE INFORMATION
Speaker: Maria (Child)	Database: Bilingual English Story Retell
Sample Date:	123 Samples Matched by Age & Grade
Current Age: 7;3, Grade: 1	112 Samples Cut at 118 Number Total Words
Context: Narration (FWAY)	Context: Narration (FWAY)

STANDARD MEASURES REPORT

LANGUAGE MEASURE	Child		DATABASE				
	Score	+/-SD	Mean	Min	Max	SD	%SD
Current Age (7;3)	7.25	0.10	7.24	7.08	7.42	0.11	2%
Compared to 123 Samples Matched by Age & Grade (ENTIRE TRANSCRIPT)							
TRANSCRIPT LENGTH							
Total Utterances	25 *	-1.43	40.03	11	67	10.52	26%
# C&I Verbal Utts	24 *	-1.09	36.23	4	67	11.24	31%
All Words Including Mazes	133 *	-1.68	299.20	81	631	98.80	33%
Elapsed Time (4:00)	4.00	-0.18	4.33	1.35	12.33	1.78	41%
INTELLIGIBILITY							
% Intelligible Utterances	100%	0.75	94.69	63.64	100.00	7.06	7%
% Intelligible Words	100%	0.56	99.15	87.06	100.00	1.51	2%
NARRATIVE STRUCTURE							
NSS Composite Score	8 **	-2.12	18.29	3	30	4.85	27%
Compared to 112 Samples Equated by Same Number of Total Words (CUT AT 118 NTW)							
SYNTAX/MORPHOLOGY							
# MLU in Words	4.92 *	-1.78	6.90	4.92	11.00	1.11	16%
# SI Composite Score	1.10	0.03	1.10	0.83	1.55	0.13	11%
SEMANTICS							
# Number Total Words (NTW)	118	0.00	118.00	118	118	0.00	0%
# Number Different Words (NDW)	40 *	-1.36	48.21	27	62	6.02	12%
# Type Token Ratio (TTR)	0.34 *	-1.36	0.41	0.23	0.53	0.05	12%
# Moving-Average TTR (100)	0.36 *	-1.35	0.43	0.21	0.54	0.05	13%
VERBAL FACILITY							
Words/Minute	33.25 *	-1.66	76.76	16.40	139.66	26.24	34%
# Maze Words as % of Total Words	13.2%	-0.18	14.58	0.00	38.86	7.38	51%
Pauses Within Utterances	11 *	1.40	3.26	0	36	5.52	169%
Pauses Between Utterances	11 *	1.01	5.46	0	36	5.46	100%
Abandoned Utterances	1	0.04	0.95	0	7	1.43	151%
ERRORS							
# % Utterances with Errors	41.7%	-0.17	45.36	0.00	86.67	21.53	47%
Number of Omissions	5	0.33	3.88	0	17	3.45	89%
Number of Error Codes	6	-0.11	6.42	0	17	3.99	62%

Calculations based on C&I Verbal Utts
* At least 1 SD (** 2 SD) from the database mean
Database selection criteria: age +/- 2 months (7;1 - 7;5), grade 1

Figure 10-32

Database Menu: Standard Measures Report (Figure 10-32)

- *Transcript Length*: María's sample length was 4.00 minutes. However, she produced fewer total utterances, fewer complete, intelligible, and verbal utterances, and fewer words (including maze words) than her age and grade-matched bilingual peers when telling the same story.
- *Narrative Structure*: The NSS composite Score, which measures the narrative structure and content, is more than 2 SD below her bilingual peers.
- *Syntax/Morphology*: Maria's MLU in words (MLUw) was 4.92, which is 1.78 standard deviations below the database mean.
- *Semantics*: She had a lower number of different words (NDW), a lower type-token ratio (TTR) and a lower Moving-Average TTR than the database samples.
- *Verbal Facility*: María's performance showed a reduced speaking rate as measured in words per minute (WPM) and an increase in pauses both within and between utterances. The numbers of mazes, errors and omissions were not significantly higher than her peers.

Comparing María's English sample to the reference databases, we can see there are several areas of concern (MLUw, NDW, WPM) relative to her age and grade-matched peers. Without testing in the native language, María would appear less language proficient than her peers, and possibly disordered.

ASSESSMENT MEASURE IN SPANISH

Because María's English proficiency was below age and grade-expected norms, it was necessary to elicit a language sample in Spanish. Approximately one week later, the clinician was able to obtain the services of an aide, fluent in Spanish, who elicited a Spanish sample from María. The elicitation process was essentially the same for Spanish as it was for English. María was seated next to the aide who told the story *Frog, Where Are You*? (Mayer, 1969) in Spanish using the script. The aide then asked María to retell the same story in Spanish. María's sample was transcribed and compared to age and grade-matched peers retelling the same story in Spanish. Comparison samples were selected from the Bilingual Spanish Story Retell reference database (see Appendix G).

Selected database samples:

117 samples matched by age (7;1 – 7;5) and grade (1st)

53 samples matched by age, grade, and same number of total words (NTW)

SALT ANALYSIS OF SPANISH SAMPLE

Maria FWAY Spanish

TRANSCRIPT INFORMATION	DATABASE INFORMATION
Speaker: María (Child)	Database: Bilingual Spanish Story Retell
Sample Date:	117 Samples Matched by Age & Grade
Current Age: 7;3, Grade: 1	53 Samples Cut at 243 Number Total Words
Context: Narration (FWAY)	Context: Narration (FWAY)

STANDARD MEASURES REPORT

LANGUAGE MEASURE	Child		DATABASE				
	Score	+/-SD	Mean	Min	Max	SD	%SD
Current Age (7;3)	7.25	0.10	7.24	7.08	7.42	0.11	2%
Compared to 117 Samples Matched by Age & Grade (ENTIRE TRANSCRIPT)							
TRANSCRIPT LENGTH							
Total Utterances	36	-0.20	38.33	5	66	11.39	30%
# C&I Verbal Utts	36	-0.04	36.47	2	66	11.12	30%
All Words Including Mazes	251	-0.24	274.87	22	512	97.62	36%
Elapsed Time (2:49)	2.82	-0.74	4.02	0.73	12.15	1.63	40%
INTELLIGIBILITY							
% Intelligible Utterances	100%	0.44	98.68	75.00	100.00	3.01	3%
% Intelligible Words	100%	0.44	99.80	96.72	100.00	0.44	0%
NARRATIVE STRUCTURE							
NSS Composite Score	17	-0.50	19.65	7	34	5.35	27%
Compared to 53 Samples Equated by Same Number of Total Words (CUT AT 243 NTW)							
SYNTAX/MORPHOLOGY							
# MLU in Words	6.75	0.06	6.71	5.30	8.03	0.60	9%
# SI Composite Score	1.29 *	1.05	1.18	1.03	1.50	0.10	9%
SEMANTICS							
# Number Total Words (NTW)	243	0.00	243.00	243	243	0.00	0%
# Number Different Words (NDW)	90 *	1.19	82.58	65	96	6.25	8%
# Type Token Ratio (TTR)	0.37 *	1.19	0.34	0.27	0.40	0.03	8%
# Moving-Average TTR (100)	0.50	0.80	0.47	0.36	0.53	0.03	7%
VERBAL FACILITY							
Words/Minute	89.11	0.58	77.37	32.74	124.86	20.13	26%
# Maze Words as % of Total Words	3.6% *	-1.32	12.22	0.41	27.46	6.54	53%
Pauses Within Utterances	0	-0.78	2.31	0	13	2.96	129%
Pauses Between Utterances	0 *	-1.09	5.39	0	17	4.92	91%
Abandoned Utterances	0	-0.72	1.06	0	7	1.47	139%
ERRORS							
# % Utterances with Errors	0.0%	-0.86	11.83	0.00	69.70	13.69	116%
Number of Omissions	0	-0.93	0.92	0	3	1.00	108%
Number of Error Codes	0	-0.62	4.36	0	39	6.99	160%

Calculations based on C&I Verbal Utts
* At least 1 SD (** 2 SD) from the database mean
Pause data based on a subset of 36 Database samples
Database selection criteria: age +/- 2 months (7;1 - 7;5), grade 1

Figure 10-33

Database Menu: Standard Measures Report (Figure 10-33)
All of María's language measures in Spanish were comparable to, and, in some areas, superior to her bilingual peers. Her MLU in words (MLUw) and speaking rate, measured in words per minute, were within normal limits. Her number of different words (NDW), TTR, and Moving Average TTR were higher than the database samples. Only 3.6% of Maria's utterances contained mazes and there were no errors or omissions in her Spanish retell.

COMPARISON OF ENGLISH AND SPANISH SAMPLES

Database Menu: Standard Measures Report (Figure 10-34)
For a comparison of María's English and Spanish performance, her English and Spanish retell samples were linked (Link menu) with the comparison based on the same number of total words (NTW = 118). The link feature is helpful when comparing two different samples as it provides the reports with the database standard deviation information in a side-by-side report. It also equates the two samples for more accurate comparison.

After the transcripts were linked, the *Database menu: Standard Measures Report* was generated. María produced 25 English utterances with 133 words in 4 minutes, and 36 Spanish utterances with 251 words in 2.82 minutes to retell the same story. Notice that her MLU in words (MLUw) in English was 4.92 and was 8.57 in Spanish. María's English vocabulary was not as diverse as her Spanish vocabulary (number of different words). Her speaking rate (words per minute) was much slower in English (33.25 vs. 89.63) due in part to the large number of pauses in her English retell. By adding the within and between pause time together, María paused for almost a minute and a half of the 4 minutes it took her to retell the story in English. There were also more mazes, omissions, and error codes in her English sample.

Maria FWAY English & Maria FWAY Spanish					
		ENGLISH Current Age: 7;3, Grade: 1 Context: Narration (FWAY) Database: Bilingual English Story Retell 123/112 Database samples		SPANISH Current Age: 7;3, Grade: 1 Context: Narration (FWAY) Database: Bilingual Spanish Story Retel 117/107 Database samples	
		STANDARD MEASURES REPORT			
LANGUAGE MEASURE		**English**		**Spanish**	
		Score	**+/-SD**	**Score**	**+/-SD**
Current Age		(7;3) 7.25	0.10	(7;3) 7.25	0.10
Compared to 123/117 Samples Matched by Age & Grade (ENTIRE TRANSCRIPT)					
TRANSCRIPT LENGTH					
Total Utterances		25 *	-1.43	36	-0.20
C&I Verbal Utts	#	24 *	-1.09	36	-0.04
All Words Including Mazes		133 *	-1.68	251	-0.24
Elapsed Time (minutes)		(4:00) 4.00	-0.18	(2:49) 2.82	-0.74
INTELLIGIBILITY					
% Intelligible Utterances		100%	0.75	100%	0.44
% Intelligible Words		100%	0.56	100%	0.44
NARRATIVE STRUCTURE					
NSS Composite Score		8 **	-2.12	17	-0.27
Compared to 112/107 Samples Equated by Same Number of Total Words (CUT AT 118/118 NTW)					
SYNTAX/MORPHOLOGY					
MLU in Words	#	4.92 *	-1.78	8.57 **	2.08
SI Composite Score	#	1.10	0.03	1.36 *	1.65
SEMANTICS					
Number Total Words (NTW)	#	118	0.00	118	0.00
Number Different Words (NDW)	#	40 *	-1.36	48	-0.47
Type Token Ratio (TTR)	#	0.34 *	-1.36	0.41	-0.47
Moving-Average TTR (100)	#	0.36 *	-1.35	0.44	-0.27
VERBAL FACILITY					
Words/Minute		33.25 *	-1.66	89.63	0.88
Maze Words as % of Total Words	#	13.2%	-0.18	3.3%	-0.91
Pauses Within Utterances		11 *	1.40	0	-0.64
Pauses Between Utterances		11 *	1.01	0 *	-1.07
Abandoned Utterances		1	0.04	0	-0.55
ERRORS					
% Utterances with Errors	#	41.7%	-0.17	0.0%	-0.80
Number of Omissions		5	0.33	0	-0.45
Number of Error Codes		6	-0.11	0	-0.63

Calculations based on C&I Verbal Utts
* At least 1 SD (** 2 SD) from the database mean
Spanish: Pause data based on a subset of 62 Database samples
Database selection criteria: age +/- 2 months (7;1 - 7;5), grade 1

Figure 10-34

Database Menu: Narrative Scoring Scheme (Figure 10-35)

María's samples were scored using the Narrative Scoring Scheme (NSS, see Appendix P), a tool to assess the structure and content of a narrative. The narrative is scored on seven features of storytelling such as introduction, character development, mental states, referencing, and cohesion. Each category can receive a score of up to five points (35 total points). SALT compared María's NSS scores to her bilingual peers. María's English NSS score (8 points out of 35) was 2.12 standard deviations below the database mean. Since her English story was limited by number of utterances, words, and by length of utterance, it is not unexpected that she scored lower on narrative form and content. Her Spanish composite NSS score was within normal limits at 17 points out of 35. She received a slightly lower score on *referencing* but all other individual category scores were within normal limits.

Maria FWAY English & Maria FWAY Spanish					
NARRATIVE SCORING SCHEME Compared to 123/117 Samples Matched by Age & Grade					
NSS Category	English			Spanish	
	Score	+/-SD		Score	+/-SD
Introduction	2	-0.80		3	0.30
Character Development	1*	-1.83		3	0.30
Mental States	1	-0.94		2	0.18
Referencing	2*	-1.45		2*	-1.45
Conflict Resolution	0**	-2.47		2	-0.51
Cohesion	0**	-2.78		2	-0.70
Conclusion	2	-0.57		3	0.41
NSS Composite Score	8**	-2.12		17	-0.27

*At least 1 SD (** 2 SD) from the database mean
Database selection criteria: age +/- 2 months (7;1 - 7;5), grade 1

Figure 10-35

Database Menu: Subordination Index (Figure 10-36)

The Subordination Index (SI, see Appendix O) is a measure of clausal density and is calculated by dividing the number of clauses by total number of utterances. After coding María's samples for SI, SALT was used to calculate the composite score and compare the results to the databases of bilingual peers. Figure 10-36 details this information with the samples linked. In her English sample María used mostly utterances with one clause. In her Spanish sample María used a greater variety with more utterances containing two clauses. Her Spanish Subordination Index score was actually above the database mean at 1.36.

SUBORDINATION INDEX					
Calculations Based on C&I Verbal Utts, Transcripts Cut at 118/118 Number Total Words (112/107 samples)					
LANGUAGE MEASURE	English			Spanish	
	Score	+/-SD		Score	+/-SD
[SI-0]	0	-0.48		0	-0.10
[SI-1]	18*	1.02		9*	-1.81
[SI-2]	2	0.23		5*	1.55
[SI-3]	0	-0.18		0	-0.41
[SI-4]	0	-0.09		0	0.00
SI Composite Score	1.10	0.03		1.36*	1.65

*At least 1 SD (** 2 SD) from the database mean*
Database selection criteria: age +/- 2 months (7;1 - 7;5), grade 1

Figure 10-36

INTERPRETATION

Performance Profile: English Language Learner
Since María has adequate Spanish skills, we can assume that she is not language impaired. Rather, María's primary difficulty is in second language acquisition. In order for a bilingual student to be considered language impaired, skills in both languages need to be below age-expected norms.

Strengths
María demonstrated good Spanish language skills with age-appropriate vocabulary, mean length of utterance, and speaking rate. Her Narrative Scoring Scheme score (measure of narrative content and form) was also within normal limits. María also used adequate syntactic complexity as her Subordination Index score was well with normal limits.

Challenges
Acquiring English as a second language is María's primary challenge. Measures of verbal fluency, words-per-minute, and increased pauses and pause time suggest that María is struggling to find English referents and sentence structure to adequately retell the story. These challenges reflect her limited knowledge of English. Examining the utterances with errors can be helpful when addressing

specific challenges. For example, María has difficulty with pronoun use (i.e., *his* for *your*). Specific English vocabulary and morphologic features of English are also challenging for her (i.e., "He's be a bird.")

CLINICAL NOTES

Role of Bilingual SLPs: As clinicians, our job in the assessment process is to ascertain whether a speaker is typically developing or language impaired. If María had been assessed first in Spanish, the decision-making process would have been completed. She is not language impaired. However, there are occasions in which it might also be advisable to follow up and test speakers like María in English. This additional testing will not modify our conclusions, but it might provide other team members critical information that would assist those who are in the process of acquiring English. If the referral specifically stated that, "María is not developing her English skills as well as her other bilingual peers," it might be beneficial to assess María's language in English in order to determine whether the teacher's concerns are warranted. English assessment would provide the teacher information on the child's strengths and weaknesses in English, and possibly afford the opportunity to collaborate with teachers in selecting appropriate materials and instructional strategies. Following this path is not necessary for our clinical decision-making process, but it will further enhance others' ability to assist speakers like María. *For more information, see ASHA's Technical Report on the role of SLPs in working with ESL instructors in school settings*[14].

PLAN/TREATMENT IDEAS
- Referral for ESL programming
- English language enrichment activities within the classroom

---

[14] http://www.asha.org/docs/html/TR1998-00145.html#sec1.3.2

Case Study 7: Malcolm
AAE Dialect Speaker

SALT Transcripts: Malcolm Nar SSS[15]

BACKGROUND

Malcolm is a 9;3 third grade student who was referred for a speech and language evaluation due to difficulty in the classroom with writing and speaking. Since Malcolm is African American and uses African American English (AAE) dialect, his teacher is wondering if his dialect is affecting his performance in school. His teacher also stated that it takes a lot of time for Malcolm to "get his message across." Writing skills are also an area of concern. Malcolm's parents and siblings speak AAE dialect at home. There is no family history of language disorder or learning disability. Malcolm uses AAE dialect at school and does not usually code switch into Standard American English (SAE) while at school.

ASSESSMENT MEASURE

A student selects story (SSS) narrative sample was collected. Malcolm retold the story of a Batman and Scooby-Doo cartoon he recently watched. The examiner used AAE dialect during the elicitation. To help determine language difference or disorder, the transcript was coded for *morphosyntactic* AAE dialect features (Craig & Washington, 2004) discussed in Chapter 8. The *phonological* AAE features were not coded in this sample. Malcolm's sample was compared to samples selected from the Narrative SSS database (see Appendix C).

Selected database samples:
  30 samples matched by age: 8;9 – 9;5
  21 samples matched by age and same number of total words (NTW)

---

[15] *Malcolm Nar SSS* is one of the sample transcripts included with the software.

SALT ANALYSIS

Malcolm Nar SSS							
TRANSCRIPT INFORMATION Speaker: Child Sample Date: Current Age: 9:3 Context: Narration (SSS)				**DATABASE INFORMATION** Database: Narrative SSS 30 Samples Matched by Age 21 Samples Cut at 287 Number Total Words Context: Narration			

STANDARD MEASURES REPORT

LANGUAGE MEASURE	Child		DATABASE				
	Score	**+/-SD**	**Mean**	**Min**	**Max**	**SD**	**%SD**
Current Age (9:3)	9.25 *	1.09	9.06	8.75	9.42	0.18	2%
Compared to 30 Samples Matched by Age (ENTIRE TRANSCRIPT)							
TRANSCRIPT LENGTH							
Total Utterances	45	-0.24	51.37	10	106	26.35	51%
# C&I Verbal Utts	43	-0.22	48.40	10	101	24.87	51%
All Words Including Mazes	412	0.03	406.60	101	870	206.14	51%
Elapsed Time (3:35)	3.58	0.39	2.99	0.70	7.07	1.52	51%
INTELLIGIBILITY							
% Intelligible Utterances	100%	0.43	99.07	89.58	100.00	2.15	2%
% Intelligible Words	100%	0.46	99.83	98.66	100.00	0.37	0%
Compared to 21 Samples Equated by Same Number of Total Words (CUT AT 287 NTW)							
SYNTAX/MORPHOLOGY							
# MLU in Words	7.25	-0.12	7.38	5.49	10.54	1.12	15%
# MLU in Morphemes	7.70	-0.35	8.13	5.98	11.36	1.22	15%
SEMANTICS							
# Number Total Words (NTW)	287	0.00	287.00	287	287	0.00	0%
# Number Different Words (NDW)	100	0.11	98.33	70	123	14.83	15%
# Type Token Ratio (TTR)	0.35	0.11	0.34	0.24	0.43	0.05	15%
# Moving-Average TTR (100)	0.51	0.04	0.50	0.39	0.60	0.06	11%
VERBAL FACILITY							
Words/Minute	114.41	-0.91	142.41	91.74	208.64	30.70	22%
# Maze Words as % of Total Words	27.2% **	3.86	9.90	2.05	17.77	4.47	45%
Pauses Within Utterances	1	-0.12	1.19	0	5	1.60	134%
Pauses Between Utterances	0	-0.37	0.81	0	9	2.20	272%
Abandoned Utterances	2	0.18	1.67	0	7	1.88	113%
ERRORS							
# % Utterances with Errors	5.0%	-0.35	7.35	0.00	21.43	6.76	92%
Number of Omissions	0	-0.56	1.19	0	9	2.14	179%
Number of Error Codes	2	-0.11	2.24	0	7	2.14	96%

 # Calculations based on C&I Verbal Utts
* At least 1 SD (** 2 SD) from the database mean
Database selection criteria: age +/- 6 months (8;9 - 9;5)

Figure 10-37

Database Menu: Standard Measures Report (Figure 10-37)

The *Standard Measures Report* reveals that most of Malcolm's language measures are in the average range (just slightly below the database mean). Malcolm is slightly older at 9.25 years of age than the database mean of 9.06 years of age. Malcolm told the narrative in the approximately the same amount of time as the database age-matched peers. His vocabulary appeared within normal limits with an age-appropriate mean length of utterance, number of different words, type token ratio, and rate of speech. Malcom did produce a high number of mazes. 27.2% of his total words were in mazes (repetitions, revisions, filled pauses). This score is 3.86 standard deviations above the database mean. Due to the high percentage of mazing, further investigation is warranted.

Additional information is provided in subsequent reports.

Database Menu: Maze Summary (Figure 10-38)

From the *Maze Summary* report, we can see that Malcolm used an abundance of part-word and phrase repetitions and revisions, indicating utterance formulation difficulty. He also had many single-word filled pauses, e.g., *uh*, *um*. Malcolm might be using filled pauses as a strategy to "buy more time" when formulating utterances. The maze distribution table shows that, as Malcolm is attempting longer utterances, he tends to have more difficulty with utterance formulation.

Malcolm Nar SSS

TRANSCRIPT INFORMATION	DATABASE INFORMATION
Speaker: Child	Database: Narrative SSS
Sample Date:	30 Samples Matched by Age
Current Age: 9;3	21 Samples Cut at 287 Number Total Words
Context: Narration (SSS)	Context: Narration

MAZE SUMMARY

Calculations Based on C&I Verbal Utts, Transcripts Cut at 287 Number Total Words (21 samples)

LANGUAGE MEASURE	Child		DATABASE				
	Score	+/-SD	Mean	Min	Max	SD	%SD
Total Verbal Utterances	40	-0.04	40.24	28	53	5.60	14%
Utterances with Mazes	22 *	1.62	13.29	3	22	5.40	41%
Average Mazes per Utterance	0.90	0.00	0.00	0.00	0.00	0.00	0%
Total Number of Mazes	36 **	2.47	16.81	3	32	7.78	46%
Number Total Words	287	0.00	287.00	287	287	0.00	0%
Total Maze Words	107 **	4.66	32.29	6	62	16.04	50%
% Maze Words/Total Words	27.2% **	3.86	9.90	2.05	17.77	4.47	45%
Average Words per Maze	2.97 **	2.58	1.43	1.00	3.00	0.60	42%
Revisions							
Part Word	3 *	1.45	1.00	0	5	1.38	138%
Word	1 *	-1.17	3.81	0	9	2.40	63%
Phrase	8 *	1.37	4.71	1	10	2.39	51%
Repetitions							
Part Word	7 **	4.25	1.38	0	4	1.32	96%
Word	10 *	1.89	3.38	0	15	3.50	104%
Phrase	12 **	5.01	1.43	0	8	2.11	148%
Filled Pauses							
Single Word	29 **	4.68	5.05	0	19	5.12	101%
Multiple Words	1 **	2.39	0.14	0	1	0.36	251%

*At least 1 SD (** 2 SD) from the database mean*

MAZE DISTRIBUTION TABLES

% of Utterances with Mazes by Utterance Length in Morphemes

	1	2	3	4	5	6	7	8	9	10	11	12	13	14	15+	Total
Child	0%	0%	0%	40%	0%	57%	0%	75%	100%	0%	0%	0%	0%	100%	100%	55%
DB Mean	5%	5%	11%	10%	18%	20%	38%	42%	31%	40%	29%	36%	51%	26%	52%	33%

Figure 10-38

Explore Menu: Word and Code List (Figures 10-39 & 10-40)

Explore Words and Codes Total Utterances Main body	
	Child
[HAD]	13

11	C And (um these two) these two bully/s, they[PRO] had[HAD] came and (uh had) had[HAD] took their game and gone[EW:left].
17	C They had[HAD] drop/ed the game and ran.
19	C (And um) and then Batman had[HAD] gave them their game back.
28	C (And i*) and (a* um) the Joker and the Penguin, (they have they had ri* they had um) they[PRO] had[HAD] scare[ZPT] all the people out of (the um the um ou* it was) the building.
30	C And they had[HAD] take[ZPT] the money.
37	C (And then they had um) and then they had[HAD] put on some skeleton/s.
40	C And then (um) Fred and Daphne they[PRO] had[HAD] ran.
41	C And then (um um the the) the Penguin and the Joker (had fell in the door where um where) had[HAD] fell in the door where Batman and Robin was[SVA].
44	C (Uh) and then (um) the Joker had[HAD] took off the mask.
45	C (And then he t*) and then the (um) Joker had[HAD] try[ZPT] to climb up to the door to see if he could (uh) reach it.
61	C Robin (h* um he had he had saw um :02 he had saw um Ro* he had) he[PRO] had[HAD] saw the Penguin.
62	C So he had[HAD] chase/ed the Penguin.
[SVA]	6
8	C (Um) on the cartoon (this this this little) this little boy (um) and a child (um ha*) had a game they was[SVA] play/ing with.
10	C And they was[SVA] sit/ing on the porch.
16	C And (um th*) they was[SVA] frightened.
34	C Batman and Robin was[SVA] already down there.
41	C And then (um um the the) the Penguin and the Joker (had fell in the door where um where) had[HAD] fell in the door where Batman and Robin was[SVA].
69	C (But th*) but they was[SVA] go/ing then.

Figure 10-39

Since Malcolm's transcript was coded for AAE dialect features, the Explore menu was used to count these codes and pull up the utterances containing them. In Figure 10-39, you can see that Malcolm used preterite *had*, e.g., "you *had* got that one before" 13 times. This AAE dialect feature would not negatively impact language measures such as mean length of utterance (MLU) or number of different words (NDW). If used often, it would lengthen MLU.

Malcolm also used one of the most common AAE features, subject-verb agreement, e.g., "but they *was* going then".

Explore Words and Codes Total Utterances Main body		
	Child	
[ZPT]	3	
28 C (And i*) and (a* um) the Joker and the Penguin, (they have they had ri* they had um) they[PRO] had[HAD] scare[ZPT] all the people out of (the um the um ou* it was) the building.		
30 C And they had[HAD] take[ZPT] the money.		
45 C (And then he t*) and then the (um) Joker had[HAD] try[ZPT] to climb up to the door to see if he could (uh) reach it.		
[PRO]	6	
11 C And (um these two) these two bully/s, they[PRO] had[HAD] came and (uh had) had[HAD] took their game and gone[EW:left].		
28 C (And i*) and (a* um) the Joker and the Penguin, (they have they had ri* they had um) they[PRO] had[HAD] scare[ZPT] all the people out of (the um the um ou* it was) the building.		
40 C And then (um) Fred and Daphne they[PRO] had[HAD] ran.		
50 C (Scooby_Doo um) Scooby_Doo, he[PRO] was at the door.		
61 C Robin (h* um he had he had saw um :02 he had saw um Ro* he had) he[PRO] had[HAD] saw the Penguin.		
67 C And then (um) Fred, he[PRO] was go/ing.		

Figure 10-40

Figure 10-40 shows that Malcolm used zero past tense, e.g., "they had *scare* all the people", 3 times. He also used appositive pronoun forms, e.g., "Scooby Doo, *he* was at the door". These features of AAE dialect, if upheld to SAE, would likely be marked as errors. This, in turn, could make Malcolm appear as though he has language impairment. However, these language features represent a language difference, not disorder, and are not considered when determining presence of language impairment.

Analyze Menu: Omissions and Errors (Figure 10-41)
Malcolm had one word-level error and one utterance-level error. This is relatively low without a specific pattern of errors.

OMISSIONS AND ERROR CODES Total Utterances 1st Speaker			
	Child		
	Total	Expanded	
Word-level Error Codes	1		
GONE[EW:LEFT]		1	
11 C And (um these two) these two bully/s, they[PRO] had[HAD] came and (uh had) had[HAD] took their game and gone[EW:left].			
Utterance-level Error Codes	1		
[EU]		1	
21 C And then just a few minute/s before that, (it was um) it was the Joker there [EU].			

Figure 10-41

INTERPRETATION

Performance Profile: AAE Dialect Speaker
Malcolm's sample contained a high percentage of mazes with repetitions, revisions, and filled pauses which is indicative of potential utterance formulation or word retrieval difficulty. Malcolm used AAE dialect. He produced a total of 28 utterances which, if compared to SAE, would look like they contained errors. Malcolm had only one valid utterance-level error and one word-level error when dialect was accounted for.

Strengths
Malcolm is an outgoing and friendly student who completed the task with enthusiasm. He is proficient in AAE dialect. Malcolm demonstrated high intelligibility. His semantic skills, as indicated by his MLU, NDW, and TTR, are within normal limits.

Challenges
Malcolm struggles with utterance formulation (and possibly word retrieval). The high number of mazes indicates difficulty with finding the right word or syntactic frame to express his thoughts. This difficulty may involve Malcolm trying to use SAE without having a solid foundation. The high number of mazes, paired with his AAE dialect, may make Malcolm appear language disordered. However, there isn't compelling evidence from his language sample to support

that diagnosis. Further investigation is warranted to identify the source of his fluency difficulties. A story retell language sample would allow for an analysis of his overall mastery of the content as well as provide more insight into his specific word or utterance formulation difficulties. In regard to his teacher's concern with writing skills, this might be due in part to "writing how he talks" with a non-standard dialect.

Clinical Impressions

It is important to correctly identify the differences between a language disorder and AAE dialect use to avoid over or under diagnosing AAE dialect speakers as language disordered. For example, the most common features of AAE are deletion of auxiliary and copula forms of "to be" along with subject-verb agreement, which would be considered errors if held to strict SAE. Other features that could be construed as errors and negatively affect language measures include undifferentiated pronoun case, multiple negation, and double modal. Some features of AAE may, in fact, increase measures such as MLU and NDW. Features such as preterite *had*, e.g., "you *had* got his toes stuck before", and completive *done*, e.g., "I think we *done* ate enough", are some examples where there are more words inserted in the utterance than if the speaker was using SAE. The take home message is that clinicians should carefully examine utterances from the language sample to determine dialect versus disorder. See Chapter 8 on African American English dialect for more information.

Ideas for Intervention
- Word retrieval tasks
- Utterance formulation work, with emphasis on increased syntactic complexity

AFTERWORD

So what's next?

Go out and collect a language sample, transcribe it, generate the analyses, and interpret the results. This book provided the fundamentals, focusing on the importance of using LSA to assess productive language. It covered the various elicitation contexts, emphasized the importance of accurate transcription, and described the reference databases available for comparison. A lot of attention was given to understanding the analysis options and interpreting the results. Little time, however, was spent on "how to"; how to elicit and record a language sample, how to play it back during the transcription phase, how to type it into the SALT editor, how to learn the transcription conventions, and how to generate the analyses.

So where can you go for help?

You have several options, depending on your style of learning. *Do you like to jump right in, only seeking help when you get stuck? Or do you prefer to complete all available training so you know as much as possible before starting?* No matter what your style, it's important for you to know about the resources available to you.

- <u>Appendices in the back of this book</u>. Find detailed descriptions of all the SALT reference databases including the protocols used for elicitation in Appendices A-L. Appendix M contains a convenient summary of the transcription conventions and Appendix N details the rules for segmenting utterances into C-units. Guidelines for applying the Subordination Index (SI), Narrative Scoring Scheme (NSS), Expository Scoring Scheme (ESS), and the Persuasion Scoring Scheme (PSS) are provided in Appendices O-R. Appendix S summarizes the analysis options and Appendix T links language measures produced by SALT to the Common Core State Standards.

- <u>SALT web site (www.saltsoftware.com)</u>. Select "Training & CEUs" for a variety of courses covering all the components of LSA using SALT. These courses are available for free. Listen to lectures, watch elicitation videos, learn and practice the transcription conventions, watch videos demonstrating how to use the software, and view case studies. Earn ASHA CEUs while you learn. SALT Software, LLC is an approved provider of ASHA CEUs and many of these courses can be taken for CEU credit. The material on the Web site is continually being improved and expanded so visit often.

- <u>Help built into the SALT software</u>. The context help, accessed by pressing the F1 function key, is particularly useful because the help it provides is specific to where you are in the software. If you are typing your sample into the SALT editor window, F1 brings up a list of all the transcription conventions with detailed explanations and examples. If you are viewing a report, F1 describes the variables included in that report. In addition, every dialogue box contains a help button and the Help menu lets you search for topics using keywords.

- <u>SALT User Guides</u>. Accessed from the SALT Help menu, these documents are in PDF format and provide detailed descriptions of all the transcription conventions, including those for Spanish and French. There are also a series of directed exercises to guide you through the mechanics of using the software.

So what are you waiting for?

One option is to go and record a language sample from anyone, child or adult, using one of the sampling protocols discussed in Chapter 2 and detailed in the appendices. Then open the SALT editor and begin transcribing the sample. This approach is for those who prefer to learn on the fly, by transcribing a sample. And this approach may work well because of the context help offered by the software. If you are typing an utterance containing a revision, for example, just press F1 and read about marking mazes. Soon you will remember that mazes are enclosed in parentheses. As you work through the transcript, you will master the frequently occurring conventions and know where to find help for the others.

An alternative learning method offers more support for learning the basics of the software. Go to the SALT web site and watch one or two elicitation videos.

Read about digital recorders. Familiarize yourself with the elicitation protocols and go out and record a language sample. Then go back to the SALT web site and work through the courses on transcription conventions. At the completion, you will be a trained transcriber. Or you may prefer to do the first two or three transcription lessons to learn the basics. Then transcribe your sample, accessing the context help built into the software and returning to the web site as needed. Refer to the SALT User Guides for directed exercises on using SALT to correct errors you may have made during transcription and to generate the reports. These lessons are designed to take you through all of the SALT features in a step-by-step format.

These learning options are available help you get the most out of SALT so you can incorporate language sample analysis into your practice as efficiently as possible.

GUIDE TO THE APPENDICES

SALT Reference Databases of English-fluent Speakers

Database	Context (Subgroup)	Age Range	Grade in School	# Samples	Location	Special Coding	Appendix
Play	Con (Play)	2;8 – 5;8	P, K	69	WI	SI	**A**
Conversation	Con	2;9 – 13;3	P, K, 1, 2, 3, 5, 7	584	WI & CA	SI	**B**
Narrative NSS	Nar (NSS)	5;2 – 13;3	K, 1, 2, 3, 5, 7	330	WI	SI	**C**
Narrative Story Retell	Nar (FWAY) Nar (PGHW) Nar (APNF) Nar (DDS)	4;4 – 7;5 7;0 – 8;11 7;11 – 9;11 9;3 – 12;8	P, K, 1 2 3 4, 5, 6	145 101 53 201	WI & CA	SI, NSS	**D**
Expository	Expo	10;7 – 18;9	5-7, 9-12	354	WI	SI, ESS	**E**
Persuasion	Pers	14;8 – 18;9 12;10 – 18;4	9-12 ----	113 66	WI Australia	SI, PSS	**F**

SALT Reference Databases of Bilingual (Spanish/English) Speakers

Database	Context (Subgroup)	Age Range	Grade in School	# Samples	Location	Special Coding	Appendix
Bilingual Spanish/English Story Retell	Nar (FWAY) Nar (FGTD) Nar (FOHO)	5;0 – 9;9 5;5 – 8;11 6;0 – 7;9	K, 1, 2, 3 K, 2 1	2,070 1,667 930	TX & CA	SI, NSS	**G**
Bilingual Spanish/English Unique Story	Nar (OFTM)	5;0 – 9;7	K, 1, 2, 3	475	TX & CA	SI, NSS	**H**

SALT Reference Databases Contributed by Colleagues

Database	Context (Subgroup)	Age Range	# Samples	Location	Appendix
Monolingual Spanish Story Retell	Nar (FWAY) Nar (FGTD) Nar (FOHO) Nar (OFTM)	5;10 – 9;11 6;4 – 10;6 6;1 – 10;1 6;9 – 10;7	366 360 188 154	Mexico	I
ENNI	Nar (ENNI)	3;11 – 10;0	377	Canada	J
Gillam Narrative Tasks	Nar (GNT)	5;0 – 11;11	500	USA	K
NZ-AU Conversation	Con	4;5 – 7;7 5;5 – 8;4	248 102	New Zealand Australia	L-1
NZ-AU Story Retell	Nar (AGL) Nar (AGL) Nar (BUS)	4;0 – 7;7 5;5 – 7;7 5;3 – 8;9	264 85 127	New Zealand Australia	L-2
NZ-AU Personal Narrative	Nar (NZPN)	4;5 – 7;7 5;5 – 8;4	228 127	New Zealand Australia	L-3
NZ-AU Expository	Expo	6;1 – 7;11 7;4 – 8;4	65 42	New Zealand Australia	L-4

Summary Guides

Topic	Appendix
Summary of SALT Transcription Conventions	M
C-Unit Segmentation Rules	N
Subordination Index (SI)	O
Narrative Scoring Scheme (NSS)	P
Expository Scoring Scheme (ESS)	Q
Persuasion Scoring Scheme (PSS)	R
Guide to the SALT Variables	S
Using SALT to Assess the Common Core	T

A

Play Database

Database	Context (Subgroup)	Age Range	Grade in School	# Samples	Location	Special Coding
Play	Con (Play)	2;8 – 5;8	P, K	69	WI	SI

Participants

Typically developing children, ranging in age from 2;8 - 5;8, were drawn from preschools in Madison and kindergarten classrooms in the Madison Metropolitan Public School District. These children, whose primary language is English, came from a variety of economic backgrounds and ability levels. "Typically developing" was determined by normal progress in school and absence of special education services. Economic background was determined by eligibility for the free lunch program. Ability level was determined by teacher rating. Age, gender, and grade data is available for all children.

Elicitation Protocol

Materials
- audio or video recorder
- Play dough, small toys, blocks etc.
- quiet location free of distractions with a table and two chairs

Preparation
Check the recorder for loudness levels. Record the date, student's name or ID, birth date, age, and grade.

Directions

Playing with play dough or small toys: Follow the child's suggestions, request directions etc. Comment on the child's activity.

"*I've bought some play dough for us to play with today. I wonder what we could make together.*"

"*Let's make ---. What do we need to do to make it*?"

"*Here are two cows. What should we do with them*?"

"*What other animals go in the barn*?"

Transcription Notes

Utterances were segmented into Communication Units (C-units) as defined in the SALT documentation. All transcripts were timed and pauses, within and between utterances, of two or more seconds in length, were marked.

Coding Notes

[EO:word] marks overgeneralization errors
[EW:word] marks other word-level errors
[EU] marks utterance-level errors

Subordination Index (SI) Coding

SI coding was applied to all samples. SI is a measure of syntactic complexity which produces a ratio of the total number of clauses (main and subordinate clauses) to the number of C-units. A clause, whether it is main or subordinate, is a statement containing both a subject and a predicate. Grammatically, a subject is a noun phrase and a predicate is a verb phrase. Main clauses can stand by themselves. Subordinate clauses depend on the main clause to make sense. They are embedded within an utterance as noun, adjective, or adverbial clauses (see Appendix O).

Acknowledgements

These samples are the result of a long-term collaboration with clinicians working in the Madison Metropolitan School District. All samples were transcribed and coded by the University of Wisconsin students working in the Language Analysis Lab. This project was funded in part by SALT Software, LLC.

Conversation Database

Database	Context (Subgroup)	Age Range	Grade in School	# Samples	Location	Special Coding
Conversation	Con	2;9 – 13;3	P, K, 1, 2, 3, 5, 7	584	WI & CA	SI

Participants

The Conversation database contains samples from typically developing English-fluent students located in Wisconsin and California. Age, gender, and grade data are available for all participants.

- *Wisconsin*: students, ranging in age from 2;9 -13;3, were drawn from preschools in Madison, the Madison Metropolitan Public School District, and rural areas in northern Wisconsin. The children were from a variety of economic backgrounds and ability levels. "Typically developing" was determined by normal progress in school and absence of special education services. Economic background was determined by eligibility for the free lunch program. Ability level was determined by teacher rating.

- *California*: students, ranging in age from 4;4 - 9;11, were drawn from two public school districts in San Diego County; San Diego City Schools and Cajon Valley School District. The students were described as typically developing and average performing in the classroom as determined by performance on standardized classroom assessments, teacher report, and absence of special education services. The participants reflected the county's demographics and were balanced by race, ethnicity, gender, and socioeconomic status. Socioeconomic status was determined by mother's highest level of education.

Elicitation Protocol

<u>Materials</u>
- audio or video recorder
- quiet location free of distractions with a table and two chairs

<u>Preparation</u>
Check the recorder for loudness levels. Record the date, student's name or ID, birth date, age, and grade.

<u>Directions</u>
Use one or more of the following conversational topics. Suggested questions and prompts are listed for each topic. Introduce at least one topic absent in time and space from the sampling condition, e.g. for holidays, *"What did you do?"* or *"What will you do?"*.

1. Classroom activities
   "Tell me about some of the things you've been doing in school lately."
   Ask about specific classroom units.

2. Holidays
   "Did you do anything special for Halloween (or appropriate holiday)?"
   "Tell me about that."
   "Are you going to do anything special for Christmas?"

3. Family activities, visits, locations, etc.
   "Are you going to visit your grandma and grandpa?"
   "Where do they live?" *"How do you get there?"* *"What do you do there?"*

4. Family pets
   "Do you have any pets at home?" *"Tell me about them."*
   "What do you have to do to take care of them?"
   "Do they ever get in trouble?"

Transcription Notes

Utterances were segmented into Communication Units (C-units). The transcripts begin and end with the student's first and last utterance, respectively. All transcripts were timed and pauses, within and between utterances, of two or more seconds in length, were marked.

Coding Notes

- [EO:word] marks overgeneralization errors
- [EW:word] marks other word-level errors
- [EU] marks utterance-level errors

Subordination Index (SI) Coding

SI coding was applied to all samples. SI is a measure of syntactic complexity which produces a ratio of the total number of clauses (main and subordinate clauses) to the number of C-units. A clause, whether it is main or subordinate, is a statement containing both a subject and a predicate. Grammatically, a subject is a noun phrase and a predicate is a verb phrase. Main clauses can stand by themselves. Subordinate clauses depend on the main clause to make sense. They are embedded within an utterance as noun, adjective or adverbial clauses (see Appendix O).

Acknowledgements

The *Wisconsin* samples are the result of a long-term collaboration with a group of speech-language pathologists working in the Madison Metropolitan School District (MMSD). We would like to express our appreciation to: Dee Boyd, Beth Daggett, Lynne Gabrielson, Laura Johnson, Mary Anne Jones, Marianne Kellman, Cathy Kennedy, Sue Knaack, Colleen Lodholtz, Kathleen Lyngaas, Karen Meissen, Chris Melgaard, Katherine Pierce, Laura Pinger, Lynn Preizler, Mary Beth Rolland, Lynda Lee Ruchti, Beth Swanson, Marianne Wood, Joan Zechman, and Rebecca Zutter-Brose for collecting the reference language samples and for sharing their clinical insights and experience in using SALT to evaluate the expressive language performance of school-age children. We would also like to acknowledge the MMSD SALT Leadership Committee for the help they provided with documenting guidelines for the elicitation and interpretation of language samples.

The *California* samples are the result of collaboration with two public school districts in San Diego County; San Diego City Schools and Cajon Valley Union Schools. We would like to thank Claudia Dunaway, from the San Diego City Schools, and Kelley Bates, from Cajon Valley, for their work on designing the protocol and organizing data collection. We would also like to thank the following San Diego City School SLPs: Cathy Lehr, Amy Maes, Roy Merrick, Peggy Schiavon, Dale Bushnell-Revell, Diana Mankowski, Jennifer Taps, Jean Janeke, Valerie Henderson, Mary Jane Zappia, Sharon Klahn, Linda Sunderland and the following Cajon Valley Union School SLPs: Marcelle Richardson, Victoria Wiley-Gire, Susan Carmody, Cathy Miller, Mary Baker, and Andrea Maher for collecting the language samples.

All samples were transcribed and coded by the University of Wisconsin students working in the Language Analysis Lab. This project was funded in part by SALT Software, LLC.

Narrative SSS Database

Database	Context (Subgroup)	Age Range	Grade in School	# Samples	Location	Special Coding
Narrative SSS	Nar (SSS)	5;2 – 13;3	K, 1, 2, 3, 5, 7	330	WI	SI

Participants

The Narrative SSS (student selects story) database consists of narrative samples from typically developing students drawn from preschools in Madison, the Madison Metropolitan Public School District, and rural areas in northern Wisconsin. Students were from a variety of economic backgrounds and ability levels. "Typically developing" was determined by normal progress in school and absence of special education services. Economic background was determined by eligibility for the free lunch program. Ability level was determined by teacher rating. Age and gender data is available for all students.

Elicitation Protocol

Materials
- audio or video recorder
- quiet location free of distractions with a table and two chairs

Preparation
Check the recorder for loudness levels. Record your name, date, student's name or ID, birth date, age, and grade.

<u>Directions</u>
Use one of the following narrative tasks. Suggested questions and prompts are listed for each task.

1. Tell about a movie s/he saw.
   "Do you go to the movies?", "Do you watch movies at home?", "Do you own any movies?", "What's your favorite movie?", "What's the last movie you saw?"

2. Tell about a book s/he read.
   "Have you read any good books lately?", "What's your favorite book?", "Have you read (insert current books likely to be of interest)*?"*

3. Retell an episode from a TV program.
   "What TV programs do you like to watch?", "Tell me about that one. I haven't seen it.", "What happened on the last one you watched?", "Do you ever watch (insert current programs likely to be of interest)*?"*

4. <u>With young children</u>: Retell a familiar story such as *Goldilocks and the Three Bears, Little Red Riding Hood,* and *The Three Little Pigs*. Picture prompts should only be used after every attempt is made to elicit spontaneous speech. This is not a labeling activity.
   "Do you know any stories?", "What is one of your favorite stories?", "Oh, I don't know that one very well. Will you tell it?", "Do you know Little Red Riding Hood, etc.? Oh, tell me about that one."

Examiner Prompts

Using overly-specific questions or providing too much information compromises the process of capturing the speaker's true language and ability level. Avoid asking questions which lead to obvious and limited responses/answers. Use open-ended prompts. Open-ended prompts *do not* provide the speaker with answers or vocabulary. They *do* encourage the speaker to try or they let the speaker know that it's ok to move on if needed. Use open-ended prompts/questions as necessary.

- **Acceptable verbal prompts include:**

  Tell me more.   *Just do your best.*
  Tell me about that/it.   *You're doing great.*
  I'd like to hear more about that/it.   *Tell me what you can.*
  That sounds interesting.   *Oh, that sounds interesting.*
  What else?   *Mhm.*
  Keep going.   *Uhhuh.*

- **Acceptable nonverbal prompts include:**

  Smiles and eye contact
  Nods of affirmation and agreement

Transcription Notes

The language samples were segmented into Communication Units (C-units). All transcripts were timed and pauses, within and between utterances, of two or more seconds in length, were marked.

Coding Notes

- [EO:word] marks overgeneralization errors
- [EW:word] marks other word-level errors
- [EU] marks utterance-level errors

Subordination Index (SI) Coding

SI coding was applied to all samples. SI is a measure of syntactic complexity which produces a ratio of the total number of clauses (main and subordinate clauses) to the number of C-units. A clause, whether it is main or subordinate, is a statement containing both a subject and a predicate. Grammatically, a subject is a noun phrase and a predicate is a verb phrase. Main clauses can stand by themselves. Subordinate clauses depend on the main clause to make sense. They are embedded within an utterance as noun, adjective or adverbial clauses (see Appendix O).

Acknowledgements

The Narrative SSS database is the result of a long-term collaboration with a group of speech-language pathologists working in the Madison Metropolitan School District (MMSD). We would like to express our appreciation to: Dee Boyd, Beth Daggett, Lynne Gabrielson, Laura Johnson, Mary Anne Jones, Marianne Kellman, Cathy Kennedy, Sue Knaack, Colleen Lodholtz, Kathleen Lyngaas, Karen Meissen, Chris Melgaard, Katherine Pierce, Laura Pinger, Lynn Preizler, Mary Beth Rolland, Lynda Lee Ruchti, Beth Swanson, Marianne Wood, Joan Zechman, and Rebecca Zutter-Brose for collecting the reference language samples and for sharing their clinical insights and experience in using SALT to evaluate the expressive language performance of school age children. We would also like to thank the MMSD SALT Leadership Committee for the help they provided with documenting guidelines for the elicitation and interpretation of language samples.

All samples were transcribed and coded by the University of Wisconsin students working in the Language Analysis Lab. This project was funded in part by SALT Software, LLC.

D

Narrative Story Retell Database

Database	Context (Subgroup)	Age Range	Grade in School	# Samples	Location	Special Coding
Narrative Story Retell	Nar (FWAY)	4;4 – 7;5	P, K, 1	145	WI & CA	SI, NSS
	Nar (PGHW)	7;0 – 8;11	2	101		
	Nar (APNF)	7;11 – 9;11	3	53		
	Nar (DDS)	9;3 – 12;8	4, 5, 6	201		

Participants

The Narrative Story Retell database contains samples from typically developing English-fluent students located in Wisconsin and California. Age, gender, and grade data are available for all participants.

- *Wisconsin* participants were drawn from the Madison Metropolitan Public School System and several Milwaukee area school districts (Brown Deer, Fox Point-Bayside, Shorewood, Waukesha, Wauwatosa, and West Allis-West Milwaukee). There are students from a variety of economic backgrounds and ability levels. "Typically developing" was determined by normal progress in school and absence of special education services. Economic background was based on eligibility in the free lunch program. Ability level was determined by teacher ratings.

- *California* participants were drawn from two public school districts in San Diego County; San Diego City Schools and Cajon Valley School District. The participants were described as typically developing and of average performance in the classroom as determined by performance on standardized classroom assessments, teacher report, and absence of special education services. The participants reflected the county's demographics and were balanced by race, ethnicity, gender, and socioeconomic status. Socioeconomic status was determined by mother's highest level of education.

Elicitation Protocol

1. Preschool, Kindergarten, and 1st Grade

There are three options for eliciting the samples. Use whichever option you prefer as they all elicit similar narratives. The database samples were elicited using the 3rd option.

- Materials
  - audio or video recorder
  - copy of the book *Frog, Where Are You?* (Mayer, 1969)
  - quiet location free of distractions with a table and two chairs

  Option 1:
  Use the FWAY script provided at the end of this appendix to tell the story to the child.

  Option 2:
  Play a recording of the FWAY story. You can record your own audio or download one from the SALT web site at www.saltsoftware.com/resources/frogstories/

  Option 3:
  Play the recording of *Frog, Where Are You?* which comes with The Strong Narrative Assessment Procedure (Strong, 1998). This audio uses a slightly different script.

- Preparation
  Check the recorder for loudness levels. Record your name, date, student's name or ID, birth date, age, and grade.

- Directions
  Seat the student next to you.

  Option 1:
  Say "*I would like to find out how you tell stories. First, I am going to tell you a story while we follow along in the book. When I have finished telling you the story, it will be your turn to tell the story using the same book.*" Tell (try not to read) the story to the student, loosely following the script (provided on the last page). You do not need to memorize the story script. Just become familiar enough with it to tell a similar story.

  Options 2 and 3:
  Say "*I would like to find out how you tell stories. First, we are going to listen to the story while we follow along in the book. When we have finished listening to the story, it will be your turn to tell the story using the same book.*" Play the audio. Turn each page while the student listens. Make sure the student is looking at the book.

  After telling the story or playing the audio, prepare the recorder to record the student's sample and say "*Now I would like you to use your own words to tell the story.*"

  Turn the book to the first page with pictures and start recording. Say "*Do the best that you can. Now you tell me the story.*"

2. **Grades 2nd, 3rd, 4th, 5th, and 6th**

   There are two options for eliciting the samples, both eliciting similar narratives. Use whichever option you prefer. Both options were used for eliciting the database samples.

   - Materials
     - audio or video recorder
     - quiet location free of distractions with a table and two chairs
     - 2 copies of the story book, one with the printed words covered
       - 2nd grade: *Pookins Gets Her Way* (Lester, 1987)

- 3rd grade: *A Porcupine Named Fluffy* (Lester, 1986)
- 4th, 5th, and 6th grade: *Doctor De Soto* (Steig, 1982)

- Preparation
  Check the recorder for loudness levels. Record your name, date, student's name or ID, birth date, age, and grade.

- Directions

  Option 1: Use the book that does not have the text covered while reading the story.

  Seat the student next to you, show the book to the student, and say *"I am helping your teacher find out how you tell stories. First, I will read this story to you while you follow along. Then I'm going to ask you to tell the story using your own words."*

  Read the story. Make sure the student is looking at the book.

  After reading the story, prepare the recorder to record the student's sample. Give the student the copy of the book which has the print covered and say *"Now I would like you to tell the story. Notice that the words are covered up. That's because I want you to use your own words to tell the story."*

  Turn to the first page with pictures and start recording. Say *"Do the best that you can. Now you tell me the story."*

  Option 2: Use both books while reading the story.

  Seat the student next to you, show the books to the student, and say *"I am helping your teacher find out how you tell stories. First, I will read this story to you while you follow along. Then I'm going to ask you to tell the story back to me using your own words."*

Give the book with the text covered to the student. Turn both books to the first page with pictures. Say, "*Notice that the words in your book are covered up. I want you to just look at the pictures and listen while I read you the story.*" Read the story. Both books are placed on the table while being read, so each person can see what page the other is on. If necessary, cue the student to turn the pages.

After reading the story say "*Now I would like you to use your own words to tell me the story.*"

Turn the student's book to the first page with pictures and start recording. Say "*Do the best that you can. Now you tell me the story.*"

3. **Examiner's role during the retell**

During the retell, move slightly away from the student turning so that eye contact is easy. The student should be in charge of page turning during the retell, but provide assistance if the student has trouble turning pages, or starts skipping too many pages. Moving away from the student promotes language and minimizes pointing.

Do not give specific cues to the student during the task. You can point to the book to focus attention or say "*Tell me more.*", "*Keep going.*", "*You are doing a great job.*", "*And then...*" if the student stops talking before the story is finished. You may also use nonverbal cues such as head nodding and smiling to promote continued talking. If the student is unable to start the task, use the prompt "*One day....*" Using overly-specific questions or providing too much information to the student compromises the process of capturing the student's true language and ability level. Open-ended prompts *do not* provide the student with answers or vocabulary. But they *do* encourage the student to try or they let the student know it is ok to move on if needed. Avoid asking the "wh" questions, who?, what?, when?, where? as these often lead to obvious and limited responses/answers.

Database Subgroups

When selecting language samples from this database, by default, the comparison is restricted to samples from the specific story listed in the transcript header. You can specify one of the following subgroups:

FWAY = *Frog, Where Are You?*
PGHW = *Pookins Gets Her Way*
APNF = *A Porcupine Named Fluffy*
DDS = *Doctor De Soto*

Transcription Notes

Utterances were segmented into Communication Units (C-units). The transcripts begin and end with the student's first and last utterance, respectively. All transcripts were timed and pauses, within and between utterances, of two or more seconds in length, were marked.

Coding Notes

- [EO:word] marks overgeneralization errors
- [EW:word] marks other word-level errors
- [EU] marks utterance-level errors

Subordination Index (SI) and Narrative Scoring Scheme (NSS) Coding

SI and NSS coding was applied to all samples.

SI is a measure of syntactic complexity which produces a ratio of the total number of clauses (main and subordinate clauses) to the number of C-units. A clause, whether it is main or subordinate, is a statement containing both a subject and a predicate. Grammatically, a subject is a noun phrase and a predicate is a verb phrase. Main clauses can stand by themselves. Subordinate clauses depend on the main clause to make sense. They are embedded within an utterance as noun, adjective or adverbial clauses (see Appendix O).

NSS is an assessment tool developed to create a more objective narrative structure scoring system. It is based upon early work on story grammar analysis by Stein and Glenn, 1979, 1982. This scoring procedure combines many of the abstract categories of Story Grammar, adding features of cohesion, connecting events, rationale for characters' behavior, and referencing. Each of the scoring categories has specific explicit examples to establish scoring criteria, reducing the abstractness of the story grammar categories (see Appendix P).

Acknowledgements

The Wisconsin samples are the result of collaboration with the Madison Metropolitan School District (MMSD) and several Milwaukee area school districts. We would like to acknowledge and thank the MMSD SALT Leadership Committee for sharing their clinical insights and experience, and for their help with selecting the story books and recruiting clinicians for data collection. The California samples are the result of collaboration with two public school districts in San Diego County; San Diego City Schools and Cajon Valley Union Schools. We would like to thank Claudia Dunaway, from the San Diego City Schools, and Kelley Bates, from Cajon Valley, for their work on designing the protocol and organizing data collection.

We would like to thank the following clinicians who collected the samples:

- Brown Deer School District: Thomas O. Malone
- Cajon Valley Union School: Mary Baker, Kelley Bates, Susan Carmody, Andrea Maher, Cathy Miller, Marcelle Richardson, Victoria Wiley-Gire
- Madison Metropolitan School District: Vicki Ashenbrenner, Dee Boyd, Kelly Chasco, Connie Daering, Beth Daggett, Lynne Gabrielson, Maureen Gonter, Tanya Jensen, Laura Johnson, Mary Anne Jones, Marianne Kellman, Cathy Kennedy, Ann Kleckner, Sue Knaack, Colleen Lodholtz, Kathleen Lyngaas, Karen Meissen, Chris Melgaard, Jane Morgan, Nicole Olson, Andrea O'Neill, Katherine Pierce, Laura Pinger, Lynn Preizler, Carolyn Putnam, Mary-Beth Rolland, Lynda Lee Ruchti, Beth Swanson, Jennifer Van Winkle, Emily Wolf, Meg Wollner, Marianne Wood, Joan Zechman, Rebecca Zutter-Brose
- San Diego City Schools: Dale Bushnell-Revell, Claudia Dunaway, Valerie Henderson, Jean Janeke, Sharon Klahn, Cathy Lehr, Amy Maes, Diana

Mankowski, Roy Merrick, Peggy Schiavon, Linda Sunderland, Jennifer Taps, Mary Jane Zappia

- <u>Shorewood School District</u>: Terry Hrycyna, Katie Koepsell
- <u>Waukesha School District</u>: Patricia Engebose Hovel, Susan Moennig, Lisa Haughney, Colleen Raupp, Christine Herro, Maureen Waterstraat
- <u>Wauwatosa School District</u>: Beth Bliss, Amy Brantley, Betsy Goldberg, Peg Hamby, Karen Malecki, Angela Quinn
- <u>West Allis-West Milwaukee School District</u>: Sarah Bartosch, Joy Behrend, Beth Beno, Ann-Guri E. Bishop, Lindsay Bliemeister, Pat Culbertson, Mary Fuchs, Nicole Gosser, Joyce King-McIver, Ellen Reitz, Jan Schmidt, Jill Vanderhoef, Michele Wolaver

All samples were transcribed and coded by the University of Wisconsin students working in the Language Analysis Lab. This project was funded in part by SALT Software, LLC.

Story Script for *Frog, Where Are You?* by Mercer Mayer, 1969.

Page	Script
1	There once was a boy who had a dog and a pet frog. He kept the frog in a large jar in his bedroom.
2	One night while he and his dog were sleeping, the frog climbed out of the jar. He jumped out of an open window.
3	When the boy and the dog woke up the next morning, they saw that the jar was empty.
4	The boy looked everywhere for the frog. The dog looked for the frog too. When the dog tried to look in the jar, he got his head stuck.
5	The boy called out the open window, "Frog, where are you?" The dog leaned out the window with the jar still stuck on his head.
6	The jar was so heavy that the dog fell out of the window headfirst!
7	The boy picked up the dog to make sure he was ok. The dog wasn't hurt but the jar was smashed.
8 - 9	The boy and the dog looked outside for the frog. The boy called for the frog.
10	He called down a hole in the ground while the dog barked at some bees in a beehive.
11	A gopher popped out of the hole and bit the boy on right on his nose. Meanwhile, the dog was still bothering the bees, jumping up on the tree and barking at them.
12	The beehive fell down and all of the bees flew out. The bees were angry at the dog for ruining their home.
13	The boy wasn't paying any attention to the dog. He had noticed a large hole in a tree. So he climbed up the tree and called down the hole.
14	All of a sudden an owl swooped out of the hole and knocked the boy to the ground.
15	The dog ran past the boy as fast as he could because the bees were chasing him.
16	The owl chased the boy all the way to a large rock.

17	The boy climbed up on the rock and called again for his frog. He held onto some branches so he wouldn't fall.
18	But the branches weren't really branches! They were deer antlers. The deer picked up the boy on his head.
19	The deer started running with the boy still on his head. The dog ran along too. They were getting close to a cliff.
20-21	The deer stopped suddenly and the boy and the dog fell over the edge of the cliff.
22	There was a pond below the cliff. They landed with a splash right on top of one another.
23	They heard a familiar sound.
24	The boy told the dog to be very quiet.
25	They crept up and looked behind a big log.
26	There they found the boy's pet frog. He had a mother frog with him.
27	They had some baby frogs and one of them jumped towards the boy.
28-29	The baby frog liked the boy and wanted to be his new pet. The boy and the dog were happy to have a new pet frog to take home. As they walked away the boy waved and said "goodbye" to his old frog and his family.

E

Expository Database

Database	Context	Age Range	Grade in School	# Samples	Location	Special Coding
Expository	Expo	10;7 – 18;9	5 – 7, 9 - 12	354	WI	SI, ESS

Introduction

The Expository database contains samples from middle and high school students, ages 10;7 through 18;9. Exposition was chosen for the following reasons:

- Exposition is central to the curriculum in middle and high school
- Exposition is included as part of state standards for speaking and writing
- Exposition challenges students to use language in context (authentic, naturalistic, real speaking and listening)
- Exposition allows documentation of oral expository skills relative to peers

Participants

354 typically developing students, ranging in age from 10;7 through 18;9, whose primary language is English.

The students were drawn from public schools in two geographic areas of Wisconsin: Milwaukee area school districts (Brown Deer, Fox Point-Bayside, Nicolet, Shorewood, Waukesha, Wauwatosa, and West Allis-West Milwaukee), and from the Madison Metropolitan School District. They were from a variety of economic backgrounds and ability levels. "Typically developing" was determined by normal progress in school and absence of special education services. Economic background was based on eligibility in the free lunch program (25%

qualified for free or reduced lunch). Ability level was determined by GPA scores and teacher reports (9% were low, 49% were average, and 42% were high). The race/ethnicity of the students was similar to that of the geographic area from which they were drawn (75% White, 13% African American, 7% Hispanic, 4% Asian, and 1% Hmong). Age, grade, and gender are provided for all samples.

Elicitation Protocol

Overview

The elicitation protocol is easy to administer and provides optimum opportunity for the student to produce a "good" expository. Following a script, the examiner asks the student to explain how to play a game or sport of the student's choosing. Discourage the student from talking about video games as they may be unfamiliar to the examiner and often result in limited content. The student is given a few minutes to complete a planning sheet which contains eight topics (Object, Preparations, Start, Course of play, Rules, Scoring, Duration, and Strategies). Listed next to each topic is a brief description of what's covered within that topic and space for making notes. Following the planning phase, the student is asked to explain the game or sport using his/her notes.

Using this protocol, expository samples tend to be between 5 – 6 minutes in length and have between 50 – 60 complete and intelligible utterances.

Script

I'm interested in finding out how well you do at giving explanations. I'm going to make a recording so I can remember what you say. If you want, you can listen to the recording when we're finished.

I want you to imagine that I am a student about your age. I'm visiting the United States from another country and I want to learn as much as I can about life in the U.S. You can help me by explaining how to play your favorite sport or game. You have lots of choices. For example, you could pick a sport, such as basketball or tennis. You could pick a board game, such as Monopoly or chess. Or you could pick a card game, such as Poker or Rummy. What sport or game do you want to pick?

The student offers an appropriate choice. If a choice is not offered or is inappropriate (such as a video game), reread the examples given above and/or add more examples to aid the student in making an appropriate choice. If the student is still having difficulty making a selection, suggest picking a game or sport recently played in the student's physical education class.

Assume that in my country we don't play [name of sport or game]. I'd like you to explain everything I would need to know to so I could learn to play. I'll expect you to talk for at least five minutes. To help you organize your thoughts, here's a list of topics I'd like you to talk about [hand the student a copy of the planning sheet found on the next page]. Please take the next few minutes to plan your explanation by taking notes in the blank spaces [indicate empty column on the right]. But don't waste time writing sentences. Just write some key words to remind you of what you want to say. You can talk about the topics in the order they are listed, or else you can number the topics any way you wish. If you don't want to take notes, you can use the backside of the list to draw a diagram or make a graphic organizer. Do you have any questions?

If student expresses difficulty with reading any portion of the checklist, read the unclear portions aloud. If the student has difficulty understanding the vocabulary, give an example from a sport or game different from the one the student has chosen.

Go ahead and start planning.

Allow enough time for student to write something for each topic on the checklist or to complete a diagram or graphic organizer. If the student stops writing or drawing before planning is finished, prompt with, "*Please do some planning for [topic name (s)].*"

I'm ready to turn on the recorder. You will be doing all the talking. I'm going to listen to what you have to say. Take as much time as you need to give a complete explanation. Remember: I expect you to talk for at least five minutes.

Turn on recording device and have the student begin speaking. After the student has finished speaking from his/her planning sheet, turn off recording device. If the student finishes speaking before five minutes has elapsed, prompt with, *"Is there anything else you can tell me?"*. Review the recording for quality before releasing the student.

Transcription Notes

The language samples were segmented into Communication Units. All transcripts were timed and pauses, within and between utterances, of two or more seconds in length, were marked.

Coding Notes
- [EO:word] marks overgeneralization errors
- [EW:word] marks other word-level errors
- [EW] marks extraneous words
- [EU] marks utterance-level errors

Subordination Index (SI) and Expository Scoring Scheme (ESS) Coding

SI and ESS coding was applied to all samples.

SI is a measure of syntactic complexity which produces a ratio of the total number of clauses (main and subordinate clauses) to the number of C-units. A clause, whether it is main or subordinate, is a statement containing both a subject and a predicate. Grammatically, a subject is a noun phrase and a predicate is a verb phrase. Main clauses can stand by themselves. Subordinate clauses depend on the main clause to make sense. They are embedded within an utterance as noun, adjective or adverbial clauses (see Appendix O).

ESS assesses the content and structure of an expository language sample, similar to how the Narrative Scoring Scheme (see Appendix P) provides an overall measure of a student's skill in producing a narrative. The ESS is comprised of 10 characteristics for completing an expository language sample. The first 8 characteristics correspond to the topics listed on the planning sheet that is given to students (see Appendix Q)

Analysis Notes

The SALT group transcribed the samples following the SALT format and performed a series of statistical analyses to describe the dataset for consistency, differences among types of expository samples, age-related changes, and differences when compared to existing conversation and narrative samples. (Malone, et al., 2008). The following summarize the results of these analyses:

- Different expository contexts (team sport, individual sport, game) do not result in significantly different outcomes. Students describing how to play a team sport provided similar samples in terms of length, vocabulary, sentence complexity as students describing an individual sport or game. This finding is very useful in that it allows students to select the type of game they know best, optimizing their performance on this task.

- Measures of language production were significantly different for expository samples than conversational and narrative samples on measures of utterance length and complexity. Students produced significantly more complex sentences in the expository samples than conversation or narratives. This finding is similar to the findings of Nippold, et al. (2005; 2008).

Acknowledgements

We gratefully acknowledge and thank Thomas O. Malone, a retired speech-language pathologist, formerly with the Brown Deer School District in Wisconsin, for being the driving force behind this project. His influence is everywhere including, but not limited to, a) recognizing the need for an expository database, b) designing the protocol used, c) recruiting clinicians from Milwaukee-area school districts, d) coding for types of subordination and applying the Expository Scoring Scheme, and e) presenting the results of the project (Malone, et al., 2008, Malone, et al., 2010).

We would like to thank the following clinicians who collected the expository samples:

- <u>Brown Deer School District</u>: Kari Anewenter, Thomas O. Malone, Katherine E. Smith
- <u>Fox Point-Bayside School District</u>: Jody Herbert
- <u>Madison Metropolitan School District</u>: Vicki Ashenbrenner, Kelly Chasco, Helen Chung, Ingrid Curcio, Alyson Eith, Sheryl Hall, Julie Hay-Chapman, Kelsey Beach Hausmann, Lynn Gabrielson, Maureen Gotner, Patty Hay-Chapman, Marie Hendrickson, Andrea Hermanson, Tanya Jensen, Laura Johnson, Abby Mahoney Kabara, Chris Melgaard, Jane Morgan, Andrea O'Neill, Nicole Olson, Nan Perschon, Carolyn Putnam, Carrie Rhode, Mary-Beth Rolland, Liz Schoonveld, Julie Scott-Moran, Jennifer Van Winkle, Helena White, Emily Wolf, Meg Wollner
- <u>Nicolet School District</u>: Karen Kingsbury
- <u>Shorewood School District</u>: Eva Gulotta, Terry Hrycyna, Katie Koepsell, Inga Siler
- <u>Waukesha School District</u>: Bill Downey, Linda Carver, Judy Ertel, Susan Fischer, Jeanne Gantenbein, Lisa Haughney, Christine Herro, Patricia Engebose Hovel, Susan Moennig, Colleen Raupp, Jennifer Theisen, Maureen Waterstraat
- <u>Wauwatosa School District</u>: Beth Bliss, Amy Brantley, Betsy Goldberg, Peg Hamby, Karen Malecki, Christine Maranan, Lynn Meehan, Kathy Meinecke, Angela Quinn, Molly Suberlak, Amanda Voigtlander
- <u>West Allis-West Milwaukee School District</u>: Sarah Bartosch, Joy Behrend, Beth Beno, Ann-Guri E. Bishop, Lindsay Bliemeister, Pat Culbertson, Mary Fuchs, Nicole Gosser, Erin Jodie, Joyce King-McIver, Ellen Reitz, Jan Schmidt, Jill Vanderhoef, Michele Wolaver.
- <u>UW-Milwaukee graduate students</u>: Taylor Hansen, Maggie Long, Maricel Schulte

Samples were transcribed and coded by the University of Wisconsin students working in the Language Analysis Lab and by the staff at SALT Software, LLC. This project was funded in part by SALT Software, LLC.

Expository Planning Sheet (*The actual form used can be downloaded from the SALT web site at www.saltsoftware.com/resources/*)

What to Talk About
When Explaining a Game or Sport

Topic	What's Covered	Notes
Object	What you have to do to win	
Preparations	Playing Area and Setup Equipment and Materials What players do to get ready	
Start	How the contest begins, including who goes first	
Course of Play	What happens during a team or player's turn, including any special plays, positions, or roles, both offensive and defensive	
Rules	Major rules, including penalties for violations	
Scoring	Different ways to score, including point values	
Duration	How long the contest lasts, including how it ends and tie breaking procedures	
Strategies	What smart players do to win, both offensively and defensively	

Please use the backside of this page for an optional diagram or graphic organizer, or for additional notes.

Persuasion Database

Database	Context	Age Range	Grade in School	# Samples	Location	Special Coding
Persuasion	Pers	USA: 14;8 – 18;9 AU: 12;10 – 18;4	USA: 9-12 AU: N/A	USA: 113 AU: 66	WI Australia	SI, PSS

Introduction

Persuasion can be defined as "the use of argumentation to convince another person to perform an act or accept the point of view desired by the persuader" (Nippold, 2007). Persuasion was chosen for the following reasons:

- It figures prominently in academic standards that cut across modes of communication: speaking, listening, reading, and writing (National Governors Association, 2010).
- Acquiring skill at persuasion is critical to success in college and career and to full participation in social and civic life.
- Persuasion challenges students to take into account their audience's perspective and to use complex language to express complex ideas.

USA Participants

Samples were elicited from typically developing students whose primary language is English. The students were drawn from public schools in two geographic areas of Wisconsin: Milwaukee area school districts, and Madison Metropolitan School District. Students were from a variety of economic backgrounds and ability levels. "Typically developing" was determined by normal progress in school and absence of special education services. Economic background was based on eligibility in the free lunch program (25% qualified for free or reduced lunch). Ability level was determined by GPA scores and teacher reports (4% were low, 25% were average, and 71% were high). The race/ethnicity of the students was similar to that of the geographic area from which they were drawn (63% White, 17% African American, 8% Hispanic, 7% Asian, and 2% Hmong, and 3% unknown). Age, grade, and gender are provided for all samples.

Australian Participants

The Australian dataset contains persuasive samples from typically developing students whose primary language is English. The students attended public schools across the state of Queensland, Australia. Schools were situated in country and metropolitan areas and students were from a range of economic backgrounds. "Typically developing" was determined by normal progress in school and absence of special education services. Economic background was based on the school's postcode and Socio-Economic Indexes for Areas (SEIFA, 2011) data. Student ability level was determined by the students' most recent performance in English (~15% obtained a C and 15% an A). The race/ethnicity of the students, as identified on the student consent form was predominantly 'Australian". Age and gender are provided for all samples. Grade in school data is not available.

Elicitation Protocol

Overview

The elicitation protocol is easy to administer and provides optimum opportunity for the student to produce a "good" persuasive argument. Following a script, the examiner asks the student to argue for a change in their school, workplace, or community. The argument is to be directed at the student's principal, boss, or government official. The student can choose an issue of personal interest or select from a list of suggested issues. The student is given a few minutes to complete a planning sheet which contains six topics (Issue Id and Desired Change, Supporting Reasons, Counter Arguments, Response to Counter Arguments, Compromises, and Conclusion). Next to each point is a brief description of what is covered within that topic and space for making notes. Following the planning phase, the student, speaking from his/her notes, is asked to persuade the examiner who stands in for the intended authority figure. The average length of the persuasion is approximately 4 minutes and contains around 33 complete and intelligible utterances.

SCRIPT
Today I want to find out how well you can persuade. That's when you talk people into changing their mind and doing something you want. I'm going to make a recording. If you want, you can listen to it when we're finished.

I would like you to pick a rule or situation you would like to see changed in your school, job, or community. Imagine that I am an adult who has the power to make the change that you want. Here are a few examples:
1. Pretend I'm the principal of your school and you want to persuade me to provide money for a special event;
OR
2. Pretend I'm your boss and you want to persuade me to change your hours or work schedule;
OR
3. Pretend I'm a government official and you want me to change the law so that taxes are raised or lowered for a specific purpose.

I expect you to talk for at least a few minutes, so be sure to pick an issue you know and care about. You can choose an issue from this list *[hand list to student]* **or else pick one of your own.**

Allow the student time to review the suggested issues before asking: **What issue have you picked?**

If the student has difficulty choosing an issue, offer assistance. Review the list together. If a proposed topic is not an arguable issue, e.g., strawberry ice cream is better than chocolate, encourage the student to pick a different issue. If a proposed issue is too narrow, encourage the student to modify it. For example, if the student wants to argue for a change to his or her individual grade in a particular class, suggest that the issue be broadened into an argument for a school-wide change to grading policy.

Once an appropriate issue has been selected, clarify the intended target of the persuasion, e.g., principal, boss, government official, by asking, **Who will you be trying to persuade?**

If there is a mismatch between the issue and the authority figure, help the student to resolve the problem. For example, if a student wishes to convince a boss to raise the minimum wage, help the student understand that this argument is best directed toward a government official.

Once a match has been established between issue and authority figure, proceed to the planning directions:

Talk to me as if I'm your [*name the appropriate authority, e.g., principal, boss, senator*] **and tell me everything you can to persuade me. To do your best job, you'll first need to organize your thoughts. Here's a list of points you'll need to cover to make a complete argument** [*hand the student a copy of the planning sheet*]. **Please take the next few minutes to plan by taking notes in these blank spaces** [*point to the empty boxes in the column on the right*]. **But don't waste time writing sentences. Just jot down some key words to remind you of what you want to say. If you don't want to take notes, you can use the reverse side to draw a diagram or make a graphic organizer. Do you have any questions? Go ahead and start planning.**

Skill at reading is not being assessed. Therefore, if the student appears to be having any difficulty understanding the planning sheet, read the text aloud to the student.

Allow enough time for the student to write something for each point on the planning sheet or to create a diagram or graphic organizer. Verify that the student has done some planning for each point. If not, prompt with, **Please do some planning for** [*name(s) of omitted point(s)*]**.**

When the student has finished planning, continue with: **When I turn on the recorder, you will be doing all the talking. I'm going to listen to what you have to say. Tell me everything you can think of. It's OK to look at your planning**

sheet to remind yourself of what you want to say. Feel free to add to what you've written. Remember: I expect you to talk for as long as you can.

Turn on the recording device and have the student begin speaking. Do not engage the student in a debate. Instead, limit your encouragement to affirmations such as: **Uhhuh, mhm, I see, OK, ah, etc.**

If the student finishes speaking before several minutes has elapsed or has not discussed one or more points on the planning sheet, prompt with: **Is there anything else you can tell me?**

When the student has finished speaking, turn off the recorder. Review the recording for quality before releasing the student. If there's time, offer to let the student listen to the recording.

Transcription Notes

The language samples were segmented into Communication Units (C-units). All transcripts were timed and pauses, within and between utterances, of two or more seconds in length, were marked.

Coding Notes
- [EO:word] marks overgeneralization errors
- [EW:word] marks other word-level errors
- [EW] marks extraneous words
- [EU] marks utterance-level errors

Subordination Index (SI) and Persuasion Scoring Scheme (PSS) Coding

SI and PSS coding was applied to all samples.

SI is a measure of syntactic complexity which produces a ratio of the total number of clauses (main and subordinate clauses) to the number of C-units. A clause, whether main or subordinate, is a statement containing both a subject and a predicate. Grammatically, a subject is a noun phrase and a predicate is a verb phrase. Main clauses can stand by themselves. Subordinate clauses depend on the main clause to make sense. They are embedded within an utterance as noun, adjective, pronominal, or adverbial clauses (see Appendix O).

The PSS assesses the structure and content of persuasive language, a critical language skill in secondary curriculum, using a scoring rubric consisting of the essential characteristics of a coherent persuasive argument. These characteristics include: 1) issue identification and desired change, 2) supporting reasons, 3) other point of view, 4) compromises, 5) conclusion, 6) cohesion, and 7) effectiveness. The first five characteristics roughly correspond to the topics from the student planning sheet (see Appendix R).

Each characteristic receives a scaled score 0-5 or NA (not applicable). The PSS scoring guide defines what is meant by Proficient/Advanced (score of 5), Satisfactory/Adequate (score of 3) and Minimal/Immature (score of 1). The scores in between, 2 and 4, are undefined, use judgment. Significant factual errors reduce the score for that topic. A score of 0 is given for student errors, e.g., not covering topic, not completing/refusing task, unintelligible productions, abandoned utterances. A score of NA (non-applicable) is given for mechanical/examiner/operator errors, e.g., interference from background noise, issues with recording (cut-offs, interruptions), examiner not following protocol, examiner asking overly specific or leading questions rather than open-ended questions or prompts.

A composite is scored by adding the total of the six characteristic scores. Maximum score = 30.

Analysis Notes

The SALT group transcribed the samples following the SALT format and performed a series of statistical analyses to describe the dataset for consistency, differences across samples from AU and USA, age-related and gender related changes, as well as topic related changes.

Acknowledgements

USA Samples: We gratefully acknowledge and thank Thomas O. Malone, a retired speech-language pathologist formerly with the Brown Deer School District, for being the driving force behind this project. His influence is everywhere including, but not limited to, designing the protocol used, recruiting clinicians from Milwaukee-area school districts, and presenting the results of the project (Heilmann, et al., 2015). We would also like to thank Dr. John Heilmann (United States) and Dr. Marleen Westerveld (Australia) for their work getting the research protocols in place and working with the school districts to obtain their approval and cooperation. We would like to thank the following clinicians and students who collected the Wisconsin persuasion samples:

- <u>Brown Deer School District</u>: Kari Anewenter
- <u>Madison Metropolitan School District</u>: Helen Chung, Alyson Eith, Sheryl Hall, Kelsey Beach Hausmann, Laura Johnson, Abby Mahoney Kabara, Chris Melgaard, Carrie Rhode, Mary-Beth Rolland, Liz Schoonveld, Helena White
- <u>Nicolet School District</u>: Karen Kingsbury
- <u>Shorewood School District</u>: Eva Gulotta, Katie Koepsell, and Inga Siler
- <u>Wauwatosa School District</u>: Amy Brantley, Peg Hamby, Christine Maranan, Kathy Meinecke, Molly Suberlak, Amanda Voigtlander
- <u>West Allis-West Milwaukee School District</u>: Sarah Bartosch, Erin Jodie
- <u>UW-Milwaukee graduate students</u>: Taylor Hansen, Maggie Long, Maricel Schulte

Australian Samples: The Australian samples were collected by speech-language pathologists employed by the Department of Education and Training, Queensland, Australia. The following clinicians assisted with the data collection: Alicia Terrey, Diane Chen, Donna Arulogan, Elizabeth Tweed, Emma Fraser, Jane Westphal, Kaitlin Scurr, Kristy Cooney, Bronte Brooke, Leanne Herbert, Lynda Miles, Melissa Gardiner, Robyn Kalkaus, Sarah Johnston, Bronte Brook.

All samples were transcribed and coded by the staff at SALT Software, LLC. We wish to thank Karen Andriacchi, Carol Cailliet, and Joyelle Divall-Rayan for their lead on the project, and the transcription staff for their help with transcription and coding.

This project was funded by SALT Software, LLC.

Persuasion Topics List

Changing the time school starts in the morning
Allowing students to leave campus during the school day without special permission
Requiring students to do graded homework
Requiring students to take foreign language classes
Allowing teachers to socialize with students on social networks such as Facebook, Twitter, Snapchat, Instagram, etc.
Including grades in physical education classes in students' grade point average
Allowing students to listen to their music using headphones during free periods
Changing the access teenagers have to entertainment that is violent or sexually suggestive; entertainment includes movies, music, and video games
Requiring school uniforms or a dress code for students
Awarding cash or other incentives to students who earn good grades
Replacing traditional textbooks with notebook computers or digital materials
Requiring cities to provide free wireless Internet access in public spaces
Requiring people to get a license in order to become parents
Allowing alternatives to jail, such as counseling or public service, for convicted criminals
Requiring colleges to pay their student athletes a salary for playing
Requiring drug tests for professional athletes
Allowing employers to require drug tests as part of their hiring procedure
Requiring workers to pay for their own work uniforms or equipment
Raising the minimum wage
Changing the minimum age for voting, drinking, driving, or holding a job
Other: Topic of your choice

Persuasion Planning Sheet (*The actual form used can be downloaded from the SALT web site at* www.saltsoftware.com/resources/)

What to Talk about When Trying to Persuade Someone

Topic	What's Covered	Notes
Issue ID and Desired Change	What rule or situation do you want changed? What would you change it to?	
Supporting Reasons	What facts or values or evidence helps your side? Be sure to include how your change would help or benefit the listener or people the listener cares about.	
Counter Arguments – Other Point of View	What are some good reasons on the other side?	
Response to Counter Arguments	What can you say to knock down or weaken the reasons on the other side? What reasons on the other side can you can agree with, either in whole or in part?	
Compromises	If you can't get your way 100%, what deals would be acceptable so each side wins a little?	
Conclusion	Briefly sum up your position: What do you want? Why do you want it? What are the first steps needed to make the change happen?	

Please use the backside of this page for an optional diagram or graphic organizer, or for additional notes.

G

Bilingual Spanish/English Story Retell Databases

Database	Context (Subgroup)	Age Range	Grade in School	# Samples	Location	Special Coding
Bilingual Spanish/English Story Retell	Nar (FWAY)	5;0 – 9;9	K, 1, 2, 3	2,070	TX & CA	SI, NSS
	Nar (FGTD)	5;5 – 8;11	K, 2	1,667		
	Nar (FOHO)	6;0 – 7;9	1	930		

Participants

The Bilingual English Story Retell and Bilingual Spanish Story Retell databases consist of English and Spanish story-retell narratives from native Spanish-speaking bilingual (Spanish/English) children. These English language learners (ELLs) were drawn from public school ELL classrooms in urban Texas (Houston and Austin), border Texas (Brownsville), and urban California (Los Angeles). The children reflect the diverse socio-economic status of these areas. Age, grade, and gender data is available for all children, and mother's education is available for many.

Additional Inclusion Criteria

1. The children were described as "typically developing" as determined by normal progress in school and the absence of special education services.

2. All children were within the following age ranges.

Grade	Age Range
K	5;0 – 6;9
1	6;0 – 7;9
2	7;0 – 8;9
3	8;1 – 9;9

3. All children were able to produce both English and Spanish narratives containing at least one complete and intelligible verbal utterance in the target language. Although the language samples may contain code-switched words (*English words in the Spanish samples or Spanish words in the English samples*), at least 80% of the words from each sample were in the target language.

Elicitation Protocol

1. General Directions

   The story retell task uses one of the following picture books:
   - *Frog, Where Are You?* by Mercer Mayer (1969)
   - *Frog Goes to Dinner* by Mercer Mayer (1974)
   - *Frog On His Own* by Mercer Mayer (1973)

   First the story is modeled for the child in the target language (*Spanish or English*). Then the child is asked to retell the same story. All instructions and prompts are given using the target language.

   Ideally, you should first assess the child in his or her native language. However, we are clearly aware that for many speech-language pathologists, assessing the child in his native language will be impossible since the majority of clinicians do not speak a language other than English. This can also be the case for clinicians who may be bilingual, but do not speak the native language of the target speaker. Thus, we suggest that clinicians first assess the child in the language in which he or she is most comfortable. If the child's performance is below average compared to age and grade-matched peers, then elicit a second sample in the other language. You may elicit the second language sample shortly after the first sample, or you may prefer to wait several weeks in between.

2. Steps

   a. Sit next to the child at a table. The book should be on the table. The audio/video recorder should be checked and ready to be turned on.

   b. Tell the story to the child, loosely following the story script provided at the end of this appendix.

      Directions to the child (Spanish sample):
      Examiner: *Aquí tengo un libro. Te voy a contar este cuento mientras miramos el libro juntos. Cuando terminemos, quiero que me vuelvas a contar el cuento en español. Okey? Vamos a mirar el primer libro. Este libro nos cuenta un cuento sobre un niño, un perro, y una rana.*

      Directions to the child (English sample):
      Examiner: *Here is a book. I am going to tell you this story while we look at the book together. When we finish, I want you to tell the story back to me in English. Ok? Let's look at the book. This book tells a story about a boy, a dog, and a frog.*

      You control the book and turn to the first picture. Tell (*not read*) the story to the child, loosely following the story script. You do not need to memorize the story script, but become familiar enough with it to tell a similar story.

   c. Leave the book with the child and move away – either at an angle facing the child or across the table. Moving away from the child helps promote language and minimize pointing. Turn on the recorder and instruct the child to tell the story back in the same language.

      Directions to the child (Spanish sample):
      Examiner: *Ahora, cuentame lo que pasó en este cuento.*

      Directions to the child (English sample):
      Examiner: *Okay, now I would like you to tell me the story.*

Refer to the following section for a list of prompts which may be used while the child retells the story. Remember, all prompts should be in the target language.

d. After the child finishes telling the story, turn off the recorder and thank the child for telling his/her story.

e. Repeat these steps to elicit the sample in the other language. You may elicit the second language sample immediately after the first, or you may prefer to wait several weeks in between.

3. Prompts

Use minimal open-ended prompts when eliciting the samples. Using overly-specific questions or providing too much information to the child compromises the process of capturing the child's true language and ability level. Open-ended prompts *do not* provide the child with answers or vocabulary. They *do* encourage the child to try or they let the child know it is ok to move on if needed. Use open-ended prompts/questions as necessary.

- Use open-ended prompts when the child:
  - is not speaking
  - says "*I don't know.*", "*Cómo se dice*?"
  - starts listing, e.g., "*boy*", "*dog*", "*jar*"

- Acceptable verbal prompts (*in the target language*) include:

Tell me more.	*Dime más.*
Just do your best.	*Haz lo mejor que puedas.*
Tell me about that.	*Dime sobre eso/esa.*
You're doing great.	*Estás haciendolo muy bien.*
I'd like to hear more about that.	*Me gustaría oír más sobre eso/esa.*
Tell me what you can.	*Dime lo que puedas.*
That sounds interesting.	*Eso/Esa suena interesante.*
What else?	*¿Qué más?*
Keep going.	*Siguele. Dale.*
Mhm . Uhhuh.	

- Acceptable nonverbal prompts include:
  Smiles and eye contact
  Nods of affirmation and agreement

- Unacceptable prompts include:

What is he doing?	*¿Qué está haciendo (él)?*
Where is he?	*¿Dónde está (él)?*
Pointing at scenes in the book while prompting	
What's this?	*¿Qué es esto?*
What's happening here?	*¿Qué está pasando/ocurriendo aquí?*

Avoid asking the "wh" questions, who?, what?, when?, where? These often lead to obvious and limited responses/answers.

What if the child code switches?

If the child uses an occasional Spanish word in the English sample, just ignore it. However, if the child uses a lot of Spanish words or phrases, prompt the child with "*in English, please*" or "*tell it to me in English*" or "*tell me the story in English*". Similarly, if the child uses a lot of English words in the Spanish sample, prompt the child with "*en Español, por favor*" or "*dimelo en Espanol*" or "*dime el cuento en Español*". Direct the child to use the target language with minimal interruption of his or her story. But keep in mind that at least 80% of the words should be in the target language in order for the sample to be valid.

Transcription Notes

The Spanish samples in the reference database were transcribed by fluent Spanish speakers. The English samples were transcribed by fluent English speakers.

Utterances were segmented into Modified Communication Units (MC-units) which were developed specifically for these samples to account for the pronoun-drop nature of the Spanish language.

The underscore was used for repetitious words or phrases within utterances. This prevented inflation of the MLU due to repetition used to provide emphasis, e.g., C dijeron|decir rana_rana_rana dónde estás|estar.

All transcripts have timing markers at the beginning and end of the sample. The initial marker indicates the child's first utterance. The final timing marker indicates the end of the child's narrative.

Coding Notes

- [EO:word] marks overgeneralization errors.
- [EW: word] marks other word-level errors.
- [EU] marks utterance-level errors.
- [CS] is a word code attached to all code-switched words (Spanish words in English transcripts or English words in Spanish transcripts).
- [I] is a word code attached to all imitations of vocabulary provided by the examiner.

The following codes were created to mark Spanish-influenced English:
- [WO] is an utterance-level code signifying words or phrases within an utterance which are out of order in Standard English. The content (semantics) of the utterance is correct; however the word order is awkward, e.g., C And then fall down the dog and the boy [WO].
- [EW] marks an extraneous or unnecessary word in the utterance that, if omitted, would make the utterance syntactically correct, e.g., C And he shout/ed and[EW] to the frog. As a general rule, do not mark more than one extraneous word in an utterance; instead, mark the utterance using the [EU] code.
- [F] was placed at the end of each utterance lacking a stated subject as a result segmenting utterances using MC-units.

Subordination Index (SI) and Narrative Scoring Scheme (NSS) Coding

SI and NSS coding was applied to all the samples in the Bilingual Spanish/English Story Retell reference databases.

SI is a measure of syntactic complexity which produces a ratio of the total number of clauses (main and subordinate clauses) to the number of C-units. A clause, whether it is main or subordinate, is a statement containing both a subject and a predicate. Grammatically, a subject is a noun phrase and a predicate is a verb phrase. Main clauses can stand by themselves. Subordinate clauses depend on the main clause to make sense. They are embedded within an utterance as noun, adjective or adverbial clauses (see Appendix O).

NSS is an assessment tool developed to create a more objective narrative content and structure scoring system. It is based upon early work on story grammar analysis by Stein and Glenn, 1979, 1982. This scoring procedure combines many of the abstract categories of Story Grammar, adding features of cohesion, connecting events, rationale for characters' behavior and referencing. Each of the scoring categories has specific explicit examples to establish scoring criteria, reducing the abstractness of the story grammar categories (see Appendix P).

Acknowledgements

Language samples for the Bilingual Spanish/English Story Retell reference databases were collected and transcribed as part of the grants HD39521 "Oracy/Literacy Development of Spanish-speaking Children" and R305U010001 "Biological and Behavioral Variation in the Language Development of Spanish-speaking Children", funded by the NICHD and IES, David Francis, P.I., Aquiles Iglesias, Co-P.I., and Jon Miller, Co-P.I.

English script for *Frog, Where Are You?* by Mercer Mayer (1969)

Page	Script
1	There once was a boy who had a dog and a pet frog. He kept the frog in a large jar in his bedroom.
2	One night while he and his dog were sleeping, the frog climbed out of the jar. He jumped out of an open window.
3	When the boy and the dog woke up the next morning, they saw that the jar was empty.
4	The boy looked everywhere for the frog. The dog looked for the frog too. When the dog tried to look in the jar, he got his head stuck.
5	The boy called out the open window, "Frog, where are you?" The dog leaned out the window with the jar still stuck on his head.
6	The jar was so heavy that the dog fell out of the window headfirst!
7	The boy picked up the dog to make sure he was ok. The dog wasn't hurt but the jar was smashed.
8-9	The boy and the dog looked outside for the frog. The boy called for the frog.
10	He called down a hole in the ground while the dog barked at some bees in a beehive.
11	A gopher popped out of the hole and bit the boy on right on his nose. Meanwhile, the dog was still bothering the bees, jumping up on the tree and barking at them.
12	The beehive fell down and all of the bees flew out. The bees were angry at the dog for ruining their home.
13	The boy wasn't paying any attention to the dog. He had noticed a large hole in a tree. So he climbed up the tree and called down the hole.
14	All of a sudden an owl swooped out of the hole and knocked the boy to the ground.
15	The dog ran past the boy as fast as he could because the bees were chasing him.
16	The owl chased the boy all the way to a large rock.

17	The boy climbed up on the rock and called again for his frog. He held onto some branches so he wouldn't fall.
18	But the branches weren't really branches! They were deer antlers. The deer picked up the boy on his head.
19	The deer started running with the boy still on his head. The dog ran along too. They were getting close to a cliff.
20-21	The deer stopped suddenly and the boy and the dog fell over the edge of the cliff.
22	There was a pond below the cliff. They landed with a splash right on top of one another.
23	They heard a familiar sound.
24	The boy told the dog to be very quiet.
25	They crept up and looked behind a big log.
26	There they found the boy's pet frog. He had a mother frog with him.
27	They had some baby frogs and one of them jumped towards the boy.
28-29	The baby frog liked the boy and wanted to be his new pet. The boy and the dog were happy to have a new pet frog to take home. As they walked away the boy waved and said "goodbye" to his old frog and his family.

Spanish script for *Frog, Where Are You?* by Mercer Mayer (1969)

Página	Papel
1	Había un niño quien tenía un perro y una rana. El tenía la rana en su cuarto en un jarro grande a su rana.
2	Una noche cuando el niño y su perro estaban durmiendo, la rana se escapó del jarro. La rana se salió por una ventana abierta.
3	Cuando el niño y el perro se despertaron la siguiente mañana, vieron que el jarro estaba vacío.
4	El niño buscó en todas partes a la rana. Aún adentro de sus botas. El perro también buscó a la rana. Cuando el perro trató de mirar adentro del jarro y no podía sacar la cabeza.
5	El niño empezó a llamar desde la ventana abierta: "Rana, ¿Dónde estás?". El perro se asomó a la ventana con el jarro todavía en la cabeza.
6	¡El jarro estaba tan pesado que hizo que el perro se cayera de cabeza por la ventana!
7	El niño fue a ver como estaba el perro. El perro no estaba herido, pero el jarro se rompió.
8-9	El niño y el perro buscaron a la rana afuera de la casa. El niño llamó a la rana.
10	El niño llamaba a la rana en un hoyo que estaba en la tierra, mientras que el perro le ladraba a unas abejas en su panal.
11	Una ardilla salió de su hueco y mordió la nariz del niño por molestarla. Mientras tanto, el perro seguía molestando a las abejas, brincaba hacia el árbol y les ladraba.
12	El panal de abejas se cayó y las abejas salieron volando. Las abejas estaban enojadas con el perro.
13	El niño no prestó ninguna atención al perro. El vió un hueco grande en un árbol y quería ver si su rana se escondía allí. Así que trepó el árbol y llamó a la rana en el hueco para ver si estaba.
14	De repente un buho salió del hueco y lanzó al niño al suelo. El buho lo vió fijamente y le dijo que se fuera.

15	El perro pasó al niño corriendo tan rápido como pudo porque las abejas lo perseguían.
16	El buho persiguió al niño hasta una piedra grande.
17	El niño se encaramó en la piedra y llamó otra vez a la rana. Se agarró a unas ramas para no caerse de la piedra.
18	¡Pero las ramas no eran ramas reales! Eran los cuernos de un venado. El venado levantó al niño con su cabeza.
19	Y el venado empezó a correr con el niño que estaba todavía en su cabeza. El perro también corrió al lado del venado. Se acercaron a un precipicio.
20-21	El venado se paró de pronto y el niño y el perro se cayeron por el precipicio.
22	Había un estanque debajo del precipicio. Aterrizaron en el estanque uno encima del otro.
23	Oyeron un sonido que conocían.
24	El niño le dijo al perro que se callara.
25	Los dos se acercaron con cuidado y miraron detrás de un tronco de un árbol.
26	Allí encontraron a la rana del niño. Había con él una rana mamá también.
27	Ellos tenían algunas ranitas bebés y una de ellas saltó hacia el niño.
28-29	La ranita quería mucho al niño y quería ser su nueva mascota. El niño y el perro estaban felices de tener una nueva rana y llevarla a casa. Cuando se iban, el niño dijo adiós a la que fue su rana y también a su familia.

English script for *Frog Goes to Dinner* by Mercer Mayer (1974)

Page	Script
1	A boy was getting dressed in his bedroom. His pet dog, frog and turtle watched as he put on his best clothes.
2	While the boy was petting the dog, the frog jumped into his coat pocket. The boy didn't know he was there.
3	As the boy left with his family, he waved and said "Goodbye" to his pets. The frog waved goodbye too.
4-5	When the boy and his family arrived at a fancy restaurant, the doorman helped them out of the car. The frog peaked out of the boy's pocket but no one noticed him.
6-7	The boy and his family sat down at a table in the restaurant. While they were looking at the menus, the frog jumped out of the boy's pocket towards the band.
8	The frog landed right in the man's saxophone! "Squeak" went the saxophone.
9	The man looked inside the saxophone to see why it made that awful noise.
10	Then the frog fell out of the horn and landed right on the saxophone player's face!
11	The saxophone player was so surprised that he fell backwards into the drum.
12-13	The drummer yelled at the saxophone player, "Look what you did to my drum- it's broken!" While they were arguing, the frog jumped away on a plate of lettuce salad.
14	The waiter didn't notice the frog. He served the salad to a woman.
15	Just as she was about to take a bite, the frog popped out of the lettuce. The woman was shocked to see the frog.
16	She screamed and fell back on her chair. The frog was frightened and he jumped away.
17	There was a man at the next table who was having a glass of wine with his wife. The frog landed right in his glass.

18	The woman complained to the waiter about getting a salad with a frog in it. She was very angry!
19	Meanwhile, when the man went to take a sip of his drink, the frog kissed him right on the nose.
20-21	The angry waiter was about to grab the frog who was waving goodbye to the man and his wife.
22-23	The waiter, who had caught the frog, was going to throw him out of the restaurant. But the boy saw the waiter carrying his frog and shouted, "Hey, that's my frog!" The boy's mother told him to be quiet.
24	The boy asked the waiter to give him back his frog.
25	The angry waiter told the boy and his family, "Take your frog and get out of this restaurant at once. Don't you ever bring that frog in here again!"
26-27	On the way home the boy's family was angry with him. The frog had ruined their dinner!
28-29	When they got home the boy's father scolded him, "You go to your room and stay there!" The dog and the turtle peaked around the corner to see what was going on.
30	When they got in his room, the boy and the frog laughed about everything that had happened at the restaurant. The more they thought about it, the more they laughed.

Spanish script for *Frog Goes to Dinner* by Mercer Mayer (1974)

Página	Papel
1	Un niño se estaba preparando para salir a cenar. Sus mascotas el perro, la tortuga, y la rana lo miraban mientras él se ponía sus mejores ropas. Estaban tristes porque sabían que él iba a salir sin ellos.
2	Mientras que el niño acariciaba al perro, la rana brincó dentro del bolsillo del niño. El niño no sabía que la rana estaba en su bolsillo.
3	Cuando la familia se iba, el niño les dijo adiós a sus mascotas. La rana también les dijo adiós.
4–5	Cuando la familia del niño llegó a un restaurante lujoso, el portero les ayudó a bajar del carro. La rana miró con cuidado desde el bolsillo.
6–7	En el restaurante se sentaron en una mesa. Mientras miraban el menú, la rana se escapó del bolsillo del niño y brincó hacia la banda musical.
8	¡La rana terminó dentro del saxofón! Cuando el músico empezó a tocar su instrumento, el sonido fue horrible.
9	Por eso, él miró dentro de su instrumento para ver que pasaba. Los otros músicos estaban muy confundidos como él.
10	¡Luego la rana le cayó y aterrizó en la cara del músico!
11	Y entonces el músico sorprendido, se cayó hacia atrás y cayó dentro del tambor.
12–13	El tocador del tambor gritó al otro músico: "¡Mira lo que pasó – mi tambor está roto! ahora, ¿Con qué voy a tocar?." Mientras ellos discutían, la rana brincó y terminó en la ensalada.
14	El mesero no se dio cuenta que la rana estaba en la ensalada. El mesero le sirvió la ensalada a una señora.
15	Cuando empezaba a comerla, la rana salió por debajo de la lechuga. La señora estaba aterrorizada al ver la rana.
16	Ella gritó y se cayó para atrás. La rana estaba asustada y salió brincando.
17	En la próxima mesa había un hombre y su esposa tomando una copa de vino. La rana se cayó en el vaso del señor.

18	La mujer se quejó de que había encontrado una rana en su ensalada. ¡Ella estaba muy enojada!
19	Mientras tanto, cuando el señor fue a tomar la copa, la rana salió y le dio un beso en la nariz.
20–21	El mesero enojado estuvo a punto de capturar la rana. El hombre y su esposa se fueron del restaurante porque no se sentían bien para comer con animales en la comida.
22–23	El mesero cuando capturó la rana, la cargó hasta la puerta para botarla. Pero el niño vió al camarero con su rana y le gritó: "¡Esa es mi rana, no la botes!" Su mamá le dijo al niño que se callara.
24	El niño estaba preocupado de que el mesero iba a botar su rana en la calle. Entonces el niño le dijo al mesero que le diera su rana.
25	El camarero les dijo al niño y su familia: "Toma tu rana y salgan de ese restaurante inmediatamente. ¡No permitimos animales ni gente que los traen en este restaurante!"
26–27	Durante el camino de vuelta, la familia del niño estaba enojada. ¡La rana arruinó la cena!
28–29	Cuando llegaron a la casa el padre del niño lo regañó y le dijo: "Vete a tu cuarto y quédate allí". El perro y la tortuga miraron de escondidas desde el rincón para ver que pasó.
30	Cuando llegaron a su cuarto, el niño y su rana se rieron de todo lo que había pasado en el restaurante. Mientras más pensaban en todo lo que había pasado, más reían.

English script for *Frog On His Own* by Mercer Mayer (1973)

Page	Script
1	One day a boy walked to the park with his dog, carrying his pet frog and turtle in a bucket.
2	After they got into the park, the frog jumped out of the bucket.
3	The frog waved goodbye to his friends as they walked away. He wanted to explore the park on his own.
4	The frog came upon some flowers. He was watching them very closely.
5	All of a sudden he snapped his tongue high into the flowers.
6	He caught a big, tasty bug for his lunch.
7	He put the bug in his mouth and realized that was a big mistake.
8	The bug was a bumblebee. It stung the frog on his tongue.
9	After a while, the frog noticed a man and woman who were having a picnic.
10	The woman reached into her picnic basket. At the same time, the frog crawled into the basket.
11	As the woman was digging around for something to eat, she felt something strange.
12	She quickly pulled her hand out of the basket to find the frog hanging on her arm.
13	The frog quickly jumped away from the couple. The woman threw a coffee cup at him. She screamed, "Don't you ever come back you nasty little frog!"
14-15	The frog hopped over to a small pond where he noticed a little boy sailing his toy boat. The boy's mother was on a bench reading.
16	The curious frog wondered if he could sail in the boat. He leapt though the air...
17	And landed, splat, on top of the sailboat.

18	The frog was too big for the sailboat and sunk it. The little boy started crying and his mother came to pull the sunken sailboat out of the water.
19	The frog swam across the pond and crawled out on the other side. He saw a woman on a bench rocking a baby stroller. Her cat was napping by the stroller.
20	The curious frog wanted to know what was inside the stroller. He took a giant leap toward it.
21	The frog landed on the baby's lap. The baby sat up and looked at the frog. It was time for the baby to have a bottle and the mom was getting it ready.
22	While the mom read her magazine she held out the bottle for her baby. The frog was going to drink the bottle while the mom wasn't looking.
23	The baby started to cry because he wanted his bottle. The cat climbed up the stroller to try to catch the frog. The mother realized what was happening and was shocked.
24-25	She picked up her baby while the cat chased after the frog.
26	The frog leapt away as fast as he could but the cat caught him by the leg.
27	The cat wrestled the frog to the ground. The frog was very frightened.
28-29	Luckily, along came the boy with his dog and turtle. The dog barked at the cat and the boy yelled, "Hey, get away from my frog!" This scared the cat who ran away as fast as he could.
30	The boy picked up his frog and started to walk home. The frog lay in the boy's arms, very tired from all of his adventures. He was happy to be back with his friends.

Spanish script for *Frog On His Own* by Mercer Mayer (1973)

Página	Papel
1	Un día un niño caminó en el parque con su perro, llevando a su rana y la tortuga en un balde.
2	Después de llegar al parque, la rana saltó del balde.
3	La rana le dijo adiós a sus amigos mientras ellos se iban. Ella quería explorar el parque sóla.
4	La rana encontró unas flores. Las miró de cerca.
5	De repente, metió la lengua en las flores.
6	Capturó un insecto grande y sabroso para el almuerzo.
7	Puso el insecto en su boca y se dio cuenta de que era un gran error.
8	El insecto era una abeja; y le picó la lengua de la rana. Y por eso a la pobre rana le dolía su lengua.
9	Después de un rato, la rana vió a un hombre y una mujer quienes estaban de día de campo.
10	La mujer metió la mano en la canasta de comida. Ella no sabía que al mismo tiempo la rana entró en la canasta.
11	Cuando la mujer intentó encontrar algo para comer, sintió algo extraño.
12	Ella rápidamente sacó su mano de la canasta y descubrió a la rana colgando de su brazo. El hombre se asustó tanto que hasta tiró su taza de café y se le cayeron sus lentes.
13	La rana se fue corriendo alejándose de la pareja. La mujer arrojó una taza de café a la rana y le gritó: "¡Odiosa ranita nunca regreses aquí!". El hombre estaba en el césped riéndose histéricamente.
14-15	La rana brincó hasta un pequeño estanque donde vio a un niñito jugando con su barco de vela.
16	La rana curiosa quería saber si podía navegar en el barco. Saltó...
17	y terminó, salpicado, encima del barco de vela.

18	La rana era demasiado grande y el barco de vela se hundió. El niñito empezó a llorar y su madre vino a sacar al barco hundido fuera del agua.
19	La rana cruzó nadando el pequeño estanque y salió al otro lado. Vio a otra mujer sentada en un banco meciendo el cochecito de un bebé. Su gato estaba dormido al lado del cochecito.
20	La rana curiosa quería saber que había en el cochecito. Así que saltó fuertemente hacia el coche.
21	La rana aterrizó en las rodillas del bebé y el bebé se sentó y miró a la rana. Ya era hora de que el bebé comiera, así que mientras la madre leía su revista le dio el tetero al bebé.
22	Y como la madre estaba entretenida leyendo, la rana trató de tomarse la leche del bebé.
23	El bebé empezó a llorar porque quería su tetero. El gato molesto subió en el cochecito para tratar de capturar a la rana. La madre se dio cuenta de lo que estaba pasando y se asustó mucho.
24-25	Ella levantó a su bebé mientras que el gato perseguía a la rana.
26	La rana salió saltando lo más rápido posible, pero el gato la atrapó por la pierna.
27	El gato luchó con la rana y ella terminó en el suelo. La rana tenía mucho miedo.
28-29	Afortunadamente, llegó el niño con su perro y su tortuga. El perro le ladró al gato y el niño gritó: "¡Deja de molestar a mi rana!". Esto asustó al gato y lo hizo salir corriendo.
30	El niño levantó a su rana y empezó el camino de regreso a la casa. La rana se acostó en los brazos del niño, muy cansada por todas sus aventuras. Estaba contenta de estar con sus amigos de nuevo.

H

Bilingual Spanish/English Unique Story Databases

Database	Context (Subgroup)	Age Range	Grade in School	# Samples	Location	Special Coding
Bilingual Spanish/English Unique Story	Nar (OFTM)	5;0 – 9;7	K, 1, 2, 3	475	TX & CA	SI, NSS

Participants

The Bilingual English Unique Story and Bilingual Spanish Unique Story databases consist of English and Spanish story **tell** (not retell) narratives from native Spanish-speaking bilingual (Spanish/English) children. These English language learners (ELLs) were drawn from public school ELL classrooms in urban Texas (Houston and Austin), border Texas (Brownsville), and urban California (Los Angeles). The children reflect the diverse socio-economic status of these areas. Age, grade, and gender data is available for all children, and mother's education is available for many.

Additional Inclusion Criteria

1. The children were described as "typically developing" as determined by normal progress in school and the absence of special education services.

2. All children were within the following age ranges.

Grade	Age Range
K	5;0 – 6;9
1	6;2 – 7;7
2	7;3 – 8;9
3	8;4 – 9;7

3. All children were able to produce both English and Spanish narratives containing at least one complete and intelligible verbal utterance in the target language. Although the language samples may contain code-switched words (*English words in the Spanish samples or Spanish words in the English samples*), at least 80% of the words from each sample were in the target language.

Elicitation Protocol

1. General Directions

   This task is a story **tell** (not retell) using the picture book *One Frog Too Many* by Mercer and Marianna Mayer (1975). The protocol assumes that the child has had experience **retelling** at least one of the frog stories from the Bilingual Spanish/English Story Retell databases (see Appendix G). This is important because the story is not modeled for the child in this protocol. The child is simply shown the pictures and then asked to tell the story.

   The examiner silently looks through the book with the child. The child is then given the book and asked to tell the story. All instructions and prompts are given using the target language.

   Ideally, you should first assess the child in his or her native language. However, we are clearly aware that, for many speech-language pathologists, assessing the child in his native language will be impossible since the majority of clinicians do not speak a language other than English. This can also be the case for clinicians who may be bilingual, but do not speak the native language of the target speaker. Thus, we suggest that clinicians first assess the child in the language in which he or she is most comfortable. If the child's performance is below average compared to age and grade-matched peers, then elicit a second sample in the other language. You may elicit the second language sample shortly after the first sample, or you may prefer to wait several weeks in between.

2. Steps

   a. Sit next to the child at a table. The book *One Frog Too Many* should be on the table. The audio/video recorder should be checked and ready to be turned on.

   b. Look at the pictures in the book.

      Directions to the child (Spanish sample):
      Examiner: *Aquí tengo un libro que no tiene palabras. Vamos a mirar las fotos en este libro. Cuando terminemos, quiero que me diga el cuento en español. Okey? Vamos a mirar el primer libro. Este libro nos cuenta un cuento sobre un niño, un perro, y una rana.*

      Directions to the child (English sample):
      Examiner: *Here is a book that doesn't have any words. We are going to look at the pictures in this book together. When we finish, I want you to tell the story to me in English. Ok? Let's look at the book. This book tells a story about a boy, a dog, and a frog.*

      You control the book while you silently look at each page together.

   c. Leave the book with the child and move away – either at an angle facing the child or across the table. Moving away from the child helps promote language and minimize pointing. Turn on the recorder and instruct the child to tell the story to you in the same language.

      Directions to the child (Spanish sample):
      Examiner: *Ahora, cuentame lo que pasó en este cuento.*

      Directions to the child (English sample):
      Examiner: *Okay, now I would like you to tell me the story.*

      Refer to the following section for a list of prompts which may be used while the child tells the story. Remember, all prompts should be in the target language.

    d. After the child finishes telling the story, turn off the recorder and thank the child for telling his/her story.

    e. Repeat these steps to elicit the sample in the other language. You may elicit the second language sample immediately after the first, or you may prefer to wait several weeks in between.

3. Prompts

Use minimal open-ended prompts when eliciting the samples. Using overly-specific questions or providing too much information to the child compromises the process of capturing the child's true language and ability level. Open-ended prompts *do not* provide the child with answers or vocabulary. They *do* encourage the child to try or they let the child know it is ok to move on if needed. Use open-ended prompts/questions as necessary.

- Use open-ended prompts when the child:
  - is not speaking
  - says "I don't know.", "Cómo se dice?"
  - starts listing, e.g., "boy", "dog", "jar"

- Acceptable verbal prompts (*in the target language*) include:

Tell me more.	*Dime más.*
Just do your best.	*Haz lo mejor que puedas.*
Tell me about that.	*Dime sobre eso/esa.*
You're doing great.	*Estás haciendolo muy bien.*
I'd like to hear more about that.	*Me gustaría oír más sobre eso/esa.*
Tell me what you can.	*Dime lo que puedas.*
That sounds interesting.	*Eso/Esa suena interesante.*
What else?	*¿Qué más?*
Keep going.	*Siguele. Dale.*
Mhm. Uhhuh.	

- Acceptable nonverbal prompts include:
  Smiles and eye contact
  Nods of affirmation and agreement

- Unacceptable prompts include:

What is he doing?	*¿Qué está haciendo (él)?*
Where is he?	*¿Dónde está (él)?*

Pointing at scenes in the book while prompting

What's this?	*¿Qué es esto?*
What's happening here?	*¿Qué está pasando/ocurriendo aquí?*

Avoid asking the "wh" questions, who?, what?, when?, where? These often lead to obvious and limited responses/answers.

What if the child code switches?

If the child uses an occasional Spanish word in the English sample, just ignore it. However, if the child uses a lot of Spanish words or phrases, prompt the child with "*in English, please*" or "*tell it to me in English*" or "*tell me the story in English*". Similarly, if the child uses a lot of English words in the Spanish sample, prompt the child with "*en Español, por favor*" or "*dimelo en Espanol*" or "*dime el cuento en Español*". Direct the child to use the target language with minimal interruption of his or her story. But keep in mind that at least 80% of the words should be in the target language in order for the sample to be valid.

Transcription Notes

The Spanish samples in the reference database were transcribed by fluent Spanish speakers. The English samples were transcribed by fluent English speakers.

Utterances were segmented into Modified Communication Units (MC-units) which were developed specifically for these samples to account for the pronoun-drop nature of the Spanish language.

The underscore was used for repetitious words or phrases within utterances. This prevented inflation of the MLU due to repetition used to provide emphasis, e.g., C dijeron|decir rana_rana_rana dónde estás|estar.

All transcripts have timing markers at the beginning and end of the sample. The initial marker indicates the child's first utterance. The final timing marker indicates the end of the child's narrative.

Coding Notes

- [EO:word] marks overgeneralization errors.
- [EW: word] marks other word-level errors.
- [EU] marks utterance-level errors.
- [CS] is a word code attached to all code-switched words (Spanish words in English transcripts or English words in Spanish transcripts).
- [I] is a word code attached to all imitations of vocabulary provided by the examiner.

The following codes were created to mark Spanish-influenced English:
- [WO] is an utterance-level code signifying words or phrases within an utterance which are out of order in Standard English. The content (semantics) of the utterance is correct; however the word order is awkward, e.g., C And then fall down the dog and the boy [WO].
- [EW] marks an extraneous or unnecessary word in the utterance that, if omitted, would make the utterance syntactically correct, e.g., C And he shout/ed and[EW] to the frog. As a general rule, do not mark more than one extraneous word in an utterance; instead, mark the utterance using the [EU] code.
- [F] was placed at the end of each utterance lacking a stated subject as a result segmenting utterances using MC-units.

Subordination Index (SI) and Narrative Scoring Scheme (NSS) Coding

SI and NSS coding was applied to all the samples in the Bilingual Spanish/English Story Retell reference databases.

SI is a measure of syntactic complexity which produces a ratio of the total number of clauses (main and subordinate clauses) to the number of C-units. A clause, whether it is main or subordinate, is a statement containing both a subject and a predicate. Grammatically, a subject is a noun phrase and a predicate is a verb phrase. Main clauses can stand by themselves. Subordinate clauses depend on the main clause to make sense. They are embedded within an utterance as noun, adjective or adverbial clauses (see Appendix O).

NSS is an assessment tool developed to create a more objective narrative content and structure scoring system. It is based upon early work on story grammar analysis by Stein and Glenn, 1979, 1982. This scoring procedure combines many of the abstract categories of Story Grammar, adding features of cohesion, connecting events, rationale for characters' behavior and referencing. Each of the scoring categories has specific explicit examples to establish scoring criteria, reducing the abstractness of the story grammar categories (see Appendix P).

Acknowledgements

Language samples for the Bilingual Spanish/English Story Retell reference databases were collected and transcribed as part of the grants HD39521 "Oracy/Literacy Development of Spanish-speaking Children" and R305U010001 "Biological and Behavioral Variation in the Language Development of Spanish-speaking Children", funded by the NICHD and IES, David Francis, P.I., Aquiles Iglesias, Co-P.I., and Jon Miller, Co-P.I.

Monolingual Spanish Story Retell Database

Database	Context (Subgroup)	Age Range	Grade in School	# Samples	Location	Special Coding
Monolingual Spanish Story Retell	Nar (FWAY)	5;10 – 9;11	1, 2, 3	366	Mexico	SI, NSS
	Nar (FGTD)	6;4 – 10;6	1, 2, 3	360		
	Nar (FOHO)	6;1 – 10;1	1, 2, 3	188		
	Nar (OFTM)	6;9 – 10;7	1, 2, 3	154		

Participants

The Monolingual Spanish Story Retell database consists of story-retell narratives from native Spanish-speaking children. These children were drawn from public school classrooms in Guadalajara, Mexico. The children reflect the socio-economic status of this area. Age, grade, and gender data is available for all children.

Additional Inclusion Criteria

The children were described as "typically developing" as determined by normal progress in school and the absence of special education services.

All children were within the following age ranges.

Grade	Age Range
1	5;10 – 8;0
2	6;4 – 9;9
3	7;10 – 10;7

Elicitation Protocol

1. General Directions

   This is a story retell task using one of the following picture books:
   - FWAY: *Frog, Where Are You*? by Mercer Mayer (1969)
   - FGTD: *Frog Goes to Dinner* by Mercer Mayer (1974)
   - FOHO: *Frog On His Own* by Mercer Mayer (1973)
   - OFTM: *One Frog Too Many* by Mercer and Marianna Mayer (1975)

   First the story is modeled for the child. Then the child is asked to retell the same story. All instructions and prompts are given in Spanish.

2. Steps

   a. Sit next to the child at a table. The book should be on the table. The audio/video recorder should be checked and ready to be turned on.

   b. Tell the story to the child loosely following the story script.

      Note that the scripts use to present the model for FWAY, FGTD, and FOHO can be found at the end of Appendix G. The scripts for OFTM are included at the end of this appendix.

      Directions to the child:
      Examiner: *Aquí tengo un libro. Te voy a contar este cuento mientras miramos el libro juntos. Cuando terminemos, quiero que me vuelvas a contar el cuento en español. Okey? Vamos a mirar el primer libro. Este libro nos cuenta un cuento sobre un niño, un perro, y una rana.*

      You control the book and turn to the first picture. Tell (not read) the story to the child, loosely following the story script. You do not need to memorize the story script, but become familiar enough with it to tell a similar story.

c. Leave the book with the child and move away – either at an angle facing the child or across the table. Moving away from the child helps promote language and minimize pointing. Turn on the recorder and instruct the child to tell the story back in the same language.

Directions to the child:
Examiner: *Ahora, cuentame lo que pasó en este cuento.*

Refer to the following section for a list of prompts which may be used while the child retells the story. Remember, all prompts should be in Spanish.

d. After the child finishes telling the story, turn off the recorder and thank the child for telling his/her story.

3. Prompts

Use minimal open-ended prompts when eliciting the samples. Using overly-specific questions or providing too much information to the child compromises the process of capturing the child's true language and ability level. Open-ended prompts do not provide the child with answers or vocabulary. They do encourage the child to try or they let the child know it is ok to move on if needed. Use open-ended prompts/questions as necessary.

- Use open-ended prompts when the child:
  is not speaking
  says "Cómo se dice?"
  starts listing, e.g., "niño", "perro", "tarro"

- Acceptable verbal prompts include:
  Dime más.
  Haz lo mejor que puedas.
  Dime sobre eso/esa.
  Estás haciendolo muy bien.
  Me gustaría oír más sobre eso/esa.
  Dime lo que puedas.

Eso/Esa suena interesante.
¿Qué más?
Siguele. Dale.
Mhm . Uhhuh.

- Acceptable nonverbal prompts include:
Smiles and eye contact
Nods of affirmation and agreement

- Unacceptable prompts include:
¿Qué está haciendo (él)?
¿Dónde está (él)?
Pointing at scenes in the book while prompting
¿Qué es esto?
¿Qué está pasando/ocurriendo aquí?

Avoid asking the "wh" questions, who?, what?, when?, where? These often lead
to obvious and limited responses/answers.

Transcription Notes

The Spanish samples in the reference database were transcribed by fluent
Spanish speakers.

Utterances were segmented into Modified Communication Units (MC-units)
which were developed specifically for these samples to account for the
pronoun-drop nature of the Spanish language.

The underscore was used for repetitious words or phrases within utterances.
This prevented inflation of the MLU due to repetition used to provide emphasis,
e.g., C dijeron|decir rana_rana_rana dónde estás|estar.

All transcripts have timing markers at the beginning and end of the sample. The
initial marker indicates the child's first utterance. The final timing marker
indicates the end of the child's narrative.

Coding Notes

- [EO:word] marks overgeneralization errors.
- [EW: word] marks other word-level errors.
- [EU] marks utterance-level errors.
- [CS] is a word code attached to all code-switched words (Spanish words in English transcripts or English words in Spanish transcripts).
- [I] is a word code attached to all imitations of vocabulary provided by the examiner.

The following codes were created to mark Spanish-influenced English:

- [WO] is an utterance-level code signifying words or phrases within an utterance which are out of order in Standard English. The content (semantics) of the utterance is correct; however the word order is awkward, e.g., *C And then fall down the dog and the boy [WO].*
- [EW] marks an extraneous or unnecessary word in the utterance that, if omitted, would make the utterance syntactically correct, e.g., *C And he shout/ed and[EW] to the frog.* As a general rule, do not mark more than one extraneous word in an utterance; instead, mark the utterance using the [EU] code.
- [F] was placed at the end of each utterance lacking a stated subject as a result segmenting utterances using MC-units.

Subordination Index (SI) and Narrative Scoring Scheme (NSS) Coding

SI and NSS coding was applied to all the samples in the Bilingual Spanish/English Story Retell reference databases.

SI is a measure of syntactic complexity which produces a ratio of the total number of clauses (main and subordinate clauses) to the number of C-units. A clause, whether it is main or subordinate, is a statement containing both a subject and a predicate. Grammatically, a subject is a noun phrase and a predicate is a verb phrase. Main clauses can stand by themselves. Subordinate clauses depend on the main clause to make sense. They are embedded within an utterance as noun, adjective or adverbial clauses (see Appendix O).

NSS is an assessment tool developed to create a more objective narrative content and structure scoring system. It is based upon early work on story grammar analysis by Stein and Glenn, 1979, 1982. This scoring procedure combines many of the abstract categories of Story Grammar, adding features of cohesion, connecting events, rationale for characters' behavior and referencing. Each of the scoring categories has specific explicit examples to establish scoring criteria, reducing the abstractness of the story grammar categories (see Appendix P).

Acknowledgements

Language samples for the Monolingual Spanish reference database were collected and transcribed as part of grant R01 HD44923 "Language and Literacy Development in Mexican Children", funded by NICHD, Goldenberg, C., PI.

Spanish script for *One Frog Too Many* by Mercer and Marianna Mayer (1975)

Página	Papel
1	Había un niño quien tenía tres animales; un perro, una rana y una tortuga. Un día vio una caja envuelta con papel regalo. La tarjeta en la caja decía que era un regalo para él.
2	Abrió la caja y se emocionó cuando vio lo que había adentro.
3	Había una ranita. Al niño, al perro y a la tortuga les gustó la ranita. Pero a la otra rana grande no le gustó. La rana grande quería seguir siendo la rana favorita del niño. Se puso celosa.
4	El niño puso la ranita al lado de sus otras mascotas y dijo: "Esta es mi nueva ranita, ¡dile hola a todos!"
5	La rana grande le dijo: "Yo soy la rana mas vieja y grande, ¡No me agradas!"
6	Entonces la rana le mordió la pata a la ranita. La ranita lloró... "¡Ay, ay!" El niño no creía que la rana grande le hiciera algo asi a la pobre ranita chiquita.
7	El niño levantó a la ranita y regañó a la rana grande: "Fue muy malo lo que hiciste. ¡Tienes que tratar bien a la ranita nueva!"
8	Las mascotas del niño lo siguieron afuera para jugar. Las dos ranas se montaron en la tortuga, pero a la rana grande todavía no le agradaba la ranita.
9	El niño, disfrazado como pirata, iba de primero en la fila.
10	Mientras tanto, la rana grande pateó a la ranita y la tumbó de la tortuga.
11	Pero cuando los demás oyeron a la ranita llorando, se dieron cuenta de lo que había pasado. Todos estaban enojados con la rana por ser tan mala con la ranita.
12 – 13	El niño llegó con todos sus animales a un estanque donde había una balsa. El niño no dejó entrar en la balsa a la rana grande. Pero a ella no le gustó que la dejaran sola en la orilla del estanque.
14 – 15	Así que la ranita no le hizo caso al niño y brincó a la balsa. Solamente la ranita se dio cuenta de que la rana había brincado en la balsa. La rana miró a la ranita con una cara muy brava.

16	Entonces la rana grande pateó a la ranita y la tumbó de la balsa.
17	La rana le sacó la lengua a la ranita y pensó: "Eso le enseñará".
18	La rana grande estaba contenta. Ahora era la única rana del niño – como solía ser antes. Pero, la tortuga le tocó la pierna al niño para avisarle lo que había pasado.
19	Cuando el niño se volteó, se asombró de lo que vio. "¿Cómo llegó la rana grande hasta la balsa? ¿y dónde está la ranita?"
20 – 21	El niño y sus mascotas se bajaron de la balsa y buscaron a la ranita. Ellos miraron por todas partes y dijeron: "Ranita, ¿Dónde estás?
22 – 23	Pero ellos no pudieron encontrarla. Durante el camino de vuelta, el niño estaba triste y empezó a llorar. La rana grande se arrepintió por lo que había hecho.
24	Cuando llegó a su casa, el niño se acostó en su cama y se puso a llorar. Sus mascotas también estaban tristes. Hasta la rana grande estaba triste.
25	Entonces, oyeron algo fuera de la ventana. Era el sonido de una ranita.
26	De repente, la ranita brincó por la ventana abierta. Todos estaban muy emocionados de ver a la ranita. Ellos creían que no la verían de nuevo, pero allí estaba.
27	La ranita brincó a la cabeza de la rana grande y se rió.
28	La rana grande decidió ser buena con la ranita desde ahora en adelante. Todos estaban muy felices.

ENNI Database

Database	Context (Subgroup)	Age Range	# Samples	Location
ENNI	Nar (ENNI)	3;11 – 10;0	377	Canada

The Edmonton Narrative Norms Instrument (ENNI) is an assessment tool for collecting language information from children aged 4 to 9 through storytelling. Pictures that portray a story are presented to a child, who then tells the story to the examiner. Picture sets were drawn for the ENNI by a professional cartoonist. They range from a simple story with 2 characters to a complex story with 4 characters.

Participants

377 typically developing children, aged 3;11-10;0, living in Edmonton, Alberta, Canada and speaking English as a first language. Children were drawn from 34 preschools, daycares, and schools in the public and separate school boards. The range of economic and ethnic backgrounds reflects the diversity in the Edmonton area, as determined by a comparison with Statistics Canada data. Teachers were asked to refer two children in the upper level of achievement, two children from the middle level, and two children in the lower level (one boy and one girl at each level). In all cases, the children who were referred for the typical development sample were not to have speech or language difficulties or any other diagnostic label such as attention deficit disorder, learning disability, or autism spectrum disorder. The children constitute the typically developing sample in the Edmonton Narrative Norms Instrument (ENNI), which also contains data from children with language impairment.

Elicitation Protocol

The task is story generation from pictures (not a story retell). Six original picture sets with animal characters are used to elicit stories, two each at three levels of complexity. The stories are controlled in pairs and systematically varied across levels for length, amount of story information, and number and gender of characters. The pictures for each story are placed in page protectors with each story in its own binder. When administering each story, the examiner first goes through all the pages so that the child can preview the story, after which the examiner turns the pages again as the child tells the story. The examiner turns the page when the child appears to be finished telling the story for a particular picture. The examiner holds the binder in such a way that he or she cannot see the pictures as the child tells the story, which means that the child needs to be explicit if the examiner is to understand the story; the child cannot legitimately use pointing in lieu of language when telling the story. The instructions emphasize that the examiner will not be able to see the pictures, so the child will have to tell a really good story in order for the examiner to understand it.

A training story is administered first consisting of a single episode 5-picture story. The purpose of the training story is to familiarize the child with the procedure and to allow the examiner to give more explicit prompts if the child has difficulty with the task. After the training story is administered, there are two story sets which may be given: Set A (Giraffe/Elephant) and Set B (Rabbit/Dog). You have the option of administering either or both sets. Both story sets were administered to all participants in the database.

When selecting language samples from the database, you have the option including both story sets or restricting the selection to a specific story set by specifying one of the following subgroups:
- Sets A & B = Set A and Set B stories
- Set A = Set A stories (Giraffe/Elephant)
- Set B = Set B stories (Rabbit/Dog)

Transcription Notes

Utterances were segmented into Communication Units (C-units), which consist either of an independent clause plus any dependent clauses or of a partial sentence. Utterances that were broken off by the speaker were counted as mazes. Timing is not indicated in the transcripts. Socioeconomic status, parental education and ethnic background are not indicated in the transcripts.

Coding Notes

The following codes were consistently used:
- [EW:word] marks word-level errors
- [EU] marks utterance-level errors

Resources

All picture sets and detailed administration and transcription instructions can be downloaded free of charge at www.rehabmed.ualberta.ca/spa/enni. The ENNI is copyrighted, including the pictures and all other materials. You are welcome to download, print, and use any of the materials for clinical, educational, or research purposes. None of the ENNI materials may be altered in any way or included in publications without permission from the authors.

Acknowledgements

Funding for this study was provided by the Children's Health Foundation of Northern Alberta. The ENNI was created by Phyllis Schneider, Rita Vis Dubé, and Denyse Hayward at the University of Alberta. The authors would like to thank Marilynn McAra, Livia Tamblin, and Linda Kaert for their assistance in data collection, and Jess Folk-Farber, Rhonda Kajner, Roxanne Lemire, Marlene May, Michelle Millson, Ignatius Nip, Michelle Trapp, and Kathy Wagner for their assistance with other aspects of the study.

K

Gillam Narrative Tasks Database

Database	Context (Subgroup)	Age Range	# Samples	Location
Gillam Narrative Tasks	Nar (GNT)	5;0 – 11;11	500	USA

Participants

The Gillam Narrative Tasks reference database consists of narrative samples from participants ranging in age from 5;0 to 11;11, including 50 five-year olds, 100 six-year olds, 100 seven-year-olds, 100 eight-year-olds, 50 nine-year-olds, 50 ten-year-olds, and 50 eleven-year-olds. There are an equal number of boys and girls at each age. Children came from four US regions (Northeast, South, Midwest, and West). Their primary language was English and they had not been identified with a disability and were not receiving any special education services. The race/ethnicity distribution of the children in the sample set is 71% white (not Hispanic), 11% black or African-American, 10% Hispanic, and 8% other or not reported.

Elicitation Protocol

Examiners collected data on children's ability to tell stories in three formats: (1) a story retell with no picture cues, (2) a story production from five sequenced pictures, and (3) a fictional narrative based on a single picture. The examiner scripts and picture stimuli that were used to elicit the narratives are available in the Test of Narrative Language (Gillam & Pearson, 2004).

- **Oral Narrative Task: McDonald's - Script Retell (no picture cues)**
  In the first narrative format, the examiner reads aloud a story about two children who go to McDonald's with their mother. Because no picture cues are provided, the child must rely on auditory memory to answer literal and inferential comprehension questions about the story. After answering the story comprehension questions, the child is asked to retell the entire McDonald's story. The child's retelling was recorded and transcribed.

- **Oral Narrative Task : Late for School - Five Sequenced Pictures**
  The examiner shows the child a sequence of five pictures that illustrate the critical events in a single-episode story that the examiner tells. After reading the story to the child, the examiner asks the child to answer nine literal and inferential comprehension questions about the characters, events, and consequences in the story. The comprehension questions and answers were not transcribed. The examiner then shows the child a sequence of five new pictures that depict a sequence of events about a boy who is late for school. The child is instructed to create a story that corresponds to the sequence of pictures. The child's oral story about the sequence of pictures was recorded and transcribed.

- **Oral Narrative Task: Aliens - Single Picture**
  The examiner tells a multi-episode story that corresponds to a picture of two children who are looking at a treasure being guarded by a dragon. The examiner asks ten literal and inferential comprehension questions about the characters, events, problems, and consequences in the story. The comprehension questions and answers were not transcribed. The examiner then shows the child a picture of two children who witness a family of aliens walking out of a spaceship that has landed in a park. The child's oral story that corresponded to the picture of a fictional event was recorded and transcribed.

Transcription Notes

Language samples were transcribed according to SALT conventions by undergraduate and graduate students in Communication Sciences and Disorders who completed a course on transcription and reached 90% or better agreement on three training transcripts. Utterances were segmented into C-units, which were defined as groups of words that could not be further divided without loss of their essential meaning. After the recording was transcribed by one research assistant, a second research assistant listened and marked disagreements with any of the original segmentation and/or coding decisions. All disagreements were resolved by a PhD level research coordinator who listened to the recording as she made a third pass through the transcripts. Timing information was not coded. Gender, age, and ethnicity information is included in the transcript header.

Acknowledgements

The narratives in this database were collected for the standardization of the Test of Narrative Language, funded by Pro-Ed Inc. Denise Hayward, PhD, supervised the transcription process while she was a post-doctoral fellow at the University of Texas at Austin. Allie Baron, Kara Bergemann, Samantha Castenuela, Jennifer Heard, Lisa Hendrix, Rebecca Garcia, Amy Grant, Tiffany Porter, Beth Schwab, and Davnee Wilson transcribed and checked the narratives. Test of Narrative Language (Gillam & Pearson, 2004).

L

New Zealand - Australia Databases

Database	Context (Subgroup)	Age Range	# Samples	Location	Section
NZ-AU Conversation	Con	NZ: 4;5 - 7;7 AU: 5;5 - 8;4	NZ: 248 AU: 102	New Zealand Australia	1
NZ-AU Story Retell	Nar (AGL & Bus)	NZ: 4;0 - 7;7 AU: 5;3 - 8;9	NZ: 264 AU: 212	New Zealand Australia	2
NZ-AU Personal Narrative	Nar (NZPN)	NZ: 4;5 - 7;7 AU: 5;5 - 8;4	NZ: 228 AU: 127	New Zealand Australia	3
NZ-AU Expository	Expo	NZ: 6;1 - 7;11 AU: 7;4 - 8;4	NZ: 65 AU: 42	New Zealand Australia	4

1. New Zealand – Australia Conversation Database

Database	Context (Subgroup)	Age Range	# Samples	Location
NZ-AU Conversation	Con	NZ: 4;5 - 7;7 AU: 5;5 - 8;4	NZ: 248 AU: 102	New Zealand Australia

General Description

This database contains oral language samples collected from participants in a conversational context; a 10 minute conversation to elicit at least 50 complete and intelligible utterances.

New Zealand Participants

This language samples collected from New Zealand are from children aged 4;5 - 7;7. The samples were collected from the participants in a conversational context. The children were randomly selected from schools in Auckland, Hamilton, and Christchurch (major urban areas in New Zealand) as well as secondary urban areas surrounding Christchurch. Approximately 80% of the participants were from the Auckland/Hamilton region to reflect New Zealand's population density in these areas. Children with diagnosed disabilities were excluded from the sample. The schools reflected a range of socio-economic areas and English was the first language of all children included in the database. There was an even gender distribution. The ethnicity of the group is comprised of the following: New Zealand European: 62%, Maori: 22%, Pasifika 5%, Asian 3%, and Other 8%.

The Group Special Education speech-language therapists involved in the project were trained by one of the researchers on the assessment procedures and language sampling protocol. Each child was seen individually in the child's school setting and was administered a New Zealand speech and language screening test and reading or letter knowledge test to gain information regarding the child's general language development. Any child who performed very poorly on the receptive language screening task (i.e., could not follow basic instructions) was excluded from the database. Children's language samples were also excluded from the database for reasons such as poor recording quality and not engaging in the task (i.e., not willing to talk). Only samples that contained over 45 complete and intelligible utterances were included.

Australian Participants

Children, aged 5;5 - 8;4, were randomly selected from the first three years of primary school, grade 0 (Prep or Foundation Year), grade 1, and grade 2, across Queensland (regional: 55; City: 72), representing the full range of socio-economic areas (1 – 10).

Ethics approval for this project was granted by the University Human Ethics Committee (PES/31/12/HREC). Approval was also granted by the Department of Education and Training, Queensland Government (550/27/1258). Of the schools who agreed to participate, teachers were asked to identify children who 1) attended Foundation Year (known as Prep; YOS1), Year 1 (YOS2), or Year 2; YOS 3); 2) spoke English as their first language; 3) were progressing normally at school; and 4) had no history of speech and/or language impairments. Consent forms were sent home to these children via the teachers. From the children for whom consent to participate was obtained, participants were randomly selected, making sure there was an equal distribution of girls and boys, and an equal number of participants across the three grades. Conversational language samples were elicited from 102 children, from grade 0 (n = 37), grade 1 (n = 32), and grade 2 (n = 33). There was an even gender distribution. These children were from the following ethnic backgrounds, as indicated by their parents on the project consent forms:

Australian (85.5%)
Aboriginal and Torres Strait Islander (3.9%)
Pacific Island (.8%)
Other (3.1%)
Non-specified (6.3%)

A total of 21 speech pathologists assisted with the data collection. These therapists received a manual, observed a demonstration video, and attended a one-hour teleconference. Each child was seen individually in the child's school setting and was administered a range of oral language tasks. Children's language samples were excluded from the database if they contained less than 40 complete and intelligible utterances. For this reason 24 transcripts were discarded (see Westerveld & Vidler, 2014). As reported in Westerveld and Vidler, samples of less than 5 minutes' duration were 1.8 times more likely to contain fewer than 50 utterances.

Elicitation Procedures

The conversation protocol aimed to elicit 50 complete and intelligible utterances from the child in 10 minutes of conversation. The protocol was adapted from interview procedures described by Evans and Craig (1992). The child was asked to bring an object from the classroom to discuss with the examiner. The examiner encouraged the child to talk about the object. The child was then asked to talk about his or her family, school, and after-school activities. To establish and maintain a productive communicative interaction, the suggestions listed by Miller (1981) were followed. These included listening and following the child's lead, maintaining the child's pace, using open-ended prompts, and adding new information when appropriate.

Transcription Notes

The utterances were segmented into Communication Units (C-units). A C-unit includes an independent clause with its modifiers (Loban, 1976). The following error codes were inserted in the transcripts: [EO] to mark overgeneralization errors, [EP] to mark pronoun errors, [EW:word] to mark word-level errors, and [EU] to mark utterance-level errors.

Database Selection Options

This database was created with two location options (New Zealand and Australia) and one ethnicity option (Maori). A language sample taken from a child can be compared against this population distribution as a whole or against a subset selected by location and/or including Maori (New Zealand) children only.

Acknowledgements

The New Zealand databases are a result of the collaboration with Gail Gillon from the Department of Communication Disorders, University of Canterbury and Marleen Westerveld from Griffith University. Speech-language therapists from Group Special Education in Auckland, Hamilton,

Christchurch, and Canterbury districts in New Zealand were involved in the collection of the language samples. The New Zealand Ministry of Education allowed the participation of Special Education speech-language therapists in the project. Financial assistance for the project was provided by the University of Canterbury, The Don Bevan Travel Scholarship, and the New Zealand Speech Language Therapists' Association.

The Australian databases are the result of a collaboration between Dr. Marleen Westerveld from Griffith University, and Kath Vidler from the Department of Education, Training, and Employment. Speech pathologists employed by the Department of Education, Training, and Employment across the State of Queensland were involved in the collection of the language samples. Financial assistance for the project was provided through a Griffith University Emerging Researcher Grant and by SALT Software LLC.

2. New Zealand – Australia Story Retell Database

Database	Context (Subgroup)	Age Range	# Samples	Location
NZ-AU Story Retell	Nar (AGL)	NZ: 4;0 - 7;7 AU: 5;3 - 8;9	NZ: 264 AU: 212	New Zealand Australia

Participants and General Description

This database contains oral language samples collected from New Zealand children, aged 4;0 - 7;7, and from Australian children, aged 5;3 - 8;9. The language samples were collected from the participants in a story retelling context using a story format and vocabulary that is familiar to children in New Zealand and Australia.

The initial data were collected in 2000/2001 from 4;6 to 7;7 year-old children who had been randomly selected from kindergartens and schools in Auckland, Hamilton, and Christchurch (major urban areas in New Zealand) as well as secondary urban areas surrounding Christchurch. Approximately 80% of the participants were from the Auckland/Hamilton region to reflect New Zealand's population density in these areas. Children with diagnosed disabilities were excluded from the sample. The schools reflected a range of socio-economic areas, and English was the first language of all children included in the database. There was an even gender distribution. The ethnicity of the group comprised of the following: New Zealand European: 62%, Maori: 22%, Pacific Island 5%, Asian 3%, Other 8%.

A second set of data was collected in November 2009 from 76 children aged 4;0 to 4;11. All children attended their local kindergarten in Christchurch, New Zealand. The kindergartens reflected a range of socio-economic areas, and English was the first language of all children. There were 58% girls and 42% boys. Ethnic make-up of the group was as follows: NZ European 89%, Maori 8%, Pacific Island 1.5%, Other 1.5%.

Two sets of samples were collected in Australia in 2012. The first set was based on the story "Ana Gets Lost". These samples were collected from 85 children (ages 5;5 to 7;7) attending the first two years of primary school: Grade 0 (Prep or Foundation) and Grade 1 across Queensland, representing the full range of socio-economic areas (1 – 10). There were 44 (52%) girls and 41 (49%) boys. All children spoke English as their first language and were progressing normally at school as indicated by their teachers. Ethnic make-up of the group was as follows: Australian 80%, Aboriginal and Torres Strait Islander 4.7%, European 3.5%, Unspecified 10.6%, Other 1.2%.

The second set of samples collected in Australia was based on the Bus story. This database contains language samples collected from Australian children attending the first three years of primary school: Grade 0 (Prep or Foundation Year), Grade 1, and Grade 2 across Queensland (regional: 55; City: 72), representing the full range of socio-economic areas (1 – 10). The language samples were collected from the participants in a narrative context, using the story retelling task "The Bus Story" (Renfrew, 1995). Ethics approval for this project was granted by the University Human Ethics Committee (PES/31/12/HREC). Approval was also granted by the Department of Education and Training, Queensland Government (550/27/1258). Of the schools who agreed to participate, teachers were asked to identify children who 1) were in their first three years of primary schooling; 2) spoke English as their first language; 3) were progressing normally at school; and 4) had no history of speech and/or language impairments. Consent forms were sent home to these children via the teachers. From the children for whom consent to participate was obtained, participants were randomly selected, making sure there was an equal distribution of girls and boys, and an equal number of participants across the three grades. A total of 127 children participated in this study, from Grade 0 (n = 44), Grade 1 (41), and Grade 2 (n = 42). These children were from the following ethnic backgrounds, as indicated by their parents on the project consent forms: Australian (85.5%), Aboriginal and Torres Strait Islander (3.9%), Pacific Island (.8%), Other (3.1%), and Non-specified (6.3%).

Other criteria

The therapists and educators involved in the project were trained by one of the researchers on the assessment procedures and language sampling protocol. Each child was seen individually in the child's school setting. Children's language samples were excluded from the database for reasons such as poor recording quality, not engaging in the task (i.e., unwilling to retell the story), or not able to retell the story without using the pictures in the book as a visual prompts.

Elicitation Procedures – Subgroup AGL

The child was required to listen to two audio-recordings of an unfamiliar story (while looking at pictures in the story book). Following the second listening of the story the child was asked to retell the story without the use of the pictures. The child listened to an English translation of the story "Ko au na galo"; *Ana Gets Lost* (Swan, 1992). The story is about a Pacific Islands girl who gets lost in the city while looking for her mum and dad. It is a 10-page 'reader' (of the type typically used in New Zealand Year 1 and 2 classrooms) with colored pictures and Tokelauan text. The story was selected for several reasons: The story has not been published in English, which minimized the chances of children being familiar with the book. Presenting text in an unknown language also prevented the children reading the text while they heard the story and thus removed any reading advantage. Having a text written in another language also provided a convincing reason for listening carefully to the recording of the English version of the text. Further, children from different cultures living in New Zealand or Australia were expected to be familiar with the story content and vocabulary translation, such as 'policeman', 'beach', and 'dairy'. The original translation of "Ko au na galo" was adapted to add a little further length and complexity to the story.

Following the first listening of the story, the child was asked eight questions about the story to evaluate oral narrative comprehension (see the language sampling protocol for New Zealand-Australia databases in the help built into SALT). To reduce the influence of story comprehension on individual children's retelling performance, all children were provided with the correct information if their answers were clearly incorrect or if they did not provide an answer.

Elicitation Procedures – Subgroup BUS

- The Bus Story (Renfrew, 1995) was administered using the standard elicitation guidelines as reported in the manual. In this task, the examiner reads the story, while the child follows along with the pictures in a wordless book (four pages containing three pictures each). After listening to the story, the child is asked "Now you tell me the story. Once upon a time, there was a ...?" (p. 5). Following the administration guidelines, only minimal or indirect prompts should be given, when needed. For example "and then?" or "so...?". The model story contains: 15 utterances (UTT), MLU: 12.4, number of different words (NDW): 102, and clausal density (CD; total number of clauses divided by the number of utterances): 1.6. Refer to Westerveld and Vidler (2015) for more information.

Transcription Notes

The utterances were segmented into Communication Units (C-units). A C-unit includes an independent clause with its modifiers (Loban, 1976). All transcripts were timed and pauses, within and between utterances, of two or more seconds in length, were marked. Age and gender information is included for all participants.

The following types of utterances were excluded from analysis by inserting an equal (=) sign in front of the utterance: 1) official title, e.g., "Ana Gets Lost", 2) comments unrelated to the story, e.g., child comments on someone entering the room, 3) official ending, e.g., *The end*.

The following error codes were inserted in the transcripts: [EO:word] to mark overgeneralization errors, [EP:word] to mark pronoun errors, [EW:word] to mark other word-level errors, and [EU] to mark utterance-level errors. [NGA] was inserted to mark an utterance that is 'not grammatically accurate'.

All New Zealand samples contained the following plus lines:
+ Context: Nar
+ Subgroup: AGL
+ Ethnicity: Maori (only included for Maori subset)
All Australian samples contained the following plus lines:
+ Context: Nar
+ Subgroup: AGL or BUS

Database Location and Ethnicity Selection Options

This database was created with two location options (New Zealand and Australia) and one ethnicity option (Maori). A language sample taken from a child can be compared against this population distribution as a whole or against a subset selected by location and/or including Maori (New Zealand) children only.

Acknowledgements

The New Zealand databases are a result of the collaboration with Gail Gillon from the Department of Communication Disorders, University of Canterbury and Marleen Westerveld from Griffith University. Speech-language therapists from Group Special Education in Auckland, Hamilton,

Christchurch, and Canterbury districts in New Zealand were involved in the collection of the language samples. The New Zealand Ministry of Education allowed the participation of Special Education speech-language therapists in the project. Financial assistance for the project was provided by the University of Canterbury, The Don Bevan Travel Scholarship, and the New Zealand Speech Language Therapists' Association.

The Australian databases are the result of a collaboration between Dr. Marleen Westerveld from Griffith University, and Kath Vidler from the Department of Education, Training, and Employment. Speech pathologists employed by the Department of Education, Training, and Employment across the State of Queensland were involved in the collection of the language samples. Financial assistance for the project was provided through a Griffith University Emerging Researcher Grant and by SALT Software LLC.

3. New Zealand – Australia Personal Narrative Database

Database	Context (Subgroup)	Age Range	# Samples	Location
NZ-AU Personal Narrative	Nar (NZPN)	NZ: 4;5 - 7;7 AU: 5;5 - 8;4	NZ: 228 AU: 127	New Zealand Australia

Participants and General Description

This database contains oral language samples collected from New Zealand children, aged 4;5 – 7;7, and from Australian children, aged 5;5 - 8;4. The language samples were collected from the participants in a personal narrative context (relating a personal experience).

The New Zealand data were collected in 2000/2001. The children were randomly selected from schools in Auckland, Hamilton, and Christchurch (major urban areas in New Zealand) as well as secondary urban areas surrounding Christchurch. Approximately 80% of the participants were from the Auckland/Hamilton region to reflect New Zealand's population density in these areas. Children with diagnosed disabilities were excluded from the sample. The schools reflected a range of socio-economic areas and English was the first language of all children included in the database. There was an even gender distribution. The ethnicity of the group comprised of the following: New Zealand European 62%, Maori 22%, Pacific Island 5%, Asian 3%, Other 8%.

The Australian data were collected in 2012 from 127 children (aged 5;5 to 8;4) attending the first three years of primary school: Grade 0 (Prep or Foundation, n = 44), Grade 1 (n = 41), or Grade 2 (n = 42) across Queensland (regional: 55, city: 72), representing the full range of socio-economic areas (1 – 10). There were 64 (50.4%) girls and 63 boys (49.6%). Of the schools who agreed to participate, teachers were asked to identify children who 1) spoke English as their first language; 2) were progressing normally at school; and 3) had no history of speech and/or language impairments. Consent forms were sent home to these children via the teachers. From the children for whom consent to participate was obtained, participants were randomly selected, making sure there was an equal distribution of girls and boys. Children were from Australian (85.2%), Aboriginal and Torres Strait Islander (4.0%), Pacific Island (0.8%), Other (3.2%), or Non-specified (6.4%) ethnic backgrounds, as indicated by their parents on the project consent forms.

The speech-language therapists involved in the project were trained by one of the researchers on the assessment procedures and language sampling protocol. Each child was seen individually in the child's school setting. Children's language samples were also excluded from the database for reasons such as poor recording quality and not engaging in the task (i.e., not giving any personal narratives).

Elicitation Procedures

The personal narrative protocol was adapted from a conversational technique developed by Peterson and McCabe (1983), called the Conversational Map. In adapting this technique, the examiner related a brief personal experience related to a photo prompt in order to encourage the child to share one of his or her personal experiences. A pocketsize photo album with a series of carefully selected photos was used for the stimulus items. Each photo was presented individually in separate sleeves of the photo album. The examiner provided a short prompting narrative with each photo followed by the question "Did anything like that ever happen to you?". If the child responded "no", the examiner turned the page of the photo album to the next photo. If the child responded "yes", a follow-up question was asked "Can you tell me about it?". The aim is to elicit at least 3 narratives and 50 C&I utterances.

The task is introduced as follows: "I brought some photos to show you." Talk about the photos as outlined in the protocol. If the child responds "no", go to the next photo. If the child says "yes", ask him/her "Can you tell me about it?"

To encourage the child to continue a personal narrative, the examiner can respond to the child's narrative by:
- Repeating the exact words of the children when they pause
- Using relatively neutral sub-prompts, such as "uh-huh"
- Saying "tell me more"
- Asking "and then what happened?"

It is very important that the examiner does NOT evaluate the child's narrative. This gives the children the opportunity to demonstrate what they can do on their own.

Transcription Notes

The utterances were segmented into Communication Units (C-units). A C-unit includes an independent clause with its modifiers (Loban, 1976). All transcripts were timed, and pauses, within and between utterances, of two or more seconds in length, were marked. Age and gender information is included for all participants.

The prompts were transcribed from (and including) the examiner's question that leads to a "yes" response from the child. For example, with the first prompt (McDonald's), <u>only transcribe the underlined italicized utterances</u>:

Oh look who's this? I went to a birthday party at McDonald's last year. *Have you ever been to McDonald's?* Child responds Yes or {Nods}. *What happened last time you went to McDonald's?*

The following plus lines were inserted as part of the header information:
+ Context: Nar
+ Subgroup: NZPN
+ Ethnicity: Maori (only included for Maori subset)

This database was created with two location options (New Zealand and Australia) and one ethnicity option (Maori). A language sample taken from a child can be compared against this population distribution as a whole or against a subset selected by location and/or including Maori (New Zealand) children only.

Acknowledgements

The New Zealand databases are a result of the collaboration with Gail Gillon from the Department of Communication Disorders, University of Canterbury and Marleen Westerveld from Griffith University. Speech-language therapists from Group Special Education in Auckland, Hamilton, Christchurch, and Canterbury districts in New Zealand were involved in the collection of the language samples. The New Zealand Ministry of Education allowed the participation of Special Education speech-language therapists in the project. Financial assistance for the project was provided by the University of Canterbury, The Don Bevan Travel Scholarship, and the New Zealand Speech Language Therapists' Association.

The Australian databases are the result of a collaboration between Dr. Marleen Westerveld from Griffith University and Kath Vidler from the Department of Education, Training, and Employment. Speech pathologists employed by the Department of Education, Training, and Employment across the State of Queensland were involved in the collection of the language samples. Financial assistance for the project was provided through a Griffith University Emerging Researcher Grant and by SALT Software LLC.

Protocol and Photos to Elicit Personal Narratives

You can download the specific protocol and photos used to elicit the samples from the SALT web site at www.saltsoftware.com/resources/.

4. New Zealand – Australia Expository Database

Database	Context (Subgroup)	Age Range	# Samples	Location
NZ-AU Expository	Expo	NZ: 6;1 - 7;11 AU: 7;4 - 8;4	NZ: 65 AU: 42	New Zealand Australia

Participants and General Description

A total of 65 six- and seven-year-old participants were recruited from three primary schools located in suburban Auckland, New Zealand (NZ). The schools were awarded mid socio-economic status based on the Ministry of Education ranking system. These children had no known history of hearing disorder, neurological disorder, or speech-language therapy, spoke English as their first language, and were progressing normally at school. The group consisted of 37 girls and 28 boys from NZ European (74%), Maori (14%), Pasifika (8%), and Other (4%) ethnic backgrounds.

A second set of data was collected in 2013 from 42 children aged 7;5 to 8;4 who attended Year 2 (year of schooling 3) of their local primary school in Queensland, Australia. Ethics approval for this project was granted by the University Human Ethics Committee (PES/31/12/HREC). Approval was also granted by the Department of Education and Training, Queensland Government (550/27/1258). The schools reflected the full range of socio-economic areas. Of the schools who agreed to participate, teachers were asked to identify children who 1) spoke English as their first language; 2) were progressing normally at school; and 3) had no history of speech and/or language impairments. Consent forms were sent home to these children via the teachers, and from the children for whom consent to participate was obtained, participants were randomly selected, making sure there was an equal distribution of girls and boys. The group consisted of 19 girls and 23 boys, from Australian (90.5%), Aboriginal and Torres Strait Islander (2.4 %), or Non-specified (7.1%) ethnic backgrounds.

This database was created with two options. A language sample taken from a child can be compared against this population distribution as a whole or against a database including NZ or AU children only.

Elicitation Procedures

Expository language generation samples were elicited using the Favorite Game or Sports (FGS) task, developed by Nippold, et al. (2005). In this task, the examiner carefully follows a script. First, the child is asked what his or her favorite game or sport is and why. The examiner then asks the child to explain the game or sport, using the pragmatically felicitous prompt "I am not too familiar with the game of [..]". Finally, the child is asked what a player should do to win a game of [..]. The child should be allowed as much time as necessary to finish the explanation. The examiner needs to make sure to show interest in the child's explanation and only use neutral responses as needed to encourage the child to continue.

Favorite Game or Sport (FGS) Task Protocol

This task was developed by Nippold, et al. (2005).
To elicit the sample, the examiner reads out the following script:

I am hoping to learn what people of different ages know about certain topics.
1. *What is your favorite game or sport?*
2. *Why is [chess, soccer, etc.] your favorite game/sport?*
3. *I'm not too familiar with the game of (chess), so I would like you to tell me all about it. For example, tell me what the goals are, and how many people may play a game. Also, tell me about the rules the players need to follow. Tell me everything you can think of about the game of (chess) so that someone who has never played it before will know how to play.*
4. *Now I would like you to tell me what a player should do in order to <u>win</u> the game of (chess). In other words, what are some key strategies that every good player should know?*

Following each prompt, the interviewer pauses, displays interest in the response, and allows the child as much time as necessary to complete the response. If the child fails to address a question or requests for the question to be repeated, the interviewer is allowed to ask the question again.

Transcription Notes

The utterances were segmented into Communication Units (C-units). A C-unit includes an independent clause with its modifiers (Loban, 1976). Utterances that did not contain a subject and a predicate were coded as fragments, i.e., [FRG] code inserted at the end of these utterances, so they could be easily excluded from analysis. The transcripts begin with the student's first utterance which pertains to the child's answer to the question what his or her favorite game or sport is. All transcripts were timed and pauses, within and between utterances, of two or more seconds in length, were marked.

The following error codes were inserted in the transcripts: [EP] to mark pronoun errors, [EO] to mark overgeneralization errors, [ES] to mark semantic errors, [EW] to mark other word-level errors, and [EU] to mark utterance-level errors. [FRG] marks utterance fragments, and [NGA] marks utterances that are 'not grammatically accurate'. All Australian samples were also coded for dependent clauses [D].

The following three types of dependent clauses were identified and coded:
- Adverbial clauses [AVC] begin with a subordinating conjunction. Examples include:
  And if they get the highest number [AVC] when the game's finished [AVC], they win [IC].
  And then once you've done that [AVC] (um) we pull out the blue mats and the (o* other k*) white mat [IC].
  And if you remember that [AVC] and you don't get hit [AVC] you win the game [IC].

- Relative clauses [RC] describe a noun and generally immediately follow the noun they describe. Examples include:
  But we (like) have to hit the person [IC] who's (um) doing that [RC].
  And he brings me to all the games [IC] that I can go to [RC].
  And you've got lines [IC] where you're allowed to go up to [RC].

- Nominal clauses name persons, places, things or ideas. These clauses often answer the question 'what'? Examples include:
  And whoever grabs the ball (um) [NOM] they (um) get to start with the ball in centre [IC].
  And that's [IC] how they lose the game sometimes [Nom].
  And whoever finishes all their beads [NOM] wins [IC].

Acknowledgements

This project was supported by a Massey University Research Fund awarded to Marleen Westerveld. All samples were collected by student clinicians under supervision, and were transcribed and coded by Massey University students. This project was funded in part by SALT Software, LLC.

The Australian database was the result of a collaboration between Dr. Marleen Westerveld from Griffith University and Kath Vidler from the Department of Education and Training. Speech pathologists employed by the Department of Education and Training across the State of Queensland were involved in the collection of the language samples. Financial assistance for the project was provided through a Griffith University Emerging Researcher Grant and by SALT Software LLC.

M

Summary of SALT Transcription Conventions

1. Transcript Format. Each entry begins with one of the following symbols. If an entry is longer than one line, continue it on the next line.

$ Identifies the speakers in the transcript; always the first line of the transcript.
       Example: $ Child, Examiner

C   Child/Client utterance. The actual character used depends on the $ speaker line.

E   Examiner utterance. The actual character used depends on the $ speaker line.

+   Typically used for identifying information such as name, age, and context.
       Example of current age: + CA: 5;7

-     Time marker.
       Example of two-minute marker: - 2:00

:   Pause between utterances of different speakers.
       Example of five-second pause: : :05

;   Pause between utterances of same speaker.
       Example of three-second pause: ; :03

=   Comment line. This information is not analyzed in any way, but is used for transcriber comments.

2. End of Utterance Punctuation. Every utterance must end with one of these six punctuation symbols.

.	Statement, comment. Do not use a period for abbreviations.	^	Interrupted utterance. The speaker is interrupted and does not complete his/her thought/utterance.
!	Surprise, exclamation.		
?	Question.	>	Abandoned utterance. The speaker does not complete his/her thought/utterance but has not been interrupted.
~	Intonation prompt. Example: E And then you have to~		

3. { } Comments within an utterance. Example: C Lookit {C points to box}.
Nonverbal utterances of communicative intent are placed in braces. Example: C {nods}.

4. Unintelligible Segments. X is used to mark unintelligible sections of an utterance. Use X for an unintelligible word, XX for an unintelligible segment of unspecified length, and XXX for an unintelligible utterance.
Example 1: C He XX today.   Example 2: C XXX.

5. **Bound Morphemes**. Words which contain a slash "/" indicate that the word is contracted, conjugated, inflected, or pluralized in a regular manner. The root word is entered in its conventional spelling followed by a slash "/" and then the bound morpheme.

English and Spanish

/S   Plural. Words that end in "s" but represent one entity are not slashed.
     Examples: kitten/s, baby/s, pants, rana/s, feliz/s, flor/s
     Irregular plurals are not marked, but are typed as spelled, e.g., leaves, mice, geese, lives, wolves.

English only

/Z   Possessive inflection.
     Examples: dad/z, Mary/z. Do not mark possessive pronouns, e.g., his, hers, ours, yours.

/S/Z Plural and Possessive. Example: baby/s/z

/ED Past tense. Predicate adjectives are not slashed.
     Examples: love/ed, die/ed, was tired, is bored

/3S 3rd Person Singular verb form. Irregular forms are not slashed.
     Examples: go/3s, tell/3s, does

/ING Verb inflection. The gerund use of the verb form is not slashed.
     Examples: go/ing, run/ing, went swimming

/N'T, /'T   Negative contractions. Irregular forms are not slashed
     Examples: can/'t, does/n't, won't

/'LL, /'M, /'D, /'RE, /'S, /'VE   Contractible verb forms.
     Examples: I/'ll, I/'m, I/'d, we/'re, he/'s, we/'ve

The following contractions were marked in the Expository and Persuasion database samples:
/H'S, /D'S, /D'D, /'US → has, does, did, us.
     Examples: He/'s been sick. What/d's he do for a living? Why/d'd the boy look for the frog? Let/'us go. In all other reference databases "let's" was not marked and the non-standard contracted forms were transcribed as two words, e.g., He has, What does.

6. **Bound Pronominal Clitics** (Spanish). Pronominal clitics may be either bound or unbound. When bound, they are preceded by a plus sign. Examples: gritándo+le, déja+lo, dá+me+lo

7. **Mazes**. Filled pauses, false starts, repetitions, and reformulations.
    ( )   Surrounds the words/part-words that fall into these categories.
       Example: C And (then um) then (h*) he left.

8. **Omissions**. Partial words, omitted words, omitted bound morphemes, and omitted pronominal clitics are denoted by an asterisk (*).
    *   Following one or more letters this indicates that a word was started but left unfinished.
      Example: C I (w* w*) want it.
    *   Preceding a word indicates that an obligatory word was omitted.
      Example: C Give it *to me.
    /*   Following a slash the * is then followed by the bound morpheme which was omitted, indicating the omission of an obligatory bound morpheme.
      Example: C The car go/*3s fast.

+*   Following a plus sign the * is then followed by the Spanish clitic which was omitted, indicating the omission of an obligatory pronominal clitic.

        Example: C Él está gritándo+*le a la rana.

9. **Overlapping Speech**. When both speakers are speaking at the same time, the words or silences that occur at the same time are surrounded by angle brackets < >.

        Example 1: C I want you to do it < > for me.   Example 2: C Can I have that <one>?

                E <Ok>.   E <Uhhuh>.

10. **Linked words**. The underscore "_" is used to link multiple words so they are treated as a single word. Examples include titles of movies and books, compound words, proper names, and words or phrases repeated multiple times.

11. **Root identification**. The vertical bar "|" is used to identify the root word.

    English uses: The root words of irregular verb forms such as "went" or "flew" are not identified.

        Linked words repeated for emphasis.

            Example: C The boy ran very very_very|very fast.

        Non-words used in error.

            Example: C He goed|go[EO:went] by hisself|himself[EW:himself].

        Shortened words.

            Example: C He was sad cuz|because they left.

    Spanish uses:

        Inflected word forms.

            Example: C Había|haber una vez un niño que tenía|tener una rana.

        Diminutives.

            Example: C El perrito|perro tumbó|tumbar las abeja/s.

        Linked words repeated for emphasis.

            Example: C Dijeron rana rana_rana|rana dónde estás.

        Non-words used in error.

12. **Sound Effects and Idiosyncratic Forms %**. The percent sign is used to identify sound effects which are essential to the meaning or structure of the utterance. Non-essential sound effects are entered as comments. Strings of the same sound are linked together.

        Example 1: C The dog went %woof_woof.   Example 2: C The dog barked {woof woof}.

    The percent sign is also used to identify idiosyncratic forms used by very young children. These are immature productions which are consistent in reference to an object, person, or situation.

        Example 1: C See %vroom {car}.   Example 2: C My %coopa {cookie}.

13. **Spelling Conventions**.
   - Filled pause words: AH, EH, ER, HM, HMM, UH, UM, MM, and any word with the code [FP]
   - Yes words: OK, AHA, MHM, UHHUH (*English & Spanish*)
                     YEAH, YEP, YES (*English only*)
                     SÍ (*Spanish only*)

- No words: NO, AHAH, MHMH, UHUH (*English & Spanish*)
                    NAH, NOPE (*English only*)
- Numbers (*examples*): 21 or TWENTYONE, 17 or DIECISIETE
- Reflexive vs Non-reflexive pronouns (Spanish only)
    The following pronouns can be used both reflexively and non-reflexively: ME, TE, SE, OS, NOS. Attach the code [X] when used reflexively.
    Examples: C El niño se[X] fue con el perro. C El perro me ayudó a conseguir la rana.
- Other English spellings:

AIN'T	GOTTA (*got to*)	LIKETA	OURS	USETA
ATTA	HMM	LOOKIT	OH, OOH	OUGHTA
BETCHA	HAFTA	NOONE	SPOSTA	WANNA
DON'T	HUH	NOPE	TRYNTA	WHATCHA
GONNA	LET'S	OOP, OOPS, OOPSY	UHOH	YOURS

14. **[ ] Codes**. Codes are used to mark words or utterances. Codes are placed in brackets [ ] and cannot contain blank spaces. Codes used to mark words are inserted at the end of a word with no intervening spaces between the code and the word.

a) Codes used to mark errors in the reference database samples:

[EO:__] used to mark overgeneralization errors.	C He falled|fall[EO:fell].
[EW:__] used to mark other word-level errors.	C He were[EW:was] look/ing.
[EW] used to mark extraneous words.	C And then the boy is a[EW] sleep/ing.
[EU] used to mark utterance-level errors.	C And they came to stop/ed [EU].
[FP] used to mark non-standard filled pause words.	C The dog (um like[FP]) fell down.

b) Other codes used in the Bilingual S/E reference database samples:

[F] used to mark fragments due to utterance segmentation with modified communication units.	C The gopher look/ed out of the hole. C and bit the boy [F].
[CS] used to mark code-switched words.	C The dog fell from la[CS] ventana[CS].
[WO] used to mark utterances with non-standard word order.	C And then fell down the dog and the boy [WO].
[I] used to mark vocabulary provided by the examiner (imitated word).	C And then the :05 <> owl[I] scare/ed him. E <Owl>.
[X] used to mark Spanish reflexive pronouns.	C El niño se[X] fue con el perro.

C-Unit Segmentation Rules

The analysis of oral language samples requires recorded speech to be segmented or divided into units. There are a few different approaches to segmenting utterances, such as phonological units, T-units, and C-units. This document describes the rules for segmenting utterances into Communication Units (C-units), a rule-governed and consistent way to segment utterances.

Disclaimer: There is variation in the literature on how to segment utterances into C-units. All of the samples in the English SALT reference databases were segmented into C-units following the rules in this document. If you intend to compare your sample with samples selected from these databases, you should segment utterances following the same rules.

Definitions

- C-Unit
  The formal definition of a C-unit is "an independent clause with its modifiers". It includes one main clause with all subordinate clauses attached to it. It cannot be further divided without the disappearance of its essential meaning.

- Clause
  A clause, whether it is the main clause or a subordinate clause, is a statement containing both a subject and a predicate. Grammatically, a subject is a noun phrase and a predicate is a verb phrase.

Segmenting Utterances into C-Units

Main clauses can stand by themselves and can be segmented into one C-unit. Subordinate clauses DEPEND on the main clause to make sense. They cannot stand alone or be separated from the main clause. So a C-unit will either consist of a main clause or a main clause with its subordinating clause(s). The following examples are broken down into main and subordinate clauses. The main clause is bolded and the subordinate clauses are underlined.

The canary was perched on a branch <u>when the man approached him.</u>
Anastasia was angry with her mother <u>because she didn't get to buy a toy.</u>
<u>When the boy looked in the jar</u> **he saw** <u>that the frog was missing.</u>

Notice the subordinate clauses cannot stand alone, or are incomplete, without the main clause. Thus, they are not separated (segmented further) from the main clause. Each of the above utterances consists of one C-unit and would be transcribed as:

C The canary was perched on a branch when the man approach/ed him.
C Anastasia was angry with her mother because she did/n't get to buy a toy.
C When the boy look/ed in the jar, he saw that the frog was missing.

Coordinating and Subordinating Conjunctions

When segmenting into C-units it is important to understand the different types of conjunctions which are used to link clauses. There are *coordinating* conjunctions and *subordinating* conjunctions.

- <u>Coordinating Conjunctions</u>

  The segmenting rule is simple when utterances contain coordinating conjunctions. These conjunctions link two main clauses which should be separated/segmented into two utterances (or two C-units) that can each stand alone. Common coordinating conjunctions include: and, but, so (but not "so that"), and then, then.

Example 1:

    C The frog was sit/ing on a lily pad.

    C And then it jump/ed in.

Example 2:

    C He had to catch the frog.

    C Or the waiter would make them leave.

Example 3:

    C He climb/ed up on the branch/s.

    C But they were/n't branch/s.

Example 4:

    C My aunt gave me money for my birthday.

    C So I use/ed it to buy some new jeans.

- Subordinating Conjunctions

Subordinating conjunctions link a main clause and a subordinate clause. A C-unit includes the main clause with all subordinate clauses attached to it. The following are examples of subordinating conjunctions:

    Early Development: because, that, when, who

    Later Development: after, before, so (that), which, although, if, unless, while, as, how, until, as__as, like, where, since, although, who, before, how, while

Examples 1:

    C He went to the store because he was out of milk.

Example 2:

    C When the boy saw it, the frog jump/ed.

Example 3:

    C The man, who usually come/3s to my exercise class, was/n't there today.

Example 4:

    C We can/'t find my cat who always run/3s away.

- **"because" and "so"**

  Always consider "because" as a subordinating conjunction. It will not start an utterance unless:

  A) It is preceded by the utterance of another speaker as in this example:

    C I like/ed the movie alot.
    E Why did you like it?
    C Because it was really funny.

    OR

  B) The subordinating clause is the first clause in the utterance as in this example:

    C Because my mom was so mad, I did my homework first thing after school.

The word "so" can either be a coordinating conjunction or a subordinating conjunction. If its usage means "so that", it is a subordinating conjunction. Otherwise it is a coordinating conjunction.

Example 1 ("so" used as a coordinating conjunction):
    C He had to go home.
    C So we could/n't go to the game.

Example 2 ("so" used as a subordinating conjunction):
    C He had to go home so his mom could take him to the dentist.

Other rules for segmenting C-units

- Sentence fragments

  Sentence fragments are counted as separate C-units when the final intonation contour of the utterance indicates that a complete thought has been spoken. For example:
  > C The boy, the dog, and the frog, they were friend/s.
  > Versus
  > C The boy, the dog, and the frog. { fragment based on intonation }
  > C They were friend/s.

- Elliptical responses

  Elliptical responses (sentence fragments) to questions or prompts from the examiner are counted as separate C-units. For example:
  > E What did you do next?
  > C Shop/ed.

- Yes/No responses or affirmations

  If a question or intonation prompt is posed, segment the yes/no response from the subsequent utterance when succeeded by a complete utterance/c-unit. Examples:
  > E Is that the Spanish teacher?
  > C No.
  > C That/'s my science teacher.

  > E Do you want to read your book now?
  > C No.
  > C I don't.

  > E Do you have any pet/s?
  > C Yeah.
  > C I have a dog.

If a Q or intonation prompt is posed, do *not* segment the Y/N response to stand alone when followed by an incomplete utterance/c unit.

> E Do you have any pet/s?
> C Yeah, a dog.

If an utterance begins with an affirmation or starter, and does not follow a question or ~ prompt, do not segment the affirmation/starter from the subsequent words.

> E I like dog/s.
> C Yeah I do too.
> E That sound/3s interesting.
> C Yeah it was.
> C It was really fun.
> C Yeah we had such a great time.

- Tags

Do not segment phrases such as "you know", "I guess", and "I mean" when they are used as tags. For example:

> C He/'s gonna live with his dad, I guess.
> C And then, you know, they were go/ing to this town.

- Questions as Tags

Do not segment questions when they are used as tags. For example:

> C They got in trouble, right?
> C He miss/ed the bus, did/n't he?
> C That movie was good, would/n't you agree?

- Dialogue Complement/Complement

Dialogue quotes which are embedded in, or as part of, an utterance are counted as one C-unit as in this example:

> C And the boy said, "That/'s my frog".

Successive main clauses that occur in dialogue quotes are counted as separate C-units. For example:
>C And he said, "I/'m ready".
>C "I want to go to the store now".

Complement:
>C She thought, "Sam was incorrect".
>C He realize/ed, nothing has changed.

- Grammatical errors

Ignore grammatical errors when segmenting utterances. For example,
>C They is[EW:are] go/ing now.
>{child said, "They is going now."}
>C We *are go/ing too.
>{child said, "We going too."}

- Pauses and intonation

Do not ignore pauses and intonation when segmenting utterances but, whenever reasonable, segment utterances based on grammar rules. When listening to speech, for example, there is sometimes a significant pause (with or without ending intonation) between a main clause and a subordinate clause. This inclines one to segment the utterance. With C-unit segmentation, however, the utterance would not be segmented as in this following example where the speaker paused for two seconds between the main clause and the subordinate clause:
>C I like/ed the movie alot :02 because it was really funny.

In the following example, however, consider pause time and intonation:
>C I like/ed the movie alot.
>: :02
>E Mhm.
>C Because it was really funny.

If there is a significant pause and ending intonation (falling for statements, rising for questions) between the speaker's first utterance and the examiner's "Mhm", segment the utterances as show above. Otherwise, give the speaker credit for subordination and transcribe these "prompt sounds" as interjections as follows:

    C I like/ed the movie alot :02 < > because it was really funny.
    E <Mhm>.

References:

The rules for C-unit segmentation were summarized from Hughes, McGillivray, and Schmidek (1997), Loban (1976), Strong (1998), and Jon Miller's class notes from Communicative Disorders 640, Fall, 1999.

Subordination Index

Introduction

This guide contains the scoring rules for the Subordination Index (SI), and directions for using the SALT 16 software to enter SI codes into a transcript and to generate the SI reports.

SI definition: SI is a measure of syntactic complexity which produces a ratio of the total number of clauses to the total number of C-units (or modified C-units for samples of bilingual Spanish/English speakers). A clause, whether it is main or subordinate, is a statement containing both a subject and a predicate. Grammatically, a subject is a noun phrase and a predicate is a verb phrase. Main clauses can stand by themselves. Subordinate clauses depend on the main clause to make sense; they are embedded within an utterance as noun, adjective, or adverbial clauses. The SI analysis counts clauses.

This measure has been used in research studies since Walter Loban first created it to document complex sentence development (Loban, 1963). The attraction of this measure is the straight forward definitions of complex syntax with a scoring system that can be completed efficiently. It still requires hand coding in that these syntactic features cannot be identified accurately using lexical lists. An added feature is that it can be used with languages other than English. Our research on Spanish-English bilingual children used the SI to quantify complex syntax across the two languages. We found that a transcript can be coded in less than 10 minutes, with most time spent on the few unique utterances. Loban demonstrated that the SI captured advancing syntactic gains from kindergarten through grade 12.

SI codes: Language samples, which have been transcribed and segmented into C-units (or modified C-units), are coded at the end of each utterance using the codes [SI-0], [SI-1], [SI-2] which means subordination index – 0 clauses, 1 clause, 2 clauses within the utterance. The code, [SI-X], should be inserted at the end of utterances which are excluded from the SI analysis set (see Scoring Rules).

SI composite score: The SI composite score is calculated by dividing the total number of clauses by the total number of utterances.

SALT reference databases: The following SALT reference databases have been coded for SI: Play, Conversation, Narrative SSS, Narrative Story Retell, Expository, Persuasion, Bilingual Spanish/English Story Retell, Bilingual Spanish/English Unique Story, and Monolingual Spanish Narrative Story Retell. Samples you code may be compared to age or grade-matched samples selected from these databases.

Disclaimer: There is variation in the literature on how to count clauses, especially for some of the special cases. The SALT reference databases were coded for SI following the rules in this document. If you intend to compare your sample with samples selected from these databases, you should code your sample following the same rules.

Scoring Rules

1. Utterances that are incomplete, unintelligible, are nonverbal, or are marked with [EU] are excluded from the SI analysis set. Titles and <u>true</u> fragments, e.g., "The end", "and the dog", are not C-units and are also excluded from the SI analysis set. These excluded utterances are coded for SI using [SI-X] and are not included in the SI composite score.

    Examples of utterances not included in SI:
    C Then he [SI-X]>
    C He went XX yesterday [SI-X].

    Examples of colloquialisms which are also not included in SI:
    C You there frog [SI-X]?
    C Frog, you in there [SI-X]?

C ¿Rana ahí [SI-X]?

These utterances are acceptable in conversation. Therefore, they are excluded from the SI analysis set so that the speaker is not penalized for not including a verb.

When an elliptical response to a question is <u>not</u> a clause, it is excluded from the SI analysis set. With elliptical responses, the missing term(s) are understood from the context. *"... they are answers to questions that lack only the repetition of the question elements to satisfy the criterion of independent predication"* (Loban, 1963).

Examples of elliptical response to a question:
> E Why did you do that?
> C Because [SI-X].
> E ¿Por qué hiciste eso?
> C Porque sí [SI-X].

When an ellipsis has clausal structure and the subject can implied, it is scored and included in SI.

Example of elliptical response with clausal structure:
> E How do you win?
> C Score the most point/s [SI-1]. –> The subject "you" was implied and scored for SI as though the subject was stated.

The following types of ellipses are given credit for verb use.
> E You should turn in your assignment.
> C I will [SI-1].

> E Did your friend come to the party?
> C He did [SI-1].

2. Ignore parenthetical remarks. Utterances which consist entirely of parenthetical remarks are excluded from the SI analysis set.

Examples:
    C The girl ((I forgot her name)) got lost [SI-1].

    C Then the ((what is that animal called)) <> ((oh yeah)) gopher bit him on the nose [SI-1].
      E <Gopher>.

Example where the child does not repeat the subject supplied by the examiner:
    C Then the ((what is that animal called)) <>bit him on the nose [SI-1].
      E <Gopher>.
In this example, the child is given credit for the subject supplied by the examiner. Repeating the subject is optional in this context.

Examples of utterances consisting entirely of parenthetical remarks:
    C ((I skip/ed a page)) [SI-X].
    C (((Um) where was I)) [SI-X]?

3. Clauses with *omitted subjects are included in the SI analysis and receive a score of SI-0.

Example of omitted subject:
    C *He got on the rock [SI-0].

Example of complex subordination with subject omission:
    C And then *he grab/ed some branch/s so he would/n't fall [SI-1].
In this example the <u>first</u> clause receives SI-0 score due to subject omission in English.

Spanish note: Spanish is a pronoun-drop language (Bedore, 1999) and, as such, omission of nouns and personal pronouns is ubiquitous and grammatical. Therefore, these subjects are not considered to be omitted. Example: C Y luego agarró unas rama/s para que no se cayera [SI-2].

4. Clauses with missing subjects due to pronoun error are included in the SI analysis and receive a score of SI-0.

    Examples:
    C There[EW:they] see the frog/s [SI-0].
    C Ahí[EW:ellos] ven a las rana/s [SI-0].
    In these examples the pronoun is a demonstrative pronoun instead of a personal pronoun (i.e. she, you, his) and therefore the clause receives a zero score.

5. Commands with implied subjects are included in the SI analysis and scored as though the subject was stated.

    Examples where the subject "you" is implied (not obligatory):
    C Give it to me [SI-1].
    C Look at this [SI-1].

6. Because of the pronoun-drop nature of Spanish, English and Spanish samples from bilingual speakers are segmented using modified C-units. Utterances containing successions of verbs without subjects are segmented and a fragment code, [F], is placed at the end of each utterance lacking a stated subject as a result of this segmentation. For these transcripts, subjects can be *implied* for fragments due to segmentation and receive SI scores.

    Examples:
    C He got on the rock [SI-1].
    C and fell off the rock [F] [SI-1].

    C Se subió a la piedra [SI-1].
    C y cayó de la piedra [F] [SI-1].

    Special case: If there is a fragment due to segmentation but the preceding utterance has an omitted subject, then you cannot imply the subject for the fragment.
    C Then *he ran [SI-0].

    C and look/ed [F] [SI-0].
Because Spanish is a pronoun-drop language, this special case does not apply to Spanish samples:
    C Luego corrió [SI-1].
    C y miró [F] [SI-1].

7. Clauses with *omitted copula (main verb) are included in the SI analysis and receive a score of SI-0.

    Examples of omitted main verb/copula:
    C (And the) and the frog *went through the big (ah) pond [SI-0].
    C (y la) y la rana *nadó por el estanque (eh) grande [SI-0].

    Examples of omitted verb in the second clause:
    C And he start/ed say/ing, "Froggy, Froggy of[EW:are] you there" [SI-1]?
    C Y empezó a decir, "¿Rana, Rana fuera[EW:estás] ahí [SI-1]?
In these examples the speaker did not state a verb in the second clause; thus that clause receives a score of zero.

8. Utterances containing omitted auxiliary verbs, bound morphemes, functor words, direct objects, and articles are included in the SI analysis (coded for SI). This includes verbs which are not conjugated correctly.

    Examples of omitted auxiliary:
    C He *is go/ing [SI-1].
    C When they *were sleep/ing the frog got out [SI-2].
    C Él *estaba yendo [SI-1].
    C Cuando ellos *estaban durmiendo la rana se salió [SI-2].

    Example of an omitted bound morpheme:
    C The boy was fall/*ing off the rock [SI-1].

    Example of an omitted article:
    C He see/3s *an owl [SI-1].
    C La rana se estaba cayendo de *la piedra [SI-1].

Examples of an omitted direct object:

C He was pour/ing coffee into the *cup [SI-1].

C Él estaba sirviendo café en la *taza [SI-1].

9. The subordinate clause within an utterance containing an omitted obligatory subordinating conjunction will not receive credit. Examples:

C There was a boy *who had a dog [SI-1].

C And the boy did/n't see *that the frog went out [SI-1].

C Había un niño *que tenía un perro [SI-1].

C Y el niño no vio *que la rana se salió [SI-1].

10. When an incorrect subordinating conjunction is used, the subordinate clause will not receive credit. Example:

C The deer was run/ing what[EW:so] he could throw the little boy in the water [SI-1].

If the word in error is a different subordinating conjunction, albeit the wrong one, the second clause may get credit. Use judgment. For example, bilingual (Spanish/English) children sometimes use the word "for" as a subordinating conjunction because the Spanish word "para," which means "for" in English, can be used as a subordinating conjunction in Spanish. In this case the subordinate clause should be given SI credit.

C The deer was run/ing for[EW:so] he could throw the little boy in the water [SI-2].

11. If a subordinating conjunction is not obligatory to the coherence of the utterance, the subordinate clause should still receive a score for SI. Examples:

C I know I want to go [SI-2].

C I think I hear something [SI-2].

The subordinating conjunction "that" can be implied in these utterances.

12. Dialogue is coded for SI. Consider the introducer, e.g., *he said*, as the main clause and what is in the quotes as the second clause. The direct quotation must have a subject and predicate in order to be considered a clause and get an SI count. Examples:

C And he *was say/ing, "Frog, where are you" [SI-2]?

C Y él *estaba diciendo, "¿Rana, dónde estás" [SI-2]?

C The boy said, "Shh" [SI-1].
C El niño dijo, "Shh" [SI-1].

Examples of commands in which the subject *you/tú* can be implied:
C The boy said, "Go away" [SI-2].
C El niño dijo, "Vete" [SI-2].

13. Semantics should be ignored when scoring SI. If the wrong content word is used by the speaker, but is grammatically acceptable, score SI accordingly. Examples:
    C The boy ran[EW:fell] off the rock [SI-1].
    C El niño se corrió[EW:cayó] de la piedra [SI-1].

14. Utterances with imitated words (coded with [I] in the examples) are included in the SI and are scored as though the imitated word originated from the speaker. Examples:
    C The <> gopher[I] came out of the hole [SI-1].
    E <Gopher>.

    C El <> topo[I] salió del hoyo [SI-1].
    E <topo>.

15. Counting Infinitives: there is variability in the literature on whether or not to count infinitives. Samples in the SALT databases do not count infinitives as clauses. Examples:
    C The boy told the dog *to be quiet* [SI-1].
    C The dog want/ed *to run away* [SI-1].
    C El niño se fue *a comprar* un perro [SI-1].
    C El perro se quería *escapar* [SI-1].

16. The utterances containing code switches will be reviewed for SI. If the majority of the utterance (at least 50%) is in the target language (English or Spanish), code for SI.

Examples of code switching and SI coding with English as the target language:

    C The rana[CS] jump/ed off the boat [SI-1].

    C El[CS] niño[CS] buscó[CS] en[CS] the hole [SI-X].   *only 2 of the 6 words are in English, so not coded for SI*

Examples of code switching and SI coding with Spanish as the target language:

    C La frog[CS] saltó del bote [SI-1].

    C The[CS] boy[CS] look/ed[CS] in[CS] el hoyo [SI-X].   *only 2 of the 6 words are in Spanish, so not coded for SI*

If the utterance has enough of the target language to score for SI but the speaker produces a partial verb in the non-target language then credit will be given for SI.

    C The boy busc|buscar[CS] in the hole [SI-1].   *(target language: English)*

    C El niño sear|search[CS] en el hoyo [SI-1]. *(target language: Spanish)*

Tricky Scoring Examples

The following table contains examples of utterances which may be tricky to score. Each utterance is given along with the rationale.

Transcript Quote	Rationale
And she get/3s all the toy/s she want/3s [SI-2]. When he was hold/ing an umbrella, he just knew he was/n't Fluffy [SI-3].	Implied subordinating conjunctions (Rule 11). Notice that in these examples the subordinating conjunction "that" can be implied.
Sit down and get to work [SI-1]. "Wait," said Dr_DeSoto [SI-2]! The boy said to the dog, "Be quiet" [SI-2].	Commands with implied "you" (Rule 5); in dialogue (Rule 12).
When it began to rain (he he um) he said, "My hat will shrink if the rain get/3s on it" [SI-4].	Notice in this relatively short utterance there are four clauses.
(Um) many player/s obviously would stretch before the game so that they would/n't (um like you know) cramp up as many people in athletics do [SI-3]. So it usually take/3s longer also because the clock stop/3s when the ball is run out of bounds [SI-3]. C And each creature also has its own special ability/s that can either destroy a creature when it come/3s in to play, or destroy a creature when it come/3s out of play, or let an opponent draw a card, or let you draw a card [SI-4].	Expository samples taken from older speakers often produce long utterances with complex subordination.
The higher your individual score, the more point/s get add/ed to your team/z score [SI-1].	The first clause does not contain a verb phrase.

Using SALT to enter SI scores (SALT 16)

The *Edit menu: Insert SI Codes* utility may be used to insert the appropriate SI code at the end of each qualifying utterance in your transcript. Each utterance is highlighted and you are prompted to select the appropriate SI code from a list.

Analyzing the SI scores (SALT 16)

The *Analyze menu: Subordination Index* report lists the count of each SI code along with the composite SI score.

Comparing your SI scores to the database samples (SALT 16)

The *Database menu: Subordination Index* report lists the count of each SI code along with the composite SI score. Scores are listed for your transcript and for the selected database samples.

Narrative Scoring Scheme

Introduction

The Narrative Scoring Scheme (NSS) is an assessment tool that provides an index of the student's ability to produce a structurally sound and coherent narrative. It was developed to create a more objective narrative structure scoring system and is based on an earlier version, Rubric for Completing a Story Grammar Analysis, developed by the Madison Metropolitan School District SALT working group, 1998, following the work of Stein and Glenn, 1979; 1982. This scoring procedure combines many of the abstract categories of Story Grammar, adding features of cohesion, connecting events, rationale for characters' behavior, and referencing. Each of the scoring categories has explicit examples to establish scoring criteria, reducing the abstractness of the story grammar categories. Heilmann, Miller, Nockerts, & Dunaway (2010) reviewed narrative scoring procedures used in research over the past 20 years detailing their sensitivity in capturing developing narrative skills. They concluded that "The NSS is an efficient and informative tool for documenting children's development of narrative macrostructure. The relationship between the NSS and microstructural measures demonstrates that it is a robust measure of children's overall oral narrative competence and a powerful tool for clinicians and researchers. The unique relationship between lexical diversity and the NSS confirmed that a special relationship exists between vocabulary and narrative organization skills in young school-age children."

The NSS scoring is done at the text level, for the most part, requiring you to review the narrative as a whole for many of the scoring categories. Scores for each category are inserted on plus lines at the end of the transcript. You can add these plus lines with the *Edit menu: Insert NSS Template* option. The SALT program summarizes these scores and calculates a total. You can then compare these scores to typical peer performance using the *Database menu* or view independently using the *Analyze menu*. You can also compare with a linked transcript to show intervention progress or language differences. This measure is key to understanding overall narrative performance.

Scoring Guidelines

Assigning NSS Scores

The NSS is scored using a 0 - 5 point scale. 5 points are given for "proficient" use, 3 points for "emerging" use, and 1 point for "immature" or "minimal" use. Scores of 2 and 4 require scorer's judgment. Scores of zero (0) are given for poor performance and for a variety of child errors including telling the wrong story, conversing with the examiner, not completing/refusing the task, abandoned utterances, unintelligibility, and when target components of the NSS are imitated. The scores for each characteristic can be considered individually or combined into a total composite score (highest possible score being 35).

Description of NSS characteristics

1. Introduction: Scores are determined by the presence, absence, and qualitative depiction of character and setting components.
2. Character Development: Scores are based on the acknowledgement of characters and their significance throughout the story.
3. Mental States: Narratives are evaluated based on the vocabulary used to convey character emotions and thought processes. The frequency as well as the diversity of mental state words is considered. For example, if a story provides frequent opportunities to verbalize anger themes and a child marks each of these with "mad," he/she will not receive as high of a score as a child who explains one opportunity using "mad," another using "angry," another using "upset," and so on. Mental state words can be either adjectives, e.g., *sad, happy, scared*, or active cognitive-state words, e.g., *believe, know, remember*.
4. Referencing: Scores are given according to the consistent and accurate use of antecedents and clarifiers throughout the story. Student's use of correct pronouns and proper names should be considered in this score.

5. Conflict/Resolution: Scores are based on the presence/absence of conflicts and resolutions required to express the story as well as how thoroughly each is described.
6. Cohesion: The sequencing of, details given to, and transitions between each event are examined.
7. Conclusion: Scores are based on the conclusion of the final event as well as the wrap-up of the entire story.

NSS Scoring Rubric

Refer to the scoring rubric at the end of this appendix for a guide to assigning scores for each of the NSS characteristics of a narrative.

Helpful Scoring Tips:
- Be familiar with the narrated story. It is recommended that the scorer have a copy of the story to reference while scoring.
- Print the narrative transcript.
- Read the transcript as fluidly/inclusively as possible, ignoring SALT transcription codes.
- Write comments and circle or flag key words/utterances such as mental state words or difficulty with referents and pronouns.
- For *each* characteristic, review the NSS before assigning a score. Read the criteria along the continuum of points. Determine what is present in the transcript and score accordingly. This will insure better intra- and inter-rater reliability.
- Conflict/Resolution and Cohesion are story grammar elements which are distributed across the entire narrative. They do not occur at one static point within the story. The scoring of these characteristics must take into account the story as a whole.
- Conflict/Resolution (CR) is based on the presence of CRs necessary for telling a complete story as well as the clarity and richness in which these story elements are expressed. A child who is missing elemental conflicts and/or resolutions will receive a proportionately lower score than a child who narrates all conflicts and resolutions necessary for advancing that story. A child who expresses these CRs clearly and comprehensively receives

a proportionately higher score than a child who narrates under-developed CRs.

- Frequently review what constitutes a score of 0 or NA. Explanations are given at the bottom of the NSS scoring rubric.
- Proficiency in assigning scores will develop with experience.

Using SALT to enter NSS scores (SALT 16)

The *Edit menu: Insert NSS Template* option may be used to insert the NSS plus line template at the bottom of your transcript. Then type the individual scores after each label.

NSS Template	Example of NSS Scoring
+ Introduction:	+ Introduction: 3
+ CharacterDev:	+ CharacterDev: 2
+ MentalStates:	+ MentalStates: 2
+ Referencing:	+ Referencing: 2
+ ConflictRes:	+ ConflictRes: 1
+ Cohesion:	+ Cohesion: 3
+ Conclusion:	+ Conclusion: 2

Analyzing the NSS scores (SALT 16)

The *Analyze menu: Narrative Scoring Scheme* report lists each individual NSS score along with the composite score.

Comparing your NSS scores to the database samples (SALT 16)

The *Database menu: Narrative Scoring Scheme* lists each individual NSS score along with the composite score. Scores are listed for your transcript and for the selected database samples.

NSS SCORING RUBRIC

Introduction

Proficient	**1) Setting**: - States general place and provides some detail about the setting, e.g., reference to the time of the setting, daytime, bedtime, season. - Setting elements are stated at appropriate place in story. **2) Characters:** - Main characters are introduced with some description or detail provided.
Emerging	**1) Setting:** - States general setting but provides no detail. - Description or elements of setting are given intermittently through story. - May provide description of specific element of setting, e.g., *the frog is in the jar*. **2) Characters:** - Characters of story are mentioned with no detail/description.
Minimal/ Immature	- Launches into story with no attempt to provide the setting.

Character Development

Proficient	- Main character(s) and <u>all</u> supporting character(s) are mentioned. - Throughout story it is clear child can discriminate between main and supporting characters, e.g., more description of, emphasis upon main character(s). - Child narrates in first person using character voice, e.g., *"You get out of my tree", said the owl.*
Emerging	- Both main and active supporting characters are mentioned. - Main characters are not clearly distinguished from supporting characters.
Minimal/ Immature	- Inconsistent mention of involved or active characters. - Character(s) necessary for advancing the plot are not present.

Mental States

Proficient	- Mental states of main and supporting characters are expressed when necessary for plot development and advancement. - A variety of mental state words are used.
Emerging	- Some use of evident mental state words to develop character(s).
Minimal/ Immature	- No use of mental state words to develop character(s).

Referencing

Proficient	- Provides necessary antecedents to pronouns. - References are clear throughout story.
Emerging	- Inconsistent use of referents/antecedents.
Minimal/ Immature	- Excessive use of pronouns. - No verbal clarifiers used. - Speaker is unaware that listener is confused.

Conflict Resolution

Proficient	- Clearly states all conflicts and resolutions critical to advancing the plot of the story.
Emerging	- Under developed description of conflicts and resolutions critical to advancing the plot of the story. **OR** - Not all conflicts and resolutions critical to advancing the plot are present.
Minimal/ Immature	- Random resolution(s) stated with no mention of cause or conflict. **OR** - Conflict mentioned without resolution. **OR** - Many conflicts and resolutions critical to advancing the plot are not present.

Cohesion

Proficient	- Events follow a logical order. - Critical events are included while less emphasis is placed on minor events. - Smooth transitions are provided between events.
Emerging	- Events follow a logical order. - Excessive detail or emphasis provided on minor events leading the listener astray. **OR** - Transitions to next event unclear. **OR** - Minimal detail given for critical events. **OR** - Equal emphasis on all events.
Minimal/ Immature	- No use of smooth transitions

Conclusion

Proficient	- Story is clearly wrapped up using general concluding statements such as "and they were together again happy as could be".
Emerging	- Specific event is concluded, but no general statement made as to the conclusion of the whole story.
Minimal/ Immature	- Stops narrating and listener may need to ask if that is the end.

Scoring

Each characteristic receives a scaled score 0-5. Proficient characteristics=5, Emerging=3, Minimal/ Immature=1. The scores in between, 2 and 4, are undefined, use judgment. Scores of 0, NA are defined below. A composite is scored by adding the total of the characteristic scores. Highest score=35.

A score of 0 is given for child errors. Examples include: telling the wrong story, conversing with examiner, not completing/refusing task, using wrong language creating inability of scorer to comprehend story in target language, abandoned utterances, unintelligibility, poor performance, and/or if components of the rubric are entirely imitated.

A score of NA (non-applicable) is given for mechanical/examiner/operator errors. Examples include: interference from background noise, issues with recording (cut-offs, interruptions), examiner quitting before child does, examiner not following protocol, and examiner asking overly specific or leading questions rather than open-ended questions or prompts.

Expository Scoring Scheme

Introduction

The Expository Scoring Scheme (ESS) assesses the content and structure of an expository language sample, similar to how the Narrative Scoring Scheme (see Appendix O) provides an overall measure of a student's skill in producing a narrative. Expository skills are critical to the curriculum in middle and high school and relate to state educational standards. The ESS is comprised of 10 characteristics for completing an expository language sample. The first 8 characteristics correspond to the topics listed on the planning sheet that is given to students. These topics, in turn, were developed based on the descriptions of sports (both individual and team) found in *Rules of the game: the complete illustrated encyclopedia of all the sports of the world* (Diagram Group, 1990). To ensure that the topics also reflected what is expected for explanations of games, The Card Game Web site (www.pagat.com) was consulted.

There is less research on this procedure than on the NSS, but clinically it captures deficits in organization, listener perspective, and overall appreciation for explaining relative situations, the overall goal of the game, the rules, and strategies to win. We believe it provides you with a valuable tool to document expository language.

Scoring Guidelines

Assigning ESS Scores

The ESS is scored using a 0 - 5 point scale. 5 points are given for "proficient" use, 3 points for "emerging" use, and 1 point for "immature" or "minimal" use. Scores of 2 and 4 require scorer's judgment. Scores of zero (0) are given for poor performance and for a variety of errors including telling the wrong story, conversing with the examiner, not completing/refusing the task, abandoned utterances, unintelligibility, and/or when target components of the ESS are imitated. Significant factual errors reduce the score for that topic. The scores for each characteristic can be considered individually or combined into a total composite score.

Description of ESS characteristics

1. Object of Contest: The main objective the game/sport
2. Preparations: What players need to do to prepare for the game/sport, including playing area, equipment, and personal preparations
3. Start of Play: The initial situation, e.g., *One football team lines up at their own 30-yard line for the kickoff, while the other team spreads out in its own territory to receive,* and how the game/sport begins
4. Course of Play: Unit of play, e.g., turn, quarter, set, as well as major roles and major plays
5. Rules: Major rules and consequences for rule violations
6. Scoring: Various ways to score and point values
7. Duration: How long the game/sport lasts using units, how the game ends, and tie breaking procedures
8. Strategy: What skilled players do to win game/sport
9. Terminology: Major terms of game/sport with definitions of new terms[16]
10. Cohesion: Overall flow of the sample, including order, covering topics completely, and smooth transitions[17]

ESS Scoring Rubric

Refer to the scoring rubric at the end of this appendix for a guide to assigning scores for each of the ESS characteristics of an expository.

---

[16] This characteristic might be analogized to the Referencing category in the NSS, which also assesses how well a student takes into account the background knowledge of the listener.

[17] Cohesion was adopted directly from the NSS; consider how well sequencing and transitioning are handled

Helpful Scoring Tips

- Be familiar with the topic of the expository, i.e., the game or sport being explained.
- Print the expository transcript.
- Read the transcript as fluidly/inclusively as possible, ignoring SALT transcription codes.
- Write comments and circle or flag key words/utterances such as those relating to terminology and rules.
- For *each* characteristic, review the ESS scoring rubric before assigning a score. Read the criteria along the continuum of points. Determine what is present in the transcript and score accordingly. This will insure better intra- and inter-rater reliability.
- Frequently review what constitutes a score of 0 or NA. Explanations are given at the bottom of the ESS scoring rubric.
- Scoring the ESS is a subjective measure by nature; however, as you gain experience, the process of scoring will become reliable.
- When beginning to score, you may want to compare your scores against the training transcripts or with another scorer. The training transcripts were scored by several scorers experienced with the ESS.

Using SALT to enter ESS scores (SALT 16)

Use the *Edit menu: Insert ESS Template* option to insert the ESS plus line template at the bottom of your transcript. Then type the individual scores after each label.

ESS Template	Example of ESS Scoring
+ Preparations:	+ Preparations: 2
+ ObjectOfContest:	+ ObjectOfContest: 3
+ StartOfPlay:	+ StartOfPlay: 3
+ CourseOfPlay:	+ CourseOfPlay: 3
+ Scoring:	+ Scoring: 4
+ Rules:	+ Rules: 3
+ Strategy:	+ Strategy: 3
+ Duration:	+ Duration: 3
+ Terminology:	+ Terminology: 3
+ Cohesion:	+ Cohesion: 3

Analyzing the ESS scores (SALT 16)

The *Analyze menu: Expository Scoring Scheme* report lists each individual ESS score along with the composite score.

Comparing your ESS scores to the database samples (SALT 16)

The *Database menu: Expository Scoring Scheme* lists each individual ESS score along with the composite score. Scores are listed for your transcript and for the selected database samples.

ESS SCORING GUIDE

Object

Proficient	Full description of the main objective.
Emerging	Mention of the main objective.
Minimal/ Immature	Mention of winner but no, or limited, description how that is determined. **OR** Description of another aspect of the contest, such as strategy or scoring.

Preparation

Proficient	1) **Playing Area**: Labels place and provides details about shape & layout. **AND/OR** 2) **Equipment**: Labels items and provides detailed description, including function. **AND/OR** 3) **Player Preparations**: Provides detailed description.
Emerging	1) **Playing Area**: Labels place and provides limited details about shape & layout. **OR** 2) **Equipment**: Labels items with limited description. **OR** 3) **Player Preparations**: Provides some description.
Minimal/ Immature	1) **Playing Area**: Labels place but no details about shape & layout. **OR** 2) **Equipment**: Labels items with no description. **OR** 3) **Player Preparations**: Provides limited description.

Start

Proficient	Describes initial situation and how play begins.
Emerging	Describes initial situation or how play begins, but not both.
Minimal/ Immature	Limited description of the initial situation or how play begins.

Course of Play

Proficient	Detailed description of: A unit of play **AND/OR** major roles **AND/OR** major plays.
Emerging	Some description of: A unit of play **AND/OR** major roles **AND/OR** major plays.
Minimal/ Immature	Limited description of: A unit of play **AND/OR** major roles **AND/OR** major plays.

Rules

Proficient	Clear statement of major rules and, when applicable, consequences for violations.
Emerging	Mentions major rules and, when applicable, consequences for violations but without full detail.
Minimal/ Immature	Minimal or no mention of major rules or consequences for violations.

Scoring

Proficient	Full description of ways to score and point values.
Emerging	Incomplete description of ways to score and point values.
Minimal/ Immature	Limited description of ways to score or point values.

Duration

Proficient	Clear description of: How long the contest lasts, including, when applicable, the units in which duration is measured **AND/OR** How the contest ends **AND/OR** Tie breaking procedures.
Emerging	Some description of: How long the contests lasts **OR** How the contest ends **OR** Tie breaking procedures.
Minimal/ Immature	Limited description of: How long the contests lasts **OR** How the contest ends **OR** Tie breaking procedures

Strategy

Proficient	Full description of some ways to win the contest that are not required by the rules but are what competent players do
Emerging	Mention of some ways to win the contest that are not required by the rules but are what competent players do,
Minimal/ Immature	Vague or incomplete mention of some ways to win the contest that are not required by the rules but are what competent players do

Terminology

Proficient	Terms of art are clearly defined whenever introduced
Emerging	Some terms of art defined, but not consistently or clearly
Minimal/ Immature	Terms of art introduced but not further defined

Cohesion

Proficient	Topics follow a logical order **AND** Topics are completely covered before moving on to another **AND** Smooth transitions between topics.
Emerging	Topics follow a logical order **OR** Topics are completely covered before moving on to another **OR** Smooth transitions between topics.
Minimal/ Immature	Little discernable order to topics, Much jumping between topics **AND** Abrupt transitions between topics.

Scoring

Each characteristic receives a scaled score 0-5. Proficient characteristics=5, Emerging=3, Minimal/ Immature=1. The scores in between, 2 and 4, are undefined, use judgment. Significant factual errors reduce the score for that topic. Scores of 0, NA are defined below. A composite is scored by adding the total of the characteristic scores. Highest score=50.

A score of 0 is given for student errors. Examples include not covering topic, explaining a different game or sport, not completing/refusing task, student unintelligibility, and abandoned utterances.

A score of NA (non-applicable) is given for mechanical/examiner/operator errors. Examples include interference from background noise, issues with recording (cut-offs, interruptions), examiner quitting before student does, examiner not following protocol, and examiner asking overly specific or leading questions rather than open-ended questions or prompts.

Persuasion Scoring Scheme

Introduction

The *Persuasion Scoring Scheme* (PSS) assesses the content and structure of a persuasive language sample. Persuasion skills relate to state educational standards and cut across modes of communication: speaking, listening, reading, and writing (National Governor's Association, 2010). The ability to persuade is critical to success in college and career and to full participation in social and civic life. The persuasion task challenges high school students to take into account the listener's perspective and to use complex language to express complex ideas. The PSS is comprised of 7 characteristics for completing a persuasive language sample. The characteristics correspond to the topics listed on the planning sheet that is given to students.

Samples contained in the SALT Persuasion reference database have all been coded for the PSS. This database can be utilized to compare a student's persuasion skills to those of his/her typically-developing peers. Clinicians can compare individual characteristics of the PSS or the composite score using the database. The persuasion task may be repeated to assess progress of persuasion skills through the high school years.

Scoring Guidelines

Assigning PSS Scores

The PSS is scored using a 0 - 5 point scale. 5 points are given for "Proficient/Advanced" production, 3 points for "Satisfactory/Adequate" production, and 1 point for "Minimal/Immature" production. Scores of 2 and 4 are undefined and require judgment. A score of 0 is given for student errors such as not completing the task when prompted, refusing the task, unintelligible production(s), and abandoned utterances leaving characteristics incomplete. A score of NA (non-applicable) is given for mechanical/examiner/operator errors, e.g., interference from background noise, issues with recording (cut-offs, interruptions), examiner not following protocol, examiner interrupting student.

PSS Scoring Rubric

Characteristic	Proficient/Advanced (5)	Satisfactory/Adequate (3)	Minimal/Immature (1)
Issue Identification and Desired Change	• Existing rule or situation is clearly understood before supporting reasons are stated • Desired change is clearly stated	• Existing rule or situation can be discerned; may require shared knowledge • Desired change can be discerned	• Speaker launches into persuasion with no mention of existing rule or situation • Desired change is difficult to determine
Supporting Reasons	• Reason(s) are comprehensive; include detail • Benefit(s) to others are clearly understood	• One or more reasons are offered to support desired change • Benefit(s) to others are unclear or omitted	• Reason(s) are confusing or vague • Significant/obvious reason(s) are not stated • Reason(s) are not plausible; do not support change
Other Point of View (Counter Arguments)	• Other point(s) of view are clearly explained; include detail • Includes language to support or refute other point of view	• Other point(s) of view are acknowledged OR • Dismissive of other point(s) of view	• Other point(s) of view are unclear or omitted
Compromises	• Includes language, with some detail, to support or refute compromising	• Compromise(s) are acknowledged OR • Dismissive of compromising	• Compromises are unclear or omitted
Conclusion	• Desired change is clearly restated/summarized • Arguments are clearly restated/summarized • Concludes using language such as, "to conclude", "therefore", "and so", "in sum", etc. • First step(s) for change are mentioned	• Desired change is restated • One or more supporting reasons are restated • Ending is inferred and/or lacks transition to conclusion, e.g., "And that's all", "that's it", "I'm done"	• Summary statement(s) are omitted • Unclear to listener that the persuasion task is completed

Cohesion	• Points are fully covered before moving on to another • Transitions between points are smooth/clear using mature language • Referents are clear • Listener can easily follow the argument	• Point are covered, but lack organization • Transitions between points are acceptable • Referencing is adequate • Listener can follow the argument with some effort	• Points are not fully covered before moving onto another • Abrupt transitions between points • Referents are unclear, hard to follow • Argument is difficult to follow
Effectiveness	• Argument is extremely compelling • Argument is entirely plausible • Argument is well stated • Mature language is used • Minimal errors of syntax/form • Supported points well • Speaker's delivery is passionate • Speaker engages listener	• Argument is compelling • Argument is plausible • Argument requires little or no clarification • Acceptable syntax/form • Speaker's delivery is clear; not necessarily passionate • Effort to persuade is evident • Speaker makes some attempt to engage listener	• Argument is minimally or not compelling • Argument is not plausible • Language is unclear • Errors of syntax/form may be prevalent • Speaker's delivery lacks effort; not passionate • Speaker makes no attempt to engage listener • Speaker uses inappropriate/immature tone

Scoring: Each characteristic receives a scaled score 0-5. Use points as a guideline to determine level of proficiency for each characteristic. Not *all* points listed in each characteristic must be present when assigning score. Proficient/Advanced = 5, Satisfactory/Adequate = 3, Minimal/Immature = 1. The scores in between, 2 and 4, are undefined; use judgment. Add the scores for the seven characteristics to yield a composite score. Highest possible score = 35.

Helpful Scoring Tips

- Print the transcript.
- Read the transcript as fluidly/inclusively as possible, ignoring SALT transcription codes.
- Write comments and circle or flag key words/utterances pertaining to points on the planning sheet

- For *each* point, review the PSS scoring rubric before assigning a score. Read the criteria along the continuum of points. Determine what is present in the transcript and score accordingly. This will insure better intra- and inter-rater reliability.
- Frequently review what constitutes a score of 0 or NA. Explanations are given at the bottom of the PSS scoring rubric.
- Scoring the PSS is a subjective measure by nature; however, as you gain experience, the process of scoring will become reliable.

Using SALT to enter PSS scores (SALT 16)

Use the *Edit menu: Insert PSS Template* option to insert the PSS plus line template at the bottom of your transcript. Then type the individual scores after each label.

PSS Template	Example of PSS Scoring
+ IssueID:	+ IssueID: 2
+ SupportReasons:	+ SupportReasons: 3
+ PointOfView:	+ PointOfView: 3
+ Compromises:	+ Compromises: 3
+ Conclusion:	+ Conclusion: 4
+ Cohesion:	+ Cohesion: 3
+ Effect:	+ Effect: 3

Analyzing the PSS scores (SALT 16)

The *Analyze menu: Persuasion Scoring Scheme* report lists each individual PSS score along with the composite score.

Comparing your PSS scores to the database samples (SALT 16)

The *Database menu: Persuasion Scoring Scheme* lists each individual PSS score along with the composite score. Scores are listed for your transcript and for the selected database samples.

S

Guide to the SALT Variables

Variables Included in the *Standard Measures Report*

	Language Measure	Description
	Current Age	Current age of speaker
TRANSCRIPT LENGTH		
	Total Utterances	Total number of utterances
#	C&I Verbal Utts (*current analysis set*)	Number of utterances in the current analysis set
	All Words Including Mazes	Total number of completed words; excludes part words
	Elapsed Time (minutes)	Elapsed time in minutes
INTELLIGIBILITY		
	% Intelligible Utterances	% of complete verbal utterances that are complete and intelligible
NARRATIVE/EXPOSITORY/PERSUASION STUCTURE		
	NSS Composite Score ESS Composite Score PSS Composite Score	Included only if the sample is a narrative/expository/persuasion (*defined by +Context: Nar, +Context: Expo, +Context: Pers*) and the Narrative/Expository/Persuasion Scoring Scheme has been applied; composite score is the sum of the individual scores
SYNTAX/MORPHOLOGY		
#	MLU in Words	Mean length of utterances in words (*excludes mazes*)
#	MLU in Morphemes	Mean length of utterances in morphemes (*excludes mazes*)
#	SI Composite Score	Included only if the sample has been coded for Subordination Index; composite score is the average of the individual scores
SEMANTICS		
#	Number Total Words (NTW)	Total number of words (*excludes mazes*)

#	Number Different Words (NDW)	Number of different word roots (*excludes mazes*)
#	Type Token Ratio (TTR)	Ratio of different words to total words (NDW/NTW)
#	Moving-Average TTR (*window length*)	Estimates TTR using a moving window, e.g., for window length of 100 words, calculates TTR for words 1–100, 2-101, 3-102, and so on to the end of the sample; final value is the average of the individual TTRs

DISCOURSE (*not included for narrative or expository samples*)

	% Responses to Questions	% of another speaker's questions that were responded to
	Mean Turn Length (words)	Mean length of speaker turn in words (*excludes mazes*)
	Utterances with Overlapping Speech	Number of utterances containing overlapping speech
	Interrupted Other Speaker	Number of times target speaker interrupted another speaker

MAZES AND ABANDONED UTTERANCES

#	Utterances with Mazes	Number of utterances that contain at least one maze
#	Number of Mazes	Total number of mazes
#	Number of Maze Words	Total number of maze words
#	Maze Words as % of Total Words	Ratio of maze words to total words (NMW/TWD)
	Abandoned Utterances	Number of abandoned utterances

VERBAL FACILITY

	Words/Minute	Number of Complete Words/Elapsed Time
#	Maze Words as % of Total Words	Ratio of maze words to total words (NMW/TWD)
	Pauses Within Utterances	Number of pauses within utterances
	Pauses Between Utterances	Number of pauses between utterances

ERRORS

#	% Utterances with Errors	Percent of utterances which contain omissions or error codes
	Number of Omissions	Number of omitted words or bound morphemes
	Number of Error Codes	Number of words or utterances coded as errors

Follow-up reports based on results of the *Standard Measures Report*

When one or more measures on the *Standard Measures Report* indicates the need for more detailed information, use the Analyze and Database menus to support your findings. Below are suggestions for where to look further.

	Language Measure	Additional Reports/Comments
	• Current Age	
	TRANSCRIPT LENGTH	

#	• Total Utterances
	• C&I Verbal Utts
	• Total Completed Words
	• Elapsed Time (minutes)
		• Read the transcript
		• Analyze menu: Summary of Utterance Types
		• Code for Narrative/Expository/Persuasion Scoring Scheme
		  – Analyze/Database menus: Narrative Scoring Scheme
		  – Analyze/Database menus: Expository Scoring Scheme
		  – Analyze/Database menus: Persuasion Scoring Scheme

	INTELLIGIBILITY	
	• % Intelligible Utterances	• Analyze menu: Standard Utterance Lists (*select unintelligible & partly intelligible*)
	NARRATIVE/EXPOSITORY/PERSUASION STRUCTURE	
	• NSS Composite Score • ESS Composite Score • PSS Composite Score	• Analyze/Database menus: Narrative Scoring Scheme • Analyze/Database menus: Expository Scoring Scheme • Analyze/Database menus: Persuasion Scoring Scheme

SYNTAX/MORPHOLOGY		
# #	• MLU in Words • MLU in Morphemes	• Analyze menu: Word and Morpheme Summary • Analyze menu: Word Root Table (*expand by words to include bound morphemes*) • Analyze menu: Bound Morpheme Table • Database menu: Words Lists, Bound Morphemes, & Utt. Distribution (*focus on bound morphemes & utt. distribution*) • Code for Subordination Index – Analyze/Database menus: Subordination Index
#	• SI Composite Score	• Analyze/Database menus: Subordination Index
SEMANTICS		
# # # #	• Number Total Words (NTW) • Number Different Words (NDW) • Type Token Ratio (TTR) • Moving-Average TTR	• Analyze menu: Word and Morpheme Summary • Analyze menu: Word Root Table (*expand if desired*) • Analyze menu: Standard Word Lists (*specify which to view*) • Analyze menu: Standard Utterance Lists (*specify which to view*) • Database menu: Words Lists, Bound Morphemes, & Utt. Distribution (*focus on word lists*) • Analyze/Database menus: Grammatical Categories (*English only*) • Analyze menu: Grammatical Category Lists (*English only*)

DISCOURSE (*not included for narrative or expository samples*)	
• % Responses to Questions • Mean Turn Length (words) • Utterances with Overlapping Speech • Interrupted Other Speaker	• Analyze/Database menus: Discourse Summary • Analyze menu: Standard Utterance Lists (*select 2nd speaker questions and look at following entries; select utterances with overlapping speech*)

VERBAL FACILITY AND RATE		
#	• Words/Minute • Maze Words as % of Total Words • Pauses Within Utterances • Pauses Between Utterances • Abandoned Utterances	• Analyze menu: Rate and Pause Summary • Analyze/Database menus: Maze Summary • Analyze menu: Standard Utterance Lists (*select utterances with mazes, utterances with pauses, and/or abandoned utterances*) • Analyze menu: Fluency Codes and Behaviors (*if sample was coded for fluency*)

ERRORS		
#	• % Utterances with Errors • Number of Omissions • Number of Error Codes	• Analyze menu: Omissions and Error Codes (*look for patterns*) • Analyze menu: Code Summary • Analyze menu: Word Code Tables • Analyze menu: Utterance Code Tables • Analyze menu: Standard Utterance Lists (*select utterances with omissions, error codes*)

Using SALT to Assess the Common Core Grades K-12

Contributed by
  Karen Andriacchi, M.S., CCC-SLP,
  Mary-Beth Rolland, M.S., CCC-SLP
  Joyelle Divall-Rayan, M.S., CCC-SLP

Below are suggested SALT elicitation protocol, language measures, and reports to document selected English Language Arts Standards in the category of Speaking and Listening state standards in literacy for grades Kindergarten through 12th grade (Common Core State Standards Initiative, 2015).

Kindergarten

State Standard - Kindergarten		Elicitation Protocol	SALT Measures/Reports to Document Standard
CCSS.ELA-Literacy.SL.K Comprehension and Collaboration	SL.K.1 Participate in conversations about kindergarten topics; listening to others and taking turns about the topic; continuing through multiple exchanges	• Play • Conversation	• Discourse Summary: %response to questions, mean turn length, utterances with overlaps, interrupted other speaker

State Standard - Kindergarten		Elicitation Protocol	SALT Measures/Reports to Document Standard
	SL.K.3 Ask and answer questions to seek help, get info, or clarify	• Play • Conversation	• Discourse Summary: %response to questions • Grammatical Categories: question words • GC Lists: question words • Standard Utterance Lists: questions
CCSS.ELA-Literacy.SL.K Presentation of Knowledge and Ideas	**SL.K.4** Describe familiar people, places, things, and events and, with prompting and support, provide additional detail	• Play • Conversation Narrative SSS	• Standard Measures Report: number different words • Standard Word Lists • Grammatical Categories • Grammatical Category Lists: adjectives, adverbs • Discourse Summary: questions and prompts • Standard Utterance Lists: responses, in context w/ utterances pre and post
	SL.K.6 Speaks audibly and expresses thoughts, feelings, and ideas clearly	• Play • Conversation Narrative SSS	• Standard Measures Report: %Intelligible utterances, words/minute, % maze words, and abandoned utterances

1ˢᵗ Grade

State Standard – 1ˢᵗ Grade		Elicitation Protocol	SALT Measures/Reports to Document Standard
CCSS.ELA-Literacy.SL.1 Comprehension and Collaboration	**SL.1.1** Participates in conversations about 1st grade topics; listening to others and taking turns about the topic; continuing via multiple exchanges; requests for clarification when needed.	• Conversation	• Discourse Summary: %response to questions, mean turn length, utterances with overlaps, interrupted other speaker

State Standard – 1st Grade		Elicitation Protocol	SALT Measures/Reports to Document Standard
	SL.1.3 Ask and answer questions to gain info or clarify.	• Conversation	• Discourse Summary: %response to questions • Grammatical Categories: question words • GCL: question words • Standard Utterance Lists: questions
CCSS.ELA-Literacy.SL.1 Presentation of Knowledge and Ideas	SL.1.4 Describe people, places, things, and events with relevant details, expressing ideas and feelings clearly.	• Conversation • Narrative SSS • Narrative Story Retell	• Standard Measures Report: number different words, %intelligibility, words/minute, % maze words, and abandoned utterances • Rate and Pause Summary • Standard Word Lists • Grammatical Categories • Grammatical Category Lists: adjectives, adverbs, existentials, intensifiers • Discourse Summary: questions and prompts • Standard Utterance Lists: responses, in context w/ utterances pre and post
	SL.1.6 Produce complete sentences when appropriate to task and situation.	• Conversation • Narrative SSS • Narrative Story Retell	• SMR; Analysis Set utterances: MLUm, MLUw • Subordination Index

2nd Grade

State Standard – 2nd Grade		Elicitation Protocol	SALT Measures/Reports to Document Standard
CCSS.ELA-Literacy.SL.2 Comprehension and Collaboration	SL.2.1 Participates in conversations about grade 2 topics; gaining the floor respectfully, with topic-appropriate turn-taking.	• Conversation	• Discourse Summary: %response to questions, mean turn length, utterances with overlaps, interrupted other speaker

State Standard – 2nd Grade		Elicitation Protocol	SALT Measures/Reports to Document Standard
	SL.2.1c Ask for clarification and further explanation as needed.	• Conversation	• Discourse Summary • GC Lists: question words • Standard Utterance Lists: questions, responses to questions…
	SL.2.2 Recount or describe key ideas or details from a text read aloud or through other media.	• Narrative Story Retell	• NSS • Grammatical Categories • Grammatical Category Lists: adjectives, adverbs, interjections, intensifiers…
	SL.2.3 Ask and answer questions about what a speaker says in order to clarify comprehension, gather additional information, or deepen understanding of topic/issue.	• Conversation	• Discourse Summary • GC Lists: question words • Standard Utterance Lists: questions, responses to questions, yes/no responses to questions, responses to intonation prompts
CCSS.ELA-Literacy.SL.2 Presentation of Knowledge and Ideas	SL.2.4 Tell a story or recount an experience with appropriate facts, relevant descriptive details, using coherent sentences.	• Narrative SSS • Narrative Story Retell	• NSS • Grammatical Categories Lists: adjectives, adverbs, prepositions… • SI • SMR: MLU, NDW, abandoned utterances • Maze Summary
	SL.2.5 Create audio recordings of stories…or recounting experiences when appropriate to clarify ideas, thoughts, and feelings.	• Narrative SSS • Narrative Story Retell	• NSS
	SL.2.6 Produce complete sentences when appropriate to task in order to provide requested detail or clarification.	• Conversation • Narrative SSS Narrative Story Retell	• SMR: MLU, abandoned utts. • Subordination Index • Standard Utterance Lists: responses to questions, yes/no responses to questions, responses to intonation prompts • NSS

3rd Grade

State Standard – 3rd Grade		Elicitation Protocol	SALT Measures/Reports to Document Standard
CCSS.ELA-Literacy.SL.3 Comprehension and Collaboration	**SL.3.1** Engage effectively in collaborative discussions (one on one); on grade three topics, building on others' ideas, expressing ideas clearly.	• Conversation	• SMR: % intelligibility, % maze words, and abandoned utterances • Rate and Pause Summary • Maze Summary • Discourse Summary
	SL.3.1b Follow rules of discourse.	• Conversation	• Discourse Summary: %response to questions, mean turn length, utterances with overlaps, interrupted other speaker
	SL.3.1c Ask questions to check understanding of information presented and stay on topic.	• Conversation	• Discourse Summary • GC Lists: question words • Standard Utterance Lists: questions
	SL.3.2 Determine the main ideas and supporting details of a text read aloud or information presented in diverse media and formats, including visually, quantitatively, and orally.	• Narrative Story Retell	• NSS
CCSS.ELA-Literacy.SL.3 Presentation of Knowledge and Ideas	**SL.3.4** Tell a story, or recount an experience with appropriate facts, and relevant descriptive details, speaking clearly, at an understandable pace.	• Narrative SSS • Narrative Story Retell	• NSS • Grammatical Categories and GC Lists: adverbs, adjectives, prepositions, existentials, intensifiers... • SMR: NDW, %Intelligibility, % maze words, abandoned utterances, words/minute, pauses, omissions, and errors • Rate and Pause Summary • Maze Summary

State Standard – 3rd Grade		Elicitation Protocol	SALT Measures/Reports to Document Standard
	SL.3.6 Speak in complete sentences when appropriate to task/situation in order to provide requested detail or clarification.	• Conversation • Narrative NSS • Narrative Story Retell	• SMR: abandoned utterances • Subordination Index • Standard Utterance Lists: responses to questions, yes/no responses to questions, responses to intonation prompts

4th Grade

State Standard – 4th Grade		Elicitation Protocol	SALT Measures/Reports to Document Standard
CCSS.ELA-Literacy.SL.4 Comprehension and Collaboration	SL.4.1 Engage effectively in collaborative discussions (one on one); on grade four topics, building on others' ideas, expressing ideas clearly.	• Conversation	• SMR: % intelligibility, % maze words, and abandoned utterances • Rate and Pause Summary • Maze Summary • Discourse Summary
	SL.4.1b Follow rules of discourse.	• Conversation	• Discourse Summary: %response to questions, mean turn length, utterances with overlaps, interrupted other speaker
	SL.4.1c Pose and respond to questions to clarify or follow-up on information, and make comments that contribute to the discussion, link to the remarks of others.	• Conversation	• Discourse Summary • GC Lists: question words • Standard Utterance Lists: questions, responses to questions, yes/no responses to questions, responses to intonation prompts (with context pre/post)

State Standard – 4th Grade		Elicitation Protocol	SALT Measures/Reports to Document Standard
	SL.4.2 Paraphrase portions of a text read aloud or information presented in diverse media and formats, including visually, quantitatively, and orally.	• Narrative Story Retell	• NSS
CCSS.ELA-Literacy.SL.4 Presentation of Knowledge and Ideas	**SL.4.4** Tell a story or recount an experience in an organized manner, using appropriate facts, and relevant descriptive details to support main ideas or themes; speak clearly, at an understandable pace.	• Narrative SSS • Narrative Story Retell • Exposition	• NSS • ESS • Grammatical Categories and GC Lists: adverbs, adjectives, prepositions, existentials, intensifiers... • SMR: NDW, %Intelligibility, % maze words, abandoned utterances, words/minute, pauses, omissions, and errors

5th Grade

State Standard – 5th Grade		Elicitation Protocol	SALT Measures/Reports to Document Standard
CCSS.ELA-Literacy.SL.5 Comprehension and Collaboration	**SL.5.1** Engage effectively in collaborative discussions (one on one, and teacher-led); on grade five topics, building on others' ideas, expressing ideas clearly.	• Conversation	• SMR: % intelligibility, mazes and abandoned utterances • Discourse Summary • Maze Summary
	SL.5.1b Follow rules of discussions/discourse.	• Conversation	• Discourse Summary: %response to questions, mean turn length, utterances with overlaps, interrupted other speaker

State Standard – 5th Grade		Elicitation Protocol	SALT Measures/Reports to Document Standard
	SL.5.1c Pose and respond to questions, make comments that contribute to the discussion, elaborate on the remarks of others.	• Conversation • Persuasion	• Discourse Summary • GC Lists: question words • Standard Utterance Lists: questions, responses to questions, yes/no responses to questions, responses to intonation prompts (with context pre/post)
CCSS.ELA-Literacy.SL.5 Presentation of Knowledge and Ideas	SL.5.4 Report on a topic or text, or present an opinion, sequencing ideas logically and using appropriate facts and relevant descriptive details to support main ideas or themes. Speak clearly at an understandable pace.	• Persuasion • Narrative SSS (from text previously read or heard) • Narrative story retell • Exposition	• PSS • NSS • ESS • Grammatical Categories and GC Lists: adverbs, adjectives, prepositions, existentials, intensifiers... • NSS • SMR: NDW, % Intelligibility, words/minute, % maze words, abandoned utterances, omissions and errors • Maze Summary • Rate and Pause Summary

6th Grade

State Standard – 6th Grade		Elicitation Protocol	SALT Measures/Reports to Document Standard
CCSS.ELA-Literacy.SL.6 Comprehension and Collaboration	S.L.6.1 Engage effectively in a range of collaborative discussions (one-on-one, and teacher-led) with diverse partners on grade 6 topics, texts, and issues, building on others' ideas and expressing their own clearly.	• Conversation	• SMR: % intelligibility, % maze words, and abandoned utterances • Discourse Summary • Maze Summary

State Standard – 6th Grade		Elicitation Protocol	SALT Measures/Reports to Document Standard
	S.L.6.1b Follow rules for collegial discussions (pragmatics/discourse).	• Conversation	• Discourse Summary: %response to questions, mean turn length, utterances with overlaps, interrupted other speaker
	S.L.6.1c Pose and respond to specific questions with elaboration and detail by making comments that contribute to the topic, text, or issue under discussion.	• Conversation • Persuasion	• Discourse Summary • GC Lists: question words • Standard Utterance Lists: questions, responses to questions, yes/no responses to questions, responses to intonation prompts (with context pre/post)
CCSS.ELA-Literacy.SL.6 Presentation of Knowledge and Ideas	**S.L.6.4** Present claims and findings, sequencing ideas logically and using pertinent descriptions, facts, and details to accentuate main ideas or themes; use appropriate eye contact, adequate volume, and clear pronunciation.	• Persuasion	• PSS • SMR: % intelligibility
	S.L.6.6 Adapt speech to a variety of contexts and tasks, demonstrating command of formal English when indicated or appropriate.	• Compare Conversation to Narrative Story Retell or Exposition	• Clinical Impressions • SI • NSS/ESS

7th Grade

State Standard – 7th Grade		Elicitation Protocol	SALT Measures/Reports to Document Standard
CCSS.ELA-Literacy.SL.7 Comprehension and Collaboration	**S.L.7.1** Engage effectively in a range of collaborative discussions (one-on-one and teacher-led) with diverse partners on grade 7 topics, texts, and issues, building on others' ideas and expressing their own clearly.	• Conversation	• SMR: % intelligibility, % maze words, and abandoned utterances • Discourse Summary • Maze Summary
	SL.7.1b Follow rules for collegial discussions.	• Conversation	• Discourse Summary: %response to questions, mean turn length, utterances with overlaps, interrupted other speaker
	SL.7.1c Pose questions that elicit elaboration and respond to others' questions and comments with relevant observations and ideas that bring the discussion back on topic as needed.	• Conversation • Persuasion	• Discourse Summary • GC Lists: question words • Standard Utterance Lists: questions, responses to questions, yes/no responses to questions, responses to intonation prompts (with context pre/post)
	SL.7.1d Acknowledge new information expressed by others and, when warranted, modify their own views.	• Persuasion	• PSS

State Standard – 7th Grade		Elicitation Protocol	SALT Measures/Reports to Document Standard
CCSS.ELA-Literacy.SL.7 Presentation of Knowledge and Ideas	SL.7.4 Present claims and findings, emphasizing salient points in a focused, coherent manner with pertinent descriptions, facts, details, and examples; use appropriate eye contact, adequate volume, and clear pronunciation.	• Persuasion	• PSS • SMR: % intelligibility, % maze words, abandoned utterances
	SL.7.6 Adapt speech to a variety of contexts and tasks, demonstrating command of formal English when indicated or appropriate.	• Compare Conversation to Narrative SSS or Exposition	• Clinical Impressions • SI • ESS

8th Grade

State Standard – 8th Grade		Elicitation Protocol	SALT Measures/Reports to Document Standard
CCSS.ELA-Literacy.SL.8 Comprehension and Collaboration	SL.8.1 Engage effectively in a range of collaborative discussions (one-on-one and teacher-led) with diverse partners on grade 8 topics, texts, and issues, building on others' ideas and expressing their own clearly.	• Conversation	• SMR: % intelligibility, % maze words, and abandoned utterances • Discourse Summary • Maze Summary
	SL.8.1b Follow rules for collegial discussions.	• Conversation	• Discourse Summary: %response to questions, mean turn length, utterances with overlaps, interrupted other speaker

State Standard – 8th Grade		Elicitation Protocol	SALT Measures/Reports to Document Standard
	SL.8.1c Pose questions connect the ideas of other speakers and respond to others' questions and comments with relevant evidence, observations, and ideas.	• Conversation • Persuasion	• Discourse Summary • GCL: question words • Standard Utterance Lists: questions, responses to questions, yes/no responses to questions, responses to intonation prompts (with context pre/post) • PSS
	SL.8.1d Acknowledge new information expressed by others, and, when warranted, qualify or justify their own views in light of the evidence presented.	• Persuasion	• PSS
CCSS.ELA-Literacy.SL.8 Presentation of Knowledge and Ideas	**SL.8.4** Present claims and findings, emphasizing salient points in a focused, coherent manner with relevant evidence, sound valid reasoning, and well-chosen details; use appropriate eye contact, adequate volume, and clear pronunciation.	• Persuasion	• PSS • SMR: % intelligibility, % maze words, abandoned utterances • Maze Summary
	SL.8.6 Adapt speech to a variety of contexts and tasks, demonstrating command of formal English when indicated or appropriate.	• Compare Conversation to Exposition	• Clinical Impressions • SI • ESS

9ᵗʰ and 10ᵗʰ Grade

State Standard – 9ᵗʰ and 10ᵗʰ Grade		Elicitation Protocol	SALT Measures/Reports to Document Standard
CCSS.ELA-Literacy. SL.9-10 Comprehension and Collaboration	SL.9-10.1 Initiate and participate effectively in a range of collaborative discussions (one-on-one, and teacher-led) with diverse partners on grades 9–10 topics, texts, and issues, building on others' ideas and expressing their own clearly and persuasively.	• Conversation • Persuasion	• SMR: % intelligibility, % maze words, and abandoned utterances • Discourse Summary • Maze Summary • PSS
	SL.9-10.1c Propel conversations by posing and responding to questions that relate the current discussion to broader themes or larger ideas; actively incorporate others into the discussion; and clarify, verify, or challenge ideas and conclusions.	• Conversation • Persuasion	• Discourse Summary • PSS
	SL.9-10.1d Respond thoughtfully to diverse perspectives, summarize points of agreement and disagreement, and, when warranted, qualify or justify their own views and understanding and make new connections in light of the evidence and reasoning presented.	• Persuasion	• PSS

State Standard – 9th and 10th Grade		Elicitation Protocol	SALT Measures/Reports to Document Standard
CCSS.ELA-Literacy. SL.9-10 Presentation of Knowledge and Ideas	**9-10.4** Present information, findings, and supporting evidence clearly, concisely, and logically such that listeners can follow the line of reasoning and the organization, development, substance, and style are appropriate to purpose, audience, and task.	• Exposition • Persuasion	• ESS • PSS • SMR: % intelligibility, % maze words, abandoned utterances, omissions, and errors • Maze Summary
	9-10.6 Adapt speech to a variety of contexts and tasks, demonstrating command of formal English when indicated or appropriate.	• Compare Conversation to Exposition or Persuasion	• Clinical Impressions • SI • ESS • PSS

11th and 12th Grade

State Standard – 11th and 12th Grade		Elicitation Protocol	SALT Measures/Reports to Document Standard
CCSS.ELA-Literacy. SL.11-12 Comprehension and Collaboration	SL.11-12.1 Initiate and participate effectively in a range of collaborative discussions (one-on-one, in groups, and teacher-led) with diverse partners on grades 11–12 topics, texts, and issues, building on others' ideas and expressing their own clearly and persuasively.	• Conversation • Persuasion	• SMR: % intelligibility, % maze words, and abandoned utterances • Discourse Summary • Maze Summary • PSS
	11-12.1c Propel conversations by posing and responding to questions that probe reasoning and evidence; ensure a hearing for a	• Persuasion	• PSS (planning sheet)

State Standard – 11th and 12th Grade		Elicitation Protocol	SALT Measures/Reports to Document Standard
	full range of positions on a topic or issue; clarify, verify, or challenge ideas and conclusions; and promote divergent and creative perspectives.		
	11-12.1d Respond thoughtfully to diverse perspectives, synthesize comments, claims, and evidence made on all sides of an issue; resolve contradictions when possible; and determine what additional information or research is required to deepen the investigation or complete the task.	• Persuasion	• PSS (planning sheet)
CCSS.ELA-Literacy. SL.11-12 Presentation of Knowledge and Ideas	**SL.11-12.4** Present information, findings, and supporting evidence, conveying a clear and distinct perspective, such that listeners can follow the line of reasoning, alternative or opposing perspectives are addressed, and the organization, development, substance, and style are appropriate to purpose, audience, and a range of formal and informal tasks.	• Persuasion	• PSS (planning sheet)
	SL.11-12.6 Adapt speech to a variety of contexts and tasks, demonstrating command of formal English when indicated or appropriate.	• Compare Conversation to Persuasion	• Clinical Impressions • SI • PSS

REFERENCES

Acarlar, F. & Johnston, J. (2006). Computer-based analysis of Turkish child language: Clinical and research applications. *Journal of Multilingual Communication Disorders, 4* (2), 30-43.

Aram, D., Morris, R., & Hall, N. (1993). Clinical and research congruence in identifying children with specific language impairment. *Journal of Speech and Hearing Research, 36* (3), 580-591.

Bedore, L.M. (1999). The acquisition of Spanish. In O. L. Taylor & L. B. Leonard (Eds.), *Language acquisition across North America: Cross-cultural competence and cross-linguistic perspectives* (157-208). San Diego, CA: Singular Publishing Group, Inc.

Bedore, L.M., Fiestas, C., Peña, E.D., & Nagy, V. (2006). Cross-language comparisons of maze use in Spanish and English in functionally monolingual and bilingual children. *Bilingualism: Language and Cognition, 9* (3), 233-247.

Bereiter C. & Englelmann S. (1966). *Teaching disadvantaged children in the preschool.* Englewood Cliffs, NJ: Prentice-Hall.

Boscolo, B., Bernstein Ratner, N., & Rescorla, L. (2002). Fluency of schoolaged children with a history of specific expressive language impairment: An exploratory study. *American Journal of Speech-Language Pathology, 11,* 41-49.

Brown, R. (1973). *A First Language.* Harvard University Press.

Channell, R. W., & Johnson, B. W. (1999). Automated grammatical tagging of child language samples. *Journal of Speech, Language, and Hearing Research, 42,* 727-734.

Coleman, C. (2013). How can you tell if childhood stuttering is the real deal? Retrieved from http://blog.asha.org/2013/09/26/how-can-you-tell-if-childhood-stuttering-is-the-real-deal/.

Common Core State Standards Initiative (2015). English Language Arts Standards. Retrieved from http://www.corestandards.org/ELA-Literacy/.

Covington, M. A., & McFall, J. D. (2010). Cutting the Gordian knot: The moving-average type–token ratio (MATTR). *Journal of Quantitative Linguistics, 17,* 94–100.

Craig, H. K., & Washington, J. A. (2004). Grade-related changes in the production of African American English. *Journal of Speech, Language, and Hearing Research, 47,* 450-463.

Crago, M., Annahatak, B., & Ningiuruvik, L. (1993). Changing patterns of language socialization in Inuit homes. *Anthropology and Educational Quarterly, 24* (3), 205-223.

Crystal, D., Garman, M., & Fletcher, P. (1976). *The grammatical analysis of language disability.* London: Edward Arnold.

Diagram Group (Ed.) (1990). *Rules of the game: the complete illustrated encyclopedia of all the sports of the world,* New York: St. Martin's Press.

Dollaghan, C., & Campbell, T.F. (1998). Nonword repetition and child language impairment. *Journal of Speech, Language, and Hearing Research, 41,* 1136-1146.

Dunn, M., Flax, J., Sliwinski, M, & Aram, D. (1996). The use of spontaneous language measures as criteria in identifying children with specific language impairment: An attempt to reconcile clinical and research incongruence. *Journal of Speech and Hearing Research, 39,* 643-654.

Evans, J., & Craig, H. (1992). Language sample collection and analysis: Interview compared to free play assessment contexts. *Journal of Speech and Hearing Research, 35,* 343–353.

Freiberg, C., Wicklund, A., & Squier, S. (2003). *Speech and Language Impairments, Assessment and Decision Making, Technical Assistance Guide*. Retrieved from http://sped.dpi.wi.gov/sites/default/files/imce/sped/pdf/slguide.pdf.

Gillam, R., & Pearson, N. (2004). *The Test of Narrative Language (TNL)*. East Moline, IL: LinguiSystems.

Gutiérrez-Clellen, V.F., & Hofstetter, R. (1994). Syntactic complexity in Spanish narratives: A developmental study. *Journal of Speech and Hearing Research, 37,* 645-654.

Gutiérrez-Clellen, V.F., Restrepo, M.A., Bedore, L., Peña, E., & Anderson, R. (2000). Language sample analysis in Spanish-speaking children: Methodological considerations. *Language, Speech, and Hearing Services in Schools, 31,* 88-98.

Hammill, D. & Newcomer, P. (1988). *Test of Language Development, Primary (TOLD-P)*. Austin, TX: Pro-Ed (Firm).

Hart, B. & Risley, T. (1999). *The Social Word of Children: Learning to Talk*. Baltimore, MD: Paul H. Brookes Publishing Co.

Haynes W. & Pindzola R. (2011). *Diagnosis and Evaluation in Speech Pathology*, CourseSmart, eTextbook, 8/E.

Heilmann, J., Malone, T., Andriacchi, K., & Westerveld, M. (2015). Don't Say No Until I Finish Talking: Persuasive Discourse of High School Students. Presented at the annual meeting of the *American Speech-Language-Hearing Association*, Denver, CO.

Heilmann, J., Miller, J., Iglesias, A., Fabiano-Smith, L., Nockerts, A., & Digney Andriacchi, K. (2008). Narrative Transcription Accuracy and Reliability in Two Languages. *Topics in Language Disorders, 28* (2), 178-188.

Heilmann, J., Miller, J., & Nockerts, A. (2010a). Sensitivity of narrative organization measures using narrative retells produced by young school-age children. *Language Testing, 27* (4), 603-626.

Heilmann, J., Miller, J., & Nockerts, A. (2010b). Using Language Sample Databases. *Language, Speech, and Hearing Services in Schools, 41*, 84-95.

Heilmann, J., Miller, J., Nockerts, A., & Dunaway, C. (2010). Properties of the Narrative Scoring Scheme Using Narrative Retells in Young School-Age Children. *American Journal of Speech-Language Pathology, 19*, 154-166.

Heilmann, J., Nockerts, A., & Miller, J. (2010). Language Sampling: Does the Length of the Transcript Matter? *Language, Speech, and Hearing Services in Schools, 41*, 393-404.

Hughes, D., McGillivray, L., Schmidek, M. (1997). *Guide to Narrative Language: Procedures for Assessment.* Eau Claire, WI: Thinking Publications.

Hunt, K. (1965). *Grammatical structures written at three grade levels* (Research Report No.3). Urbana, IL: National Council of Teachers of English.

Justice, L., Bowles, R., Kaderavek, J., Ukrainetz, T., Eisenberg S., & Gillam, R. (2006). The Index of Narrative Microstructure: A clinical tool for analyzing school-age children's narrative performances. *American Journal of Speech-Language Pathology, 15*, 177-191.

Kohnert, K., Kan, P.F., & Conboy, B.T. (2010). Lexical and grammatical associations in sequential bilingual preschoolers. *Journal of Speech, Language, and Hearing Research, 53*, 684-698.

Leadholm, B. & Miller, J. (1992). *Language sample analysis: The Wisconsin Guide*. Madison, WI: Wisconsin Dept. of Public Instruction.

Lee, L. & Canter, S. (1971). Developmental Sentence Scoring: A Clinical Procedure for Estimating Syntactic Development in Children's Spontaneous Speech. *Journal of Speech and Hearing Disorders, 36,* 315-340.

LENA™ Research Foundation (2015). Retrieved from http://www.lenafoundation.org/.

Lester, H. (1987). *Pookins Gets Her Way*, Boston, MA: Houghton Mifflin Co.

Lester, H. (1986). *A Porcupine Named Fluffy*, Boston, MA: Houghton Mifflin Co.

Loban, W. (1976). *Language development: Kindergarten through grade twelve*. Urbana, IL: National Council of Teachers of English.

Loban, W. (1963). *The Language of Elementary School Children.* Urbana, IL: National Council of Teachers of English.

Long, S.H., Fey, M.E., and Channell, R.W. (2008). *Computerized Profiling*. Cleveland, OH: Case Western Reserve University.

Malone, T., Heilmann, J., Miller, J.F., DiVall-Rayan, J., & M. Rolland (2010, November). Reaching the Tweeners: Extending Two SALT Databases to Grades 5-6. Presented at the annual meeting of the *American Speech-Language-Hearing Association*, Philadelphia, PA.

Malone, T., Miller, J., Andriacchi K., Heilmann J., Nockerts, A., Schoonveld, E. (2008), Let Me Explain: Teenage Expository Language Samples, Presented at the *American Speech and Hearing Association*, Chicago, IL.

Mayer, M. (1974). *Frog Goes to Dinner,* New York, NY: Dial Press.

Mayer, M. (1973). *Frog On His Own,* New York, NY: Dial Press.

Mayer, M. (1969). *Frog, Where Are You?,* New York, NY: Dial Press.

Mayer, M. & Mayer, M. (1975). *One Frog Too Many,* New York, NY: Dial Press.

McWhinney, B. (2000). *The CHILDES project: Tools for analyzing talk. Third Edition.* Mahwah, NJ: Lawrence Erlbaum Associates.

Miller, J. (1981). *Assessing Language Production in Children: Experimental Procedures, Second Edition*, New York: Allyn and Bacon.

Miller, J., Andriacchi, K., & Nockerts, A. (in press). Using Language Sample Analysis to Assess Spoken Language Production in Adolescents. *Language, Speech, and Hearing Services in Schools.*

Miller, J., Heilmann, J., Nockerts, A., Iglesias, A., Fabiano, L., & Francis, D. (2006). Oral language and reading in bilingual children. *Journal of Learning Disabilities Research to Practice, 21* (1), 30-43.

Miller, J., & Iglesias, A. (2015). *Systematic Analysis of Language Transcripts (SALT), Version 16* [Computer software]. SALT Software, LLC.

Miller, J. & Klee, T. (1995). Quantifying language disorders in children. In P. Fletcher and B. MacWhinney (Eds.), *The handbook of child language* (545-572). Oxford, UK: Basal Blackwell.

National Center for Education Statistics (2006). The condition of education 2006. Retrieved from http://nces.ed.gov/pubs2006/2006071.pdf.

National Governors Association Center for Best Practices, Council of Chief State School Officers (2010). *Common Core Standards, English Language Arts & Literacy in History/Social Studies, Science, and Technical Subjects.* Washington, D.C.: National Governors Association Center for Best Practices, Council of Chief State School Officers. Retrieved from http://www.corestandards.org/ELA-Literacy.

Nelson, N. W. (2014a). Classroom-based writing assessment. In A. Stone, E. Silliman, B. Ehren, & G. Wallach (Eds.), *Handbook of Language and Literacy Development and Disorders* (2nd ed., pp. 524-543). New York, NY: Guilford Press.

Nelson, N. W. (2014b). Integrating language assessment, instruction, and intervention in an inclusive writing lab approach. In B. Arfé, J., Dockrell, & V. Berninger (Eds.), *Writing development in children with hearing loss, dyslexia, or oral language problems* (pp. 273-300). New York, NY: Oxford University Press.

Nippold, M. (2010). *Language Sampling with Adolescents*. San Diego, CA: Plural Publishing Inc.

Nippold, M. (2007). *Later language development: school-age children, adolescents, and young adults (3rd Edition)*. Austin, TX: Pro-Ed.

Nippold, M., Hesketh L., Duthie, J., & Mansfield, T. (2005). Conversational Versus Expository Discourse: A Study of Syntactic Development in Children, Adolescents, and Adults. *Journal of Speech, Language, and Hearing Research, 48*, 1048-1064.

Nippold, M., Mansfield, T., Billow, J. & Tomblin, J.B., (2008) Expository Discourse in Adolescents With Language Impairments: Examining Syntactic Development. *American Journal of Speech-Language Pathology,* (17) 356–366.

Olswang, L., Bain, B. & Johnson, G. (1991). Using Dynamic Assessment with children with language disorders. In S. Warren & J. Reichle (Eds.), *Causes and effects in communication and language intervention*. Baltimore, MD: Brookes Publishing Co.

Parker, M. & Brorson, K. (2005). A comparative study between mean length of utterance in morphemes (MLUm) and mean length of utterance in words (MLUw). *First Language, 25* (3), 365-376.

Paul, R. (2007). *Language Disorders from Infancy through Adolescence: Assessment and Intervention (3rd Edition)*. St. Louis, MO: Mosby.

Peterson, C, McCabe A. (1983). *Developmental psycholinguistics: Three ways of looking at a child's narrative*. New York: Plenum.

Plante, E., & Vance, R. (1994). Selection of preschool language tests: A data-based approach. *Language, Speech, and Hearing Services in Schools, 25*, 15-24.

Renfrew, C. E. (1995). *The Bus Story Test: A test of narrative speech (3rd Edition)*. Oxford, UK.

Rice M., Smolik, F., Perpich, D., Thompson, T., Rytting, N., & Blossom, M. (Apr 2010). Mean Length of Utterance Levels in 6-Month Intervals for Children 3 to 9 Years With and Without Language Impairments, *Journal of Speech, Language, and Hearing Research, 53*, 333-349.

Rojas R., & Iglesias, A. (2010). Using language sampling to measure language growth. *Perspectives on Language Learning and Education, 17* (1), 24-31.

Rojas, R., & Iglesias, A. (2009, March 3). Making a case for language sampling. *The ASHA Leader, 14* (3), 10–11, 13.

Schneider, P., Dubé, R. V., & Hayward, D. (2005). *The Edmonton Narrative Norms Instrument*. Retrieved from www.rehabmed.ualberta.ca/spa/enni/.

Semel, E., Wiig, E., & Secord, W. (2003). *Clinical Evaluation of Language Fundamentals – Fourth Edition (CELF-4)*. San Antonio, TX: Psychological Corporation.

Shin, H. B., & Kominski, R. A. (2010). Language use in the United States: 2007. *American Community Survey Reports*, ACS-12. U.S. Census Bureau, Washington, DC.

Socio-Economic Indexes for Areas (2011). *Australian Bureau of Statistics, Census for Population and Housing, Australia, 2011*. Retrieved from http://www.abs.gov.au/ausstats/abs@.nsf/mf/2033.0.55.001/.

Steig, W. (1982). *Doctor De Soto*, New York: NY: Farrar, Straus, and Giroux.

Stein, N., & Glenn, C. (1982). Children's concept of time: The development of a story schema. In W.J. Friedman (Ed.), *The developmental psychology of time* (255-282). New York: Academic Press.

Stein, N., & Glenn, C. (1979). An analysis of story comprehension in elementary school children. In R. Freedle (Ed.), *New directions in discourse processing* (53-120). Noorwood, NJ: Ablex.

Strong, C. (1998). *The Strong Narrative Assessment Procedure*. Eau Claire, WI: Thinking Publications.

Swan, E. (1992). *Ko au na galo* (Ana gets lost).Wellington, New Zealand: Learning Media, Ministry of Education.

Swanson, C.B. (2009). *Perspectives on a population: English-Language Learners in American schools*. Bethesda, MD: Editorial Projects in Education.

Templin, M. (1957). *Certain Language Skills in Children: Their developmental and inter-relationships*. Minneapolis, MN: University of Minnesota Press.

Thordardottir E. (2005). Early lexical and syntactic development in Quebec French and English: implications for cross-linguistic and bilingual assessment. *International Journal of Language & Communication Disorders*, *40* (3), 243-278.

Van Zaalen-Op 't Hof Y1, Wijnen F., De Jonckere PH. (2009). Differential diagnostic characteristics between cluttering and stuttering—part one. *Journal of Fluency Disorders*, *34* (3), 137-54.

Westerveld, M. & Gillon, G. (2010a). Profiling oral narrative ability in young school aged children. *International Journal of Speech-Language Pathology, 12* (3), 178-189.

Westerveld, M. & Gillon, G. (2010b). Oral narrative context effects on poor readers' spoken language performance: Story retelling, story generation and personal narratives. *International Journal of Speech-Language Pathology, 12* (2), 132-141.

Westerveld, M., Gillon, G., & Miller, J. (2004). Spoken language samples of New Zealand children in conversation and narration. *International Journal of Speech-Language Pathology, 6* (4), 195-208.

Westerveld, M. Gillon, G., & Moran, K. (2008). A longitudinal investigation of oral narrative skills in children with mixed reading disability. *International Journal of Speech-Language Pathology, 10* (3), 132-145.

Westerveld, M. & Heilmann, J. (June, 2010). Narrative Analysis: The effects of geographical location on children's spoken language performance. Presented at the *Symposium on Research on Child Language Disorders*, Madison, Wisconsin.

Westerveld, M. F., & Vidler, K. (2015). The use of the Renfrew Bus Story with 5- to 8-year-old Australian children. *International Journal of Speech-Language Pathology, 17*(3), 304-313. doi: 10.3109/17549507.2015.1024168.

Wisconsin Administrative Code (2011). *Areas of impairment: Speech or Language Impairment. PI* 11.36 (5). Retrieved from https://docs.legis.wisconsin.gov/code/admin_code/pi/11/36

Wolfram W. & Shilling-Estes N. (1998), *American English: Dialects and Variation.* Oxford (UK) & Malden (MA): Blackwell.

Woodcock, RW. (1991). Woodcock Language Proficiency Battery-Revised: English and Spanish. Riverside Publishing; Itasca, IL.

INDEX